ALGEBRA

An Introductory Course

VOLUME I

MORRIS BRAMSON has been Chairman, Department of Mathematics, Martin Van Buren High School, Queens, New York; Instructor of Mathematics, Adelphi University, Garden City, New York; Adjunct Lecturer of Mathematics Education, York College, City University of New York; and Supervisor of General Studies, The Brandeis School, Lawrence, New York.

ALGEBRA

An Introductory Course

VOLUME I

MORRIS BRAMSON

When ordering this book, please specify *either*
R 204 W *or* ALGEBRA: AN INTRODUCTORY
COURSE, VOLUME I

Dedicated to serving

our nation's youth

AMSCO SCHOOL PUBLICATIONS, INC.
315 Hudson Street   New York, N.Y. 10013

ISBN 0-87720-240-0

PREFACE

Algebra: An Introductory Course provides students with a gradual, progressive development of algebraic concepts, skills, and applications. Although this book should be particularly helpful to students who have experienced some difficulty in learning mathematics, it places strong emphasis on basic algebra.

The first three chapters introduce students to formulas, simple equations, and the use of equations in the solution of simple verbal problems. The only prerequisite for these topics is some skill in the arithmetic of positive whole numbers.

For those students who lack the necessary basic skills, however, a complete review of the arithmetic of whole numbers is provided in Appendix I.

Further reviews of arithmetic skills and concepts are interspersed throughout this book. Chapter 4 provides a review of arithmetic fractions followed by an introduction to algebraic fractions and the solution of simple fractional equations. Chapter 5 follows a similar sequence of arithmetic review and algebraic development for decimal fractions and decimal equations. Chapter 6 develops the concepts of ratio and proportion and makes use of algebraic skills in the solution of problems of these types. Chapter 7 reviews the basic skills and concepts of percentage and illustrates the use of simple equations in solving percentage problems.

In the treatment of topics throughout *Algebra: An Introductory Course*, excessive abstraction and rigorous theory are avoided. Mathematical ideas and processes are explained in concrete terms and grow out of a need for them in everyday situations.

In addition to algebra and related arithmetic, basic geometric concepts are illustrated and explained. Chapter 8 reviews linear measure and focuses on the metric system. The concepts of area and volume are carefully developed here, and they are applied to a variety of situations. Exponents are introduced in connection with the area of a square and the volume of a cube.

The algebra of signed numbers, followed by monomial and polynomial expressions, is developed in Chapters 9 and 10. The solution of equations is then expanded in Chapter 11 to use signed numbers and the new skills. Then equations are used to solve more difficult verbal problems of assorted types.

Chapter 12 introduces students to the techniques of graphing linear equations. This skill is then applied in Chapter 13 to the graphic solution of inequalities.

Throughout the book, new terms are defined in simple, concise language. Each new concept is followed by numerous illustrative problems whose detailed solutions are presented in a step-by-step manner that is easy for students to follow.

After each new type of problem has been introduced and illustrated, it is followed by an ample set of well-graded exercises. These range considerably in difficulty so as to provide for individual differences in student ability. Exercises are often related to science, social science, business, industry, and other areas of mathematics.

For those students interested in a glimpse of a more theoretical, rigorous approach to algebra, an introduction to set theory is given in Appendix II.

The author expresses his thanks and appreciation to Mr. Harold Baron, Chairman of the Mathematics Department of August Martin High School, New York City, who carefully read the manuscript and made many helpful criticisms and valuable suggestions.

MORRIS BRAMSON

CONTENTS

1 THE FORMULA

2 SOLVING SIMPLE EQUATIONS

3 SOLVING PROBLEMS BY USING EQUATIONS

4 COMMON FRACTIONS AND SIMPLE FRACTIONAL EQUATIONS

5 DECIMAL FRACTIONS AND SIMPLE DECIMAL EQUATIONS

6 RATIO AND PROPORTION

7 PERCENTAGE

THE FORMULA

1

1. Meaning of a formula

In everyday living, we frequently use abbreviations and shorthand expressions to represent groups of words. Most people know that UN represents United Nations and that NFL means National Football League. If your history teacher refers to 600 BC, what does BC represent? What is FBI an abbreviation of?

We also use shorthand expressions for ideas in mathematics, science, social science, business, and industry. When these ideas are mathematical, they usually involve mathematical symbols as well as letters. For example, if it <u>costs</u> a man $40 to buy a radio and he wishes to make a <u>gain</u> of $10, he must <u>sell</u> the radio for $50. The selling price is found by adding the cost to the gain. This rule can be written as

$$\textbf{Selling price} = \textbf{Cost} + \textbf{Gain}$$

We may write this rule in a shorthand manner as

$$S = C + G$$

where S represents <u>selling price</u>, C represents <u>cost</u>, and G represents <u>gain</u>. The terms are related by the mathematical symbols = and +. This total expression is called a ***formula***. In a formula, the letters are not only abbreviations for words, but also represent quantities.

In the work that follows in Chapters 1, 2, and 3, it is assumed that you have some basic arithmetic skills in handling whole numbers and fractions. If you find that you are having difficulty, review the arithmetic of whole numbers in Appendix I. If you are having trouble with fractions, review these in Chapters 4 and 5.

2. Using formulas

Let us use the above formula, $S = C + G$, to solve a simple problem:

ILLUSTRATIVE PROBLEM 1

An electric toaster costs a dealer $72.50 and he wishes to make a gain of $12.25. For how much must he sell it?

Solution: $S = C + G$

$S = \$72.50 + \$12.25$

$S = \$84.75$ (*answer*)

In this solution, we perform the following steps:

Step 1: Write the formula.
Step 2: Substitute the given values in the formula.
Step 3: Perform the mathematical operations indicated by the symbols in the formula.

The use of letters to represent numbers makes up one of the basic features of *algebra*. We are later going to use algebra to solve more difficult problems of this type, and we shall find that using the above steps is most helpful in getting our solutions.

Many of you have already learned some of the properties of a *triangle* (a 3-sided figure as shown in the diagram). The *perimeter* of the figure is the distance around it, or the sum of the lengths of the sides. If we represent the lengths of the sides by *r*, *s*, and *t*, we may find the perimeter, *p*, by the formula

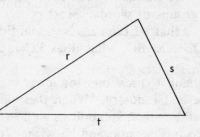

$$p = r + s + t$$

ILLUSTRATIVE PROBLEM 2

If the lengths of the sides of a triangle are 12 inches, 15 inches, and 21 inches, find its perimeter.

Solution: $p = r + s + t$

$p = 12 + 15 + 21$

$p = 48$ inches   (*answer*)

If the three sides of a triangle are equal, it is called an *equilateral triangle*, as in the figure. If we represent each side by *s*, then the perimeter formula tells us that

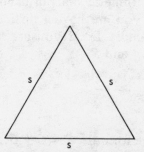

$$p = s + s + s$$

We may write this as $p = 3 \times s$ or $p = 3 \cdot s$ or $p = 3s$.

In algebra, we usually avoid the "times" sign ($\times$) because it resembles the letter *x* and may lead to confusion. When writing a product of numbers, we prefer the center dot ($\cdot$) to the $\times$ sign. When writing a product of letters or of numbers and letters, we usually omit the multiplication sign entirely. The above formula is usually written $p = 3s$.

ILLUSTRATIVE PROBLEM 3

Find the perimeter of an equilateral triangle when the length of each side is $6\frac{1}{2}$ inches.

Solution: $p = 3s$

$p = 3 \cdot 6\frac{1}{2}$

$p = 19\frac{1}{2}$ inches   (*answer*)

ILLUSTRATIVE PROBLEM 4

A retailer sells ties for 4 dollars each.
a. Write a formula for the amount of money, A, in dollars that he receives for selling t ties.
b. Use the formula from part **a** to find the amount of dollars he receives for 15 ties.

Solution:

a. The amount of dollars he receives is the product of 4 and t. Thus,

$$A = 4t$$

b. $A = 4t$
$A = 4 \cdot 15$
$A = 60$ dollars   (*answer*)

Exercises

1. A mechanic earns $3 an hour.

    a. If he works h hours, write a formula for his salary, S.

    b. Using this formula, find his salary for a 40-hour week.

2. An auto travels on a highway at 55 miles per hour.

    a. Write a formula for the distance, d, in miles that the auto travels in t hours.

    b. What distance does the auto travel in 4 hours?

3. A plane is cruising at 250 miles per hour.

    a. Write a formula for the distance, d, in miles flown by the plane in t hours.

    b. How many miles will the plane fly in 6 hours?

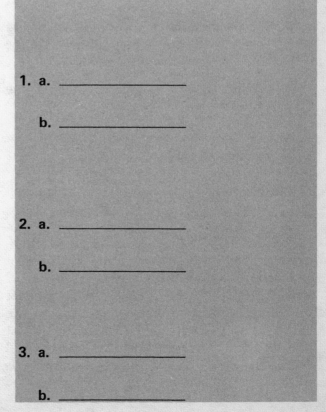

1. a. _____

   b. _____

2. a. _____

   b. _____

3. a. _____

   b. _____

4. a. Write a formula for the distance, d, traveled by an object in t hours if its rate of travel is r miles per hour.

b. A satellite is traveling around the earth at the rate of 10,000 miles per hour. How many miles does it travel in 15 minutes?

5. a. A merchant buys shirts for $3.50 each. Write a formula for his cost, C, of n shirts.

b. What is his cost per dozen for these shirts?

6. a. The driver of an auto determines how much gas he uses per mile (consumption, C) by dividing the distance covered in miles (d) by the number (N) of gallons of gas he uses. Write a formula for finding C.

b. How many miles per gallon does an auto travel if it uses 8 gallons to cover 100 miles?

7. a. Write a formula for the number of inches, I, in F feet.

b. How many inches long is a $4\frac{1}{2}$-foot board?

8. a. A classroom has r rows of seats with s seats in each row. Write a formula for the number, N, of seats in the room.

b. Find the number of seats in a room with 6 rows and 7 seats in each row.

4. a. _____

b. _____

5. a. _____

b. _____

6. a. _____

b. _____

7. a. _____

b. _____

8. a. _____

b. _____

3. Combining like terms

In determining the perimeter of an equilateral triangle, we say that $p = 3s$ is the same as $p = s + s + s$ because we know that adding a number to itself 3 times is the same as multiplying it by 3. When we multiply a number by a letter, we call the number the *numerical coefficient* of the letter. Thus, in the product $3s$, 3 is the numerical coefficient of s. In the expression $5x$, what is the numerical coefficient of x? In the expression $\frac{1}{4}d$, what is the numerical coefficient of d? The d in this expression is called the *literal factor*.

When we have a product of letters or of numbers and letters, the product is called a *term*. Thus, $3s$ is a term and $5b$ is a term. The expression $3s + 5b$ is a sum of two terms. How many terms are in $2a + 3b - 4c$?

The terms $5a$ and $3a$ are called *like terms* because they have a *common literal factor*. It is possible to add or subtract like terms if we recall how we added like quantities in arithmetic. For example,

$$5 \text{ eggs} + 2 \text{ eggs} = 7 \text{ eggs}$$
$$8 \text{ feet} - 3 \text{ feet} = 5 \text{ feet}$$
$$4 \text{ hours} + 6 \text{ hours} = 10 \text{ hours}$$

In a like manner, we say that

$5a + 2a = 7a$

$8f - 3f = 5f$

$4h + 6h = 10h$

We add and subtract like terms just as we do in arithmetic. Thus,

Add: $4b$ Subtract: $5r$
   $\underline{6b}$ $\underline{3r}$
  $10b$ $2r$

Rule: To add or subtract like terms, we add or subtract their numerical coefficients and multiply the result by their common literal factor.

Note that we cannot add 5 eggs and 2 shoes. In a like manner, we cannot combine $5a + 2b$ into one term.

However, we can add 5 nickels and 1 penny to 2 nickels and 3 pennies to get a sum of 7 nickels and 4 pennies. In algebra, we can show the addition like this:

$5n + 1p$
$\underline{2n + 3p}$
$7n + 4p$

We usually write $1p$ as just p with the 1 understood.

Examples

1. $4m + 3m = 7m$ 2. $8t - 3t = 5t$

3. Add: $7k$ 4. Add: $5x$
    $\underline{4k}$ $\underline{8x}$
    $11k$ $13x$

5. $7h + 4h - h = 11h - h = 10h$

6. Add: $2a + 7b$ 7. $6r - 6r = 0 \cdot r = 0$
    $\underline{4a + 2b}$
    $6a + 9b$

8. $10a - 3b + 4a = 14a - 3b$

9. $12x - 4x + 7y = 8x + 7y$

Exercises

1. State the numerical coefficient of each of the following:

   a. $4t$

   b. $7m$

   c. $\frac{1}{2}p$

   d. r

2. State whether the expressions are *like* terms or *unlike* terms and write the sum in each case:

   a. $3x$ and $5x$

   b. $4t$ and t

   c. $4m$ and $3n$

   d. $2y$ and $\frac{1}{2}y$

3. Combine like terms:

   a. $4r + 7r =$

   b. $3s + 5s - 2s =$

   c. $8x - x =$

   d. $5y - 5y =$

   e. $6t + 2\frac{1}{2}t =$

   f. $8p - 2p + 5p =$

   g. Add: $7m$
            $\underline{8m}$

   h. Add: $4y$
            $5y$
            $\underline{3y}$

4. Add:

   a. $2x + 3y$
      $\underline{5x + 4y}$

   b. $a + 6b$
      $\underline{3a + 5b}$

   c. $r + 2s + \ t$
      $\underline{4r + 3s + 5t}$

   d. $3m + \ 9$
      $\underline{2m + 11}$

5. Simplify the following formulas by combining like terms wherever possible:

   a. $p = 2a + 3a + 5b$

   b. $T = 3m + d + 2m$

   c. $c = 4r - 2r + 3s$

1. a. _____ b. _____
     c. _____ d. _____

2. a. _____ b. _____
     c. _____ b. _____

3. a. _____ b. _____
     c. _____ d. _____
     e. _____ f. _____
     g. _____ h. _____

4. a. _____ b. _____
     c. _____ d. _____

5. a. _____
     b. _____
     c. _____

4. Order of operations

In order to join a certain club, a man has to pay $5 down and then $2 every month. The formula for his total payment, T, after n months is given by

$$T = 5 + 2n$$

Now suppose we wish to find his total payment after 10 months. Substituting in the formula, we obtain

$$T = 5 + 2 \times 10$$

If we add the 5 and 2 first and then multiply by 10, we obtain 70. If we multiply 2 by 10 first and then add 5, we obtain 25. Which is correct?

Apparently it is not clear here as to which operation to perform first. In order to avoid this kind of confusion, mathematicians have agreed upon the following rule for the order of operations:

Rule: Reading from left to right, first perform the operations of multiplication and division. Then perform the operations of addition and subtraction.

Using this rule in the above problem,

$$T = 5 + 2 \times 10$$

$$T = 5 + 20$$

$$T = 25$$

The dues for 10 months are $25.

Exercises

In 1 to 7, find the value of each expression.

1. $6 + 5 \times 7$

2. $9 \div 3 - 1$

3. $5 \times 6 + 7 \times 8$

4. $9 \times 2 - 3 \times 4$

5. $8 \times 5 \div 20$

6. $18 - 6 \div 3$

7. $6 + 6 \times 6 - 6 \div 6$

8. In the triangle, two sides are equal and are designated by the letter r. The third side is designated by the letter s.

a. Write a formula for the perimeter, p, of this triangle.

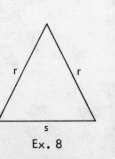

Ex. 8

Examples

1. $3 \cdot 5 + 8 = 15 + 8 = 23$

2. $12 \div 2 - 3 = 6 - 3 = 3$

3. $8 \cdot 3 - 6 \div 2 = 24 - 3 = 21$

1. _____

2. _____

3. _____

4. _____

5. _____

6. _____

7. _____

8. a. _____

b. Find the perimeter of the triangle if $r = 8$ and $s = 10$.

c. Find the perimeter of the triangle if $r = 12\frac{1}{2}$ and $s = 9\frac{1}{4}$.

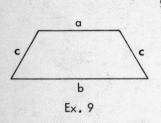

Ex. 9

9. In the four-sided figure, two sides are equal and are designated by the letter c. The other two sides are designated by the letters a and b.

a. Write a formula for the perimeter, p.

b. Find p if $a = 12$, $b = 15$, and $c = 10$.

10. An auto rental service charges $6 per day to rent a car and $.03 per mile for each mile driven. The formula for the cost in dollars, C, of renting a car for d days and driving m miles is $C = 6d + .03m$.

a. Find the cost of renting a car for 4 days and driving 300 miles.

b. Find the cost of renting a car for 6 days and driving 460 miles.

11. A movie theatre has an admission charge of $2 for adults and $1 for children.

a. Write a formula for the total receipts, R, in dollars of the theatre on a day when there are a adults and c children admitted.

b. Using the formula, find the total receipts on a day when 456 adults and 237 children are admitted.

12. On a certain test, pupils are awarded 5 points for each correct answer but are penalized for a wrong answer by having 2 points deducted. The formula for computing the total number of points is

$$P = 5c - 2w$$

where c is the number of correct answers and w is the number of wrong answers.

b. _____

c. _____

9. a. _____

b. _____

10. a. _____

b. _____

11. a. _____

b. _____

a. How many points did a boy receive if he had 15 correct answers and 5 wrong answers?

b. How many points did a girl receive if she had 10 correct answers and 10 wrong answers?

5. Using parentheses in formulas

Suppose we wish to find the perimeter of a rectangle of length l and width w, as in the figure. We may write the formula for the perimeter as

$$p = l + w + l + w \quad \text{or} \quad p = 2l + 2w$$

Another way of writing this is

$$p = 2(l + w)$$

where the quantity *in the parentheses* is to be obtained *first*; that is, the numerical values of l and w are to be added *first*, and then the sum is to be multiplied by 2. (See commutative, associative, and distributive principles in Appendix I, pages 279 and 285.)

Let us assume that the length of a rectangle is 30 inches and its width is 20 inches. The perimeter would then be

$$p = 2(l + w)$$

$$p = 2(30 + 20)$$

$$p = 2 \cdot 50 = 100 \text{ inches}$$

Note that the same result would be obtained by the other form of the formula:

$$p = 2l + 2w$$

$$p = 2 \cdot 30 + 2 \cdot 20$$

$$p = 60 + 40 = 100 \text{ inches}$$

These examples illustrate the following rule:

Rule: When several operations are indicated in a numerical expression, those grouped within parentheses are to be completed *first*. Then multiplication and division are done before addition and subtraction.

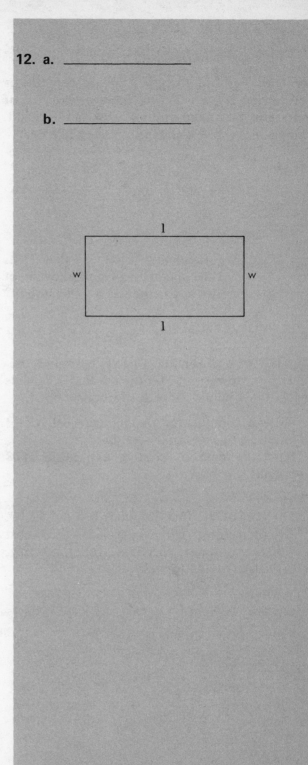

12. a. _____

b. _____

ILLUSTRATIVE PROBLEM 1

Find the value of $3 \times (9 - 7) + 2$.

Solution: Perform the operation in parentheses first, giving $3 \times 2 + 2$. Now the accepted rule of operations tells us to multiply first and then add, giving $6 + 2 = 8$. We arrange our work like this:

$3 \times (9 - 7) + 2$

$3 \times 2 + 2$

$6 + 2$

8 (*answer*)

Note: We frequently write $3 \times (9 - 7)$ as $3(9 - 7)$ where the operation of multiplication of 3 and the quantity in parentheses is understood.

ILLUSTRATIVE PROBLEM 2

The cost of sending a parcel by railway between two towns is $2.00 for the first 3 pounds and $.30 per pound for each additional pound.

a. Write a formula for finding the cost, C, of sending a package of p pounds.
b. Find the cost of sending a package of 8 pounds.

Solution:
a. The cost of the first 3 pounds is a flat $2.00. The remaining $(p - 3)$ pounds then cost $.30 per pound. Therefore, the total cost, C, is given by the formula

$C = 2.00 + .30(p - 3)$

b. If $p = 8$, we have

$C = 2.00 + .30(8 - 3)$

$C = 2.00 + .30 \times 5$

$C = 2.00 + 1.50$

$C = \$3.50$ (*answer*)

Exercises

1. Find the value of:

   a. $(4 + 3) \times 7$ **b.** $10 + 4 \times (5 - 2)$

   c. $18 \div (4 + 2)$ **d.** $(25 - 10) \div 2$

   e. $(6 + 11 - 3) \div 7$ **f.** $(12 - 3) \times (7 + 4)$

1. a. _____   **b.** _____

   c. _____   **d.** _____

   e. _____   **f.** _____

2. In the formula $L = 5 + d(n - 1)$:

   a. find L, when $d = 2$ and $n = 10$;

   b. find L, when $d = 3$ and $n = 20$;

   c. find L, when $d = 2\frac{1}{2}$ and $n = 15$.

3. The formula used to convert from Fahrenheit readings (F) on a thermometer to Celsius readings (C) is

$$C = \tfrac{5}{9}(F - 32)$$

   a. The boiling point of water is $212°$ F. Convert this to a Celsius reading.

   b. Convert a Fahrenheit reading of $68°$ F to a Celsius reading.

4. A limousine charges 60¢ for the first mile and 40¢ for each additional mile. The formula for the cost, C, of riding m miles is then

$$C = 60 + 40(m - 1)$$

   a. Find the cost of making a trip of 8 miles.

   b. Find the cost of a $4\frac{1}{2}$-mile trip.

5. The cost of sending a certain telegram is 60¢ for the first 10 words and 5¢ for each additional word. The formula for finding the cost, C, in cents, of sending a telegram of n words is

$$C = 60 + 5(n - 10)$$

   a. Find the cost of sending a telegram of 18 words.

   b. Find the cost of sending a telegram of 25 words.

6. **a.** Write a formula for the cost, c, of borrowing a book from a lending library for d days if the cost for the first 3 days is 25¢ and the cost for each additional day is 5¢.

   b. Find the cost of borrowing a book for a week.

6. Obtaining formulas from tables

   The owner of a movie theatre posts a table to be used by his employees to find the cost of

2. a. _____

   b. _____

   c. _____

3. a. _____

   b. _____

4. a. _____

   b. _____

5. a. _____

   b. _____

6. a. _____

   b. _____

different numbers of tickets. Here is the table:

Number of tickets (n)	1	2	3	4	5	6
Cost of tickets (c)	1.25	2.50	3.75	5.00	6.25	7.50

From this table, we can readily determine a formula for c in terms of n. Note that the cost per ticket is $1.25 and, therefore, the formula is

$$c = 1.25n$$

Using the formula, we can find the cost of any number of tickets.

Thus, for $n = 20; c = 1.25 \times 20 = \$25.00$.

The formula, therefore, is a shorthand way of summarizing the table.

An airline lists the following table showing the time in London (L) that corresponds to the time in New York (N):

London time (L)	6	7	8	9	10	11	12	13
New York time (N)	1	2	3	4	5	6	7	8

This is based on the 24-hour clock used by airlines. Can you write a formula to show how L is related to N? We may use either $L = N + 5$ or $N = L - 5$. As before, the formula is a shorthand summary of the table.

Exercises

In 1 to 5, write a formula to express the relationship shown in each table.

1.

Number of tickets (n)	1	2	3	4	5
Cost in dollars (c)	1.50	3.00	4.50	6.00	7.50

1. _____

2.

Number of inches (i)	12	24	36	48	60
Number of feet (f)	1	2	3	4	5

2. _____

3.

H	1	2	3	4	5
W	8	9	10	11	12

4.

K	9	11	13	15	17
L	6	8	10	12	14

5.

Husband's age (h)	27	30	33	36	40
Wife's age (w)	23	26	29	32	36

(This table shows the relationship of a man's age to his wife's age.)

6. This table shows the conversion from British pounds (P) to U.S. dollars (D) at one time.

British pounds (P)	1	2	3	4	5
U.S. dollars (D)	2.40	4.80	7.20	9.60	12.00

   a. Write a formula relating D to P.

   b. How many dollars would be received for 10 British pounds?

Chapter review exercises

1. A pentagon is a five-sided figure. In the pentagon shown, all five sides are equal and are designated by s.

   a. Write a formula for the perimeter, p, of this pentagon.

   Ex. 1

   b. Find the perimeter of the base of the Pentagon building in Washington, D.C., each side of which is 921 feet.

2. In a certain test consisting of Parts I and II, a pupil gets 3 points for each correct answer in Part I and 2 points for each correct answer in Part II.

   a. Write a formula for the total number of

3. _____

4. _____

5. _____

6. a. _____

   b. _____

1. a. _____

   b. _____

points, P, received for a correct answers in Part I and b correct answers in Part II.

b. Using the formula, find the total number of points received by a student getting 15 correct answers in Part I and 16 correct in Part II.

3. a. Using the formula $C = \frac{5}{9}(F - 32)$, find the Celsius reading corresponding to 32° F, the freezing point of water.

b. Normal body temperature is 98.6° F. What is this in the Celsius scale?

4. The cost of a long-distance telephone call is 80¢ for the first three minutes and 20¢ for each additional minute.

a. Write a formula for the total cost, T, of a phone call lasting m minutes.

b. Using the formula, find the total cost of an 8-minute call?

5. A repair man receives $2 per hour regular pay and $1\frac{1}{2}$ times this rate for overtime pay.

a. Write a formula for the salary, S, earned by a man who works r hours at regular pay and V hours overtime.

b. Using the formula, find the salary of a man who works 40 hours in a week at regular pay and 8 hours overtime.

6. a. Write a formula for the average (A) of three numbers r, s, t.

b. Using the formula, find the average of three test scores: 78, 83, 90.

7. The following table shows a man's weekly salary, S, for working h hours per week:

h	10	15	20	25	30	35	40
S	$30	$45	$60	$75	$90	$105	$120

a. Write a formula for S in terms of h.

b. Using the formula, find what the man earns for 38 hours of work.

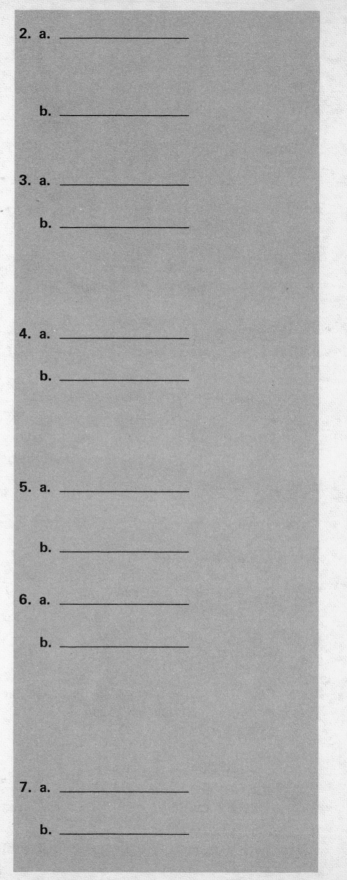

2. a. _____

   b. _____

3. a. _____

   b. _____

4. a. _____

   b. _____

5. a. _____

   b. _____

6. a. _____

   b. _____

7. a. _____

   b. _____

Check your arithmetic skills

1. Add:

    a. 129   **b.** 9497   **c.** 357
        958   6364   22
        787   4269   1845
        436   9785   639

2. Subtract:

    a. 637   **b.** 805   **c.** 835
        265   276   397

3. Multiply:

    a. 27   **b.** 43   **c.** 27
       ×6   ×27   ×40

    d. 220   **e.** 807
       ×30   ×28

4. Divide:

    a. $4\overline{)56}$ **b.** $11\overline{)352}$ **c.** $31\overline{)9.641}$

    d. $69\overline{)483}$ **e.** $25\overline{)2300}$

5. A lumber yard had 12,280 feet of a certain plank. If 6252 feet are used, how many feet of this plank remain?

6. Find the total weight of 6875 metal blocks if each block weighs 97 pounds.

7. A job requires 480 hours. How many 8-hour days is this?

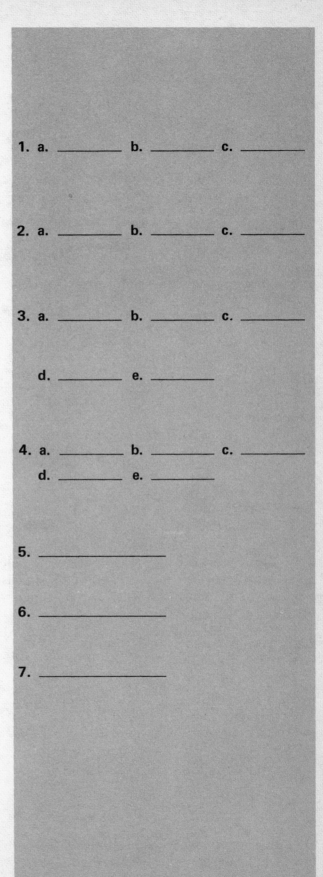

1. a. _____ b. _____ c. _____

2. a. _____ b. _____ c. _____

3. a. _____ b. _____ c. _____

    d. _____ e. _____

4. a. _____ b. _____ c. _____

    d. _____ e. _____

5. _____

6. _____

7. _____

SOLVING SIMPLE
EQUATIONS

2

1. Meaning of an equation

Consider the following statements:

$$4 + 3 = 7$$
$$8 \times 3 = 12 \times 2$$
$$9 - 3 = 6$$

Each states that the two quantities are equal and, therefore, each is a statement of equality. In mathematics, a statement of equality is called an *equation*.

Which of the following are equations?

$$10 + 2 = 12$$
$$19 - 8$$
$$7 + 4$$
$$\frac{120}{6} = 20$$

The equation $5 + 4 = 9$ consists of two quantities, $5 + 4$ and 9. The quantity $5 + 4$ is on the left side of the equals sign and is called the *left member* of the equation. What do you think we call the quantity on the right side of the equals sign?

In the following equations, identify the left member and the right member:

$$15 = 5 \times 3$$
$$9 \times 4 = 18 \times 2$$
$$5y = 35$$
$$n = 14 + 3$$
$$\frac{p}{4} = 3$$
$$x + 8 = 12$$

In some of these equations, a letter has been used to represent a missing number. In $x + 8 = 12$, it is clear that 4 is the value of x which makes the equation true because $4 + 8 = 12$. In $5y = 35$, it is clear that 7 is the value of y which makes this equation true because $5 \times 7 = 35$.

The value of the letter which makes the equation a true statement is called the **root** of the equation. In $\frac{p}{4} = 3$, when p is replaced by 12 the equation is a true statement. Thus, 12 is the root of the equation.

Exercises

By trying various numbers, find the root of each equation.

1. $6m = 18$ **2.** $x + 3 = 9$ **3.** $y - 3 = 12$

4. $\dfrac{r}{3} = 5$ **5.** $14 + t = 20$ **6.** $s + \dfrac{1}{4} = 1$

7. $15 = x + 9$ **8.** $21 = p - 2$

1. _____   **2.** _____   **3.** _____

4. _____   **5.** _____   **6.** _____

7. _____   **8.** _____

2. Solving equations by addition or subtraction

Find the roots of the following equations:

$y + 7 = 10$

$y + 5 = 8$

$y + 4 = 7$

$y + 2 = 5$

$y = 3$

Note that in each equation the root is 3. Equations having the same root are called **equivalent equations**. In order to find the root of a given equation, we must change the given equation to an equivalent equation where the root is obvious, as in the last equation above, $y = 3$.

We may think of an equation as a **balance scale**, where the left and right pans of the scale are similar to the left and right members of an equation. If the scale is balanced to begin with, we may maintain the balance if we add to or remove equal weights from both pans. Likewise, if we add or subtract the same number to or from both members of an equation, we will obtain an equivalent equation.

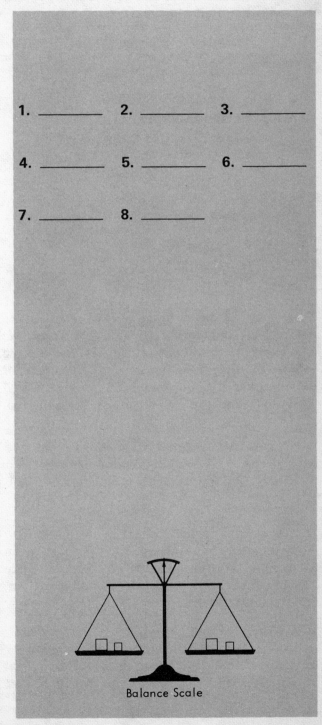

Balance Scale

This principle is very useful in finding the roots of many equations. For example, consider the equation

$$y + 5 = 12$$

Since the y and 5 are added, we can obtain y alone on the left side by subtracting 5. But the **balance principle** requires that we subtract 5 from the right member also to obtain an equivalent equation. Hence we have

$$\begin{array}{ll} y + 5 = 12 & \text{(original equation)} \\ \underline{-5 \quad -5} & \text{(subtract 5 from both members} \\ y = 7 & \text{(root)} \end{array}$$

We can check this equation by replacing y by 7 in the original equation.

Check: $y + 5 = 12$

$$7 + 5 = 12$$
$$12 = 12 \checkmark$$

Let us find the root of the equation $x + 3 = 10$:

$$\begin{array}{ll} x + 3 = 10 & \\ \underline{-3 \quad -3} & \\ x = 7 & \text{(root)} \end{array}$$

Clearly, $x = 7$ checks in the original equation. We refer to this principle as the **subtraction principle of equality**. In like manner, we may also use the **addition principle of equality**. For example, if we start with the equation $m - 5 = 11$, we would now add 5 to both members of the equation. Thus

$$\begin{array}{ll} m - 5 = 11 & \text{(original equation)} \\ \underline{+5 \quad +5} & \text{(add 5 to both members)} \\ m = 16 & \text{(equivalent equation or root)} \end{array}$$

Principle: If we add the same number to both members of an equation, the result is an equivalent equation. If we subtract the same number from both members of an equation, the result is an equivalent equation.

When we find the root of an equation by changing it to an equivalent equation whose root is obvious (as above), we say that we are **solving** the equation or finding its **solution**.

Exercises

Solve each of the following equations and check:

1. $y + 7 = 18$

2. $m - 14 = 20$

3. $x + 3 = 12$

4. $r + 2\frac{1}{2} = 5\frac{1}{2}$

5. $s - 2.7 = 5.5$

6. $10 + t = 20$

7. $14 = a + 11$

8. $k - 2 = 8\frac{1}{4}$

9. $k + 12 = 12$

10. $4\frac{3}{4} = n + \frac{3}{8}$

11. $p - .13 = 2.9$

12. $w - \frac{2}{3} = 1\frac{1}{2}$

1. _____   2. _____

3. _____   4. _____

5. _____   6. _____

7. _____   8. _____

9. _____   10. _____

11. _____   12. _____

3. Solving equations by division

Determine by inspection the root of each of the following equations:

$$6n = 24$$
$$3n = 12$$
$$2n = 8$$
$$n = 4$$

Note that these equations are **equivalent** since $n = 4$ is a root of all four equations. Now let us see how we obtain one of these equations from the other.

Recall that, when we write $5x$, both 5 and x are **factors** of the expression; that is, the 5 and the x are *multiplied* together to obtain the product $5x$. In such a product, we refer to the numeral 5 as the **coefficient** of x. In the expression $6a$, 6 would be the coefficient of a.

Let us divide the product 3×7 by both of the factors:

$$\frac{3 \times 7}{3} = \frac{21}{3} = 7 \quad \text{and} \quad \frac{3 \times 7}{7} = \frac{21}{7} = 3$$

Thus, if we divide a product of two numbers by one of them, we get the other number. For example,

$$\frac{8 \times 5}{8} = \frac{40}{8} = 5 \quad \text{and} \quad \frac{8 \times 5}{5} = \frac{40}{5} = 8$$

By what number must we divide $7m$ to get m?

Now let us return to the four equations we saw at the start of this section:

$$6n = 24$$

$$3n = 12$$

$$2n = 8$$

$$n = 4$$

Note that the last three equations could be obtained from the first equation by dividing both members of the equation $6n = 24$ first by 2, then by 3, and then by 6.

These examples suggest the following *division principle of equality*:

Principle: If we divide both sides of an equation by the same number, the result is an equivalent equation.

ILLUSTRATIVE PROBLEM 1

Solve and check: $8x = 32$

Solution: By what number must we divide $8x$ in order to get x? Obviously, by 8. Hence, we must also divide the right member by 8.

$$8x = 32 \quad \text{(original equation)}$$

$$\frac{8x}{8} = \frac{32}{8} \quad \text{(division principle of equality)}$$

$$x = 4 \quad \text{(equivalent equation or root)}$$

Check: $\quad 8x = 32$ (original equation)

$$8 \cdot 4 = 32 \quad \text{(substitute } x = 4\text{)}$$

$$32 = 32 \quad \checkmark$$

ILLUSTRATIVE PROBLEM 2

Solve and check: $6y = 45$

Solution:

$$6y = 45$$

$$\frac{6y}{6} = \frac{45}{6}$$

$$y = 7\tfrac{1}{2}$$

Check: $6y = 45$

$$6 \cdot 7\tfrac{1}{2} = 45$$

$$45 = 45 \;\checkmark$$

Note that, in equations of this type, we always divide both members of the equation by the coefficient of the unknown term. In illustrative problem 1 we divided by 8, the coefficient of x. In illustrative problem 2 we divided by 6, the coefficient of y.

Exercises

Find the root of each equation and check.

1. $5x = 20$ **2.** $8y = 96$

3. $7d = 28$ **4.** $6m = 50$

5. $2b = 7.4$ **6.** $12z = 100$

7. $.2r = 68$ **8.** $.04t = .76$

9. $15 = 3k$ **10.** $11n = 0$

11. $15p = 225$ **12.** $0 = 5s$

1. _____   2. _____

3. _____   4. _____

5. _____   6. _____

7. _____   8. _____

9. _____   10. _____

11. _____   12. _____

4. Solving equations by multiplication

In a manner similar to that used in section 3, we can solve equations such as $\dfrac{n}{5} = 7$. We know that $3 \times \dfrac{11}{3} = 11$ and that $5 \times \dfrac{8}{5} = 8$.

These examples indicate that, in general,

$$5 \times \frac{n}{5} = n$$

and suggest the approach to use in solving equations such as $\dfrac{n}{5} = 7$. Just as we were able to *divide* both members of an equation by the same quantity and arrive at an equivalent equation, we may also *multiply* both members by the same quantity and arrive at an equivalent equation whose solution is obvious. Let us solve $\frac{n}{5} = 7$:

$$\frac{n}{5} = 7 \qquad \text{(original equation)}$$

$$5 \times \frac{n}{5} = 7 \times 5 \quad \text{(multiply both members by 5)}$$

$$n = 35 \qquad \text{(equivalent equation or root)}$$

Check: $\qquad \frac{n}{5} = 7 \quad$ (original equation)

$$\frac{35}{5} = 7 \quad \text{(substitute } n = 35)$$

$$7 = 7 \; \checkmark$$

This illustration suggests the following *multiplication principle of equality:*

Principle: If we multiply both sides of an equation by the same number, the result is an equivalent equation.

Exercises

In 1 to 6, solve and check.

1. $\frac{n}{4} = 8$

2. $\frac{b}{11} = 7$

1. _____ 2. _____

3. $\frac{c}{3} = 9$

4. $14 = \frac{k}{5}$

3. _____ 4. _____

5. $\frac{3r}{4} = 2\frac{1}{2}$

6. $\frac{x}{10} = 3.4$

5. _____ 6. _____

7. What is $5 \times \frac{1}{5}n$ equal to?

7. _____

8. What is $\frac{2}{3} \times \frac{3}{2}k$ equal to?

8. _____

In 9 to 14, solve and check.

9. $\frac{1}{5}x = 12$

10. $\frac{1}{3}y = 9$

9. _____ 10. _____

11. $\dfrac{3}{2}t = 21$ **12.** $\dfrac{x}{.5} = 12.6$

13. $\dfrac{p}{4} = 0$ **14.** $1 = \dfrac{3r}{9}$

11. _____   **12.** _____

13. _____   **14.** _____

5. Solving equations by two steps

In solving some equations, it becomes necessary to use two principles of equality in succession before arriving at an equivalent equation whose solution is obvious.

For example, let us solve the equation $4x - 3 = 17$:

$$
\begin{array}{ll}
4x - 3 = 17 & \\
\underline{+3 \quad +3} & \text{(addition property of equality)} \\
4x \quad\;\; = 20 &
\end{array}
$$

This equation is equivalent to the original equation, but requires further simplification. Thus,

$$4x = 20$$

$$\frac{4x}{4} = \frac{20}{4} \quad \text{(division principle of equality)}$$

$$x = 5$$

We would obtain the same result here if we used the division principle first and then the addition property; however, at this stage, it is simpler to use the addition property first.

Now let us check this solution in the original equation.

Check:
$$4x - 3 = 17$$
$$4 \cdot 5 - 3 = 17 \quad \text{(substitute } x = 5\text{)}$$
$$20 - 3 = 17$$
$$17 = 17 \;\checkmark$$

ILLUSTRATIVE PROBLEM

Solve for y and check: $\dfrac{y}{4} + 3 = 15$

Solution: Let us begin by first subtracting 3 from both members.

$$\frac{y}{4} + 3 = 15$$

$$\frac{-3 \quad -3}{\frac{y}{4} \quad = 12}$$

Now multiply both members by 4.

$$4 \times \frac{y}{4} = 12 \times 4$$

$$y = 48 \quad (answer)$$

Check: $\frac{y}{4} + 3 = 15$ (original equation)

$$\frac{48}{4} + 3 = 15 \quad (\text{substitute } y = 48)$$

$$12 + 3 = 15$$

$$15 = 15 \checkmark$$

Exercises

Solve and check the following equations:

1. $2p - 7 = 11$

2. $3y + 5 = 17$

3. $4r + 1 = 22$

4. $2r - 8 = 9$

5. $7n + 3 = 3$

6. $8 + 5t = 28$

7. $\frac{s}{4} + 5 = 15$

8. $10 + \frac{k}{3} = 18$

9. $2a - 3.8 = 5.0$

10. $3y + .2 = 9.2$

11. $3p - \frac{1}{4} = 8$

12. $5t + .2 = 10.7$

13. $\frac{m}{3} + 2 = 6$

14. $6r - 2 = 5.2$

15. $\frac{2}{3}x + 1 = 1$

16. $\frac{5}{8}z = 50$

17. $4a - \frac{1}{2} = 11\frac{1}{2}$

18. $.04x + 3 = 3.08$

1. _____

2. _____

3. _____

4. _____

5. _____

6. _____

7. _____

8. _____

9. _____

10. _____

11. _____

12. _____

13. _____

14. _____

15. _____

16. _____

17. _____

18. _____

6. Combining like terms in equations

In Chapter 1, we learned how to add or subtract *like terms*. For example, $2a + 5a = 7a$ and $8m - 2m = 6m$.

We may use this principle in solving an equation which has a sum or difference in like terms in one of its members.

ILLUSTRATIVE PROBLEM 1

Solve and check: $2x + 3x = 15$

Solution:

$$2x + 3x = 15$$
$$5x = 15 \quad \text{(combine like terms)}$$
$$\frac{5x}{5} = \frac{15}{5} \quad \text{(divide both members by 5)}$$
$$x = 3 \quad (\textit{answer})$$

Check:

$$2x + 3x = 15$$
$$2(3) + 3(3) = 15 \quad \text{(substitute } x = 3)$$
$$6 + 9 = 15$$
$$15 = 15 \ \checkmark$$

Recall here that $2(3)$ is another way of writing $2 \cdot 3$ or 2×3. This notation was already used in Chapter 1.

ILLUSTRATIVE PROBLEM 2

Solve and check: $7y - 4y = 21$

Solution:

$$7y - 4y = 21$$
$$3y = 21 \quad \text{(combine like terms)}$$
$$\frac{3y}{3} = \frac{21}{3} \quad \text{(divide both members by 3)}$$
$$y = 7 \quad (\textit{answer})$$

Check:

$$7y - 4y = 21 \quad \text{(original equation)}$$
$$7(7) - 4(7) = 21 \quad \text{(substitute } y = 7)$$

$$49 - 28 = 21$$
$$21 = 21 \ \checkmark$$

In checking, it is important to substitute in the *original* equation. If we substitute in an equivalent equation, we may have already made a mistake in obtaining the equivalent equation from the original.

Exercises

Solve and check the following equations:

1. $5m + 2m = 14$

2. $32 = 10y - 2y$

3. $x + 4x = 30$

4. $8 = 2.5k + 1.5k$

5. $p + 2p + 3p = 180$

6. $\frac{3}{2}t + \frac{5}{2}t = 50$

7. $14.2r - 4.2r = 30$

8. $390 = 4n + 2n$

9. $\frac{8}{5}y - \frac{7}{5}y = 6$

10. $2.40 = c + .20c$

11. $3t + \frac{1}{2}t = 28$

12. $4\frac{1}{2}x - 2\frac{3}{4}x = 14$

1. _____   2. _____

3. _____   4. _____

5. _____   6. _____

7. _____   8. _____

9. _____   10. _____

11. _____   12. _____

7. More difficult equations: Unknown terms on both sides

ILLUSTRATIVE PROBLEM

Solve and check: $5x = 21 + 2x$

Here terms involving the unknown quantity are in both members of the equation. We must, therefore, subtract $2x$ from both sides so as to bring like terms to one side.

Solution:

$$5x = 21 + 2x$$
$$\underline{-2x = \quad\quad -2x}$$
$$3x = 21$$

$$\frac{3x}{3} = \frac{21}{3}$$

$$x = 7$$

Check:

$$5x = 21 + 2x \quad \text{(original equation)}$$
$$5(7) = 21 + 2(7) \quad \text{(substitute } x = 7\text{)}$$
$$35 = 21 + 14$$
$$35 = 35 \ \checkmark$$

Exercises

Solve and check the following equations:

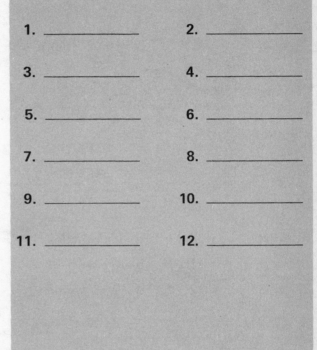

1. $7y = 15 + 2y$ **2.** $9m = 33 - 2m$ 1. _____   2. _____

3. $5t = 24 + t$ **4.** $3 - p = 8p$ 3. _____   4. _____

5. $1.1k = 30 + .5k$ **6.** $3\frac{1}{2}x = 18 + 1\frac{1}{2}x$ 5. _____   6. _____

7. $11r = 36 - 7r$ **8.** $3t + 6 = 55 - 4t$ 7. _____   8. _____

9. $4b + 8 = 20 + b$ **10.** $2.3y = 40 - .2y$ 9. _____   10. _____

11. $8z + 24 = 5z - 12$ **12.** $4c - 3 = 47 - c$ 11. _____   12. _____

Chapter review exercises

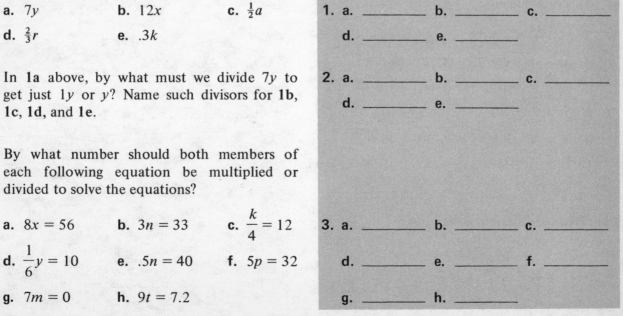

1. In each of the following, name the numerical coefficient:

   a. $7y$ **b.** $12x$ **c.** $\frac{1}{2}a$

   d. $\frac{2}{3}r$ **e.** $.3k$

1. a. _____ b. _____ c. _____
   d. _____ e. _____

2. In **1a** above, by what must we divide $7y$ to get just $1y$ or y? Name such divisors for **1b**, **1c**, **1d**, and **1e**.

2. a. _____ b. _____ c. _____
   d. _____ e. _____

3. By what number should both members of each following equation be multiplied or divided to solve the equations?

   a. $8x = 56$ **b.** $3n = 33$ **c.** $\dfrac{k}{4} = 12$

   d. $\dfrac{1}{6}y = 10$ **e.** $.5n = 40$ **f.** $5p = 32$

   g. $7m = 0$ **h.** $9t = 7.2$

3. a. _____ b. _____ c. _____
   d. _____ e. _____ f. _____
   g. _____ h. _____

4. Solve and check each equation in exercise 3.

5. What number must be added to or subtracted from both members of each following equation in order to solve the equation?

a. $r + 7 = 15$ b. $t - 9 = 11$

c. $8 + x = 20$ d. $y - 2\frac{1}{2} = 7\frac{1}{2}$

e. $n + 2.3 = 17$ f. $18 = k - 7$

g. $r + 5 = 5$ h. $y - .07 = 4.2$

6. Solve and check each equation in exercise 5.

7. Solve and check the following equations:

a. $2x + 3 = 15$ b. $4 + 8n = 44$

c. $3p - 6 = 12$ d. $2y + \frac{1}{2} = 6\frac{1}{2}$

e. $.5 + 2k = 7.1$ f. $5a + 9 = 9$

g. $\dfrac{5}{8}y = 40$ h. $\dfrac{3z}{10} = 12$

i. $3n - n + 4 = 15$ j. $28 + 4r = 54$

k. $8x + 4 - x = 25$ l. $\frac{1}{2}t + 1 = 17$

m. $2a - 6 = 0$ n. $\frac{2}{3}t - 7 = 17$

o. $5r + 3r = 80$ p. $.3c + .02c = 6.4$

q. $7p + 4 - p = 34$ r. $6x = 36 - 3x$

s. $5y - 4 = 2y + 8$ t. $12z - 19 = 7z + 11$

Check your arithmetic skills

1. Evaluate: a. $10 - 4 + 2 + 6$

   b. $14 + 16 - 3 + 10 - 4 - 6$

2. Add:

   a. 8768   **b.** 9,568   **c.** 85,416
       2436   76   78,959
       6832   800   20,048
       4095   19,875

2. a. _____ b. _____ c. _____

3. Subtract:

   a. 390   **b.** 709
       169   594

   c. 2807   **d.** 8700
       998   5008

3. a. _____ b. _____

   c. _____ d. _____

4. Multiply:

   a. 89   **b.** 509
    ×76   ×87

   c. 847   **d.** 699
    ×79   ×507

4. a. _____ b. _____

   c. _____ d. _____

5. Divide:

   a. 21⟌882   **b.** 82⟌2952   **c.** 23⟌943
   d. 78⟌3978   **e.** 67⟌5963

5. a. _____ b. _____ c. _____
   d. _____ e. _____

6. A tank contained 5356 gallons of oil. If 686 gallons were used, how many gallons remained?

6. _____

7. A bar of iron 18 feet long weighs 1134 pounds. What is the weight per foot?

7. _____

8. A building is 28 stories high. Each story is 14 feet high. What is the height in feet of the building?

8. _____

SOLVING PROBLEMS
BY USING EQUATIONS

3

1. Algebraic representation

The equation provides us with a very powerful tool for solving many mathematical problems. But, before we can solve these problems, we must first become familiar with the way certain words or phrases in English are *translated* into the symbols and letters of algebra.

In Chapter 1, we learned how to use letters to represent numbers. If n represents a certain number, $7n$ represents seven times that number. What is 7 more than the number n? Seven more than 4 is $4 + 7$, or 11. Hence, 7 more than n is $n + 7$.

What is 7 less than n? Again, think of what you would do with two numbers. Seven less than 10 is $10 - 7$, or 3. Thus, 7 less than n is $n - 7$.

Certain algebraic symbols may be expressed in words in several different ways. A few of these are listed below:

Algebraic Expression	Word Expression
$3n$	3 times n 3 multiplied by n the product of 3 and n
$x + 7$	7 more than x the sum of x and 7 x increased by 7
$t - 5$	t diminished by 5 t decreased by 5 5 less than t the difference of t and 5 5 subtracted from t
$\dfrac{m}{9}$ or $m \div 9$	one-ninth of m m divided by 9 the quotient of m and 9

ILLUSTRATIVE PROBLEMS

1. Bill is 3 years older than Tom. If Tom is t years old, express Bill's age algebraically.

Solution: Bill is $(t + 3)$ years old.

2. Jim's father is 3 times as old as he is. If Jim is y years old, express his father's age algebraically.

Solution: His father is $3y$ years old.

3. Mary has n dollars. Anne has 3 less than twice what Mary has. Express Anne's amount algebraically.

Solution: Anne has $(2n - 3)$ dollars.

4. How many feet are in p inches?

Solution: How would we change 24 inches to feet? We would divide 24 by 12. Likewise, we divide p by 12 so that p inches $= \dfrac{p}{12}$ feet.

Exercises

1. If n represents a number, write algebraically:

  a. 10 more than n

  b. 3 less than n

  c. 5 times n

  d. 7 more than twice n

  e. n decreased by 9

  f. 30 diminished by 5 times n

  g. one-half of n

  h. the product of n and 12

  i. the quotient of 48 divided by n

  j. 17 less than four times n

  k. $\frac{2}{3}$ of n increased by 12

1. a. _____
   b. _____
   c. _____
   d. _____
   e. _____
   f. _____
   g. _____
   h. _____
   i. _____
   j. _____
   k. _____

2. Represent algebraically:

  a. 7 more than t

  b. 18 less than k

  c. 5 times r

  d. s decreased by 14

  e. p divided by 9

  f. 8 less than 6 times x

  g. y increased by 3

  h. 25 decreased by m

  i. one-half of q

2. a. _____
   b. _____
   c. _____
   d. _____
   e. _____
   f. _____
   g. _____
   h. _____
   i. _____

j. n subtracted from 8

k. p increased by q

l. r decreased by s

m. 5 less than 8 times t

n. 32 more than $\frac{9}{5}$ of c

j. _____

k. _____

l. _____

m. _____

n. _____

3. If x and y represent two numbers, write algebraically:

a. the product of the two numbers

b. the quotient of the first number divided by the second

c. the sum of the two numbers

d. the first number diminished by twice the second number

3. a. _____

b. _____

c. _____

d. _____

4. State in words a meaning of each of the following algebraic expressions:

a. $r + 4$

b. $m - 7$

c. $6t$

d. $2n - 5$

e. $\dfrac{y}{12}$

f. $\frac{1}{2}x + 8$

g. $13 - k$

h. $\dfrac{p}{4} - 6$

i. $a - b$

j. $p + 2q$

4. a. _____

b. _____

c. _____

d. _____

e. _____

f. _____

g. _____

h. _____

i. _____

j. _____

In 5 to 22, express the result algebraically.

5. A man is now k years old.

a. Express his age 10 years from now.

b. Express his age 10 years ago.

5. a. _____

b. _____

6. Jim had 60 cents and spent c cents. How many cents did he have left?

6. _____

7. An apple costs *p* cents. How much will a dozen apples cost?

7. _____

8. a. If 10 toys cost $30, how much does each toy cost?

8. a. _____

   b. If 10 toys cost *x* dollars, express the cost of each toy.

b. _____

9. A man is *h* years old and his wife is *w* years old. How much older is the man than his wife?

9. _____

10. The length of a rectangle is *f* feet and the width is 3 feet shorter. Express the width.

10. _____

11. How many feet are there in:

   a. 1 yard?   **b.** 5 yards?

   c. 7 yards?   **d.** *y* yards?

11. a. _____   b. _____

     c. _____   d. _____

12. How many cents are there in:

   a. 1 dime?   **b.** 3 dimes?   **c.** *n* dimes?

12. a. _____ b. _____ c. _____

13. A bus travels 40 miles per hour. How far does it go in:

   a. 3 hours?   **b.** 5 hours?   **c.** *t* hours?

13. a. _____ b. _____ c. _____

14. The side of a square is *s* inches in length. Express its perimeter.

14. _____

15. If we represent a whole number by *n*, how do we represent the next whole number?

15. _____

16. How many yards are there in:

   a. 3 feet?   **b.** 6 feet?

   c. 12 feet?   **d.** *f* feet?

16. a. _____   b. _____

     c. _____   d. _____

17. Bob has *b* dollars.

   a. If Arthur has 8 dollars more than Bob, represent Arthur's amount.

17. a. _____

   b. Represent the sum of Bob's amount and Arthur's amount.

b. _____

18. John is x years old. His father is 3 times as old as John.

   a. Represent his father's age.

   b. Represent the difference between the father's and son's ages.

19. Eggs cost c cents per dozen.

   a. How much does 1 egg cost?

   b. Represent the cost of 5 eggs.

20. The width of a rectangle is k feet. If the length is 10 more than twice the width, represent the length.

21. Represent the sum of p and q diminished by twice r.

22. A boy bought 8 articles, each costing c cents. How much change should he receive from a $5.00 bill?

18. a. _____

    b. _____

19. a. _____

    b. _____

20. _____

21. _____

22. _____

2. Writing algebraic equations

We are now prepared to solve problems by means of equations. We will start with some simple problems that may easily be done by arithmetic processes alone. In order to develop greater skill in algebra, however, we will form equations and solve them.

ILLUSTRATIVE PROBLEM 1

If 12 is added to a certain number, the result is 35. Find the number. Form an equation for this problem; solve and check it.

Solution: Let n = the certain number. Then:

$$n + 12 = 35 \quad \text{(equation)}$$
$$\underline{-12 \quad -12}$$
$$n \quad\quad = 23 \quad \text{(\emph{answer})}$$

Check: To check the solution to a verbal problem, check it in the *original* problem. Thus, if 12 is added to 23, the result is 35, and this checks.

ILLUSTRATIVE PROBLEM 2

Five times a number diminished by 18 is 42. Find the number.

Solution: Let x = the number. Then:

$$5x - 18 = 42 \quad \text{(equation)}$$
$$\underline{+18 \quad +18}$$
$$5x \quad\quad = 60$$

$$\frac{5x}{5} = \frac{60}{5}$$

$$x = 12 \quad \text{(answer)}$$

Check: Five times $12 = 60; 60 - 18 = 42.$ ✓

ILLUSTRATIVE PROBLEM 3

A boy, who is 12 years old, is $\frac{1}{3}$ as old as his father. How old is his father?

Solution: Let y = the father's age in years. Then:

$$\tfrac{1}{3}y = 12 \quad \text{(equation)}$$

Multiply both members by 3:

$$y = 36 \quad \text{(answer)}$$

Check: 12 is $\frac{1}{3}$ of 36.

The steps in solving "word problems" are as follows:

a. Read the problem carefully.
b. Determine what is given and what is to be found.
c. Represent one of the unknown quantities by a letter.
d. Represent any other unknown quantities in terms of this letter.
e. Write the equation which expresses the meaning of the problem.
f. Solve the equation.
g. Check the answers in the wording of the problem.

Exercises

In 1 to 10, solve each problem by forming an equation. Then solve the equation and check in the *original* problem. Give the equation as part of your answer.

1. If 8 is added to a certain number, the sum is 84. Find the number.

2. Eleven times a certain number is 132. Find the number.

3. One-third of a number is 83. Find the number.

4. If 14 is subtracted from a certain number, the result is 72. Find the number.

5. Twice a certain number increased by 15 is 35. Find the number.

6. If three times a certain number is diminished by 17, the result is 28. Find the number.

7. There are 32 pupils in a class. The number of girls is 3 times the number of boys. How many boys are in the class?

8. In 14 days, a man earned $308. How much did he earn each day?

9. Three-sevenths of a number is 24. Find the number.

10. A football player scored one-fourth of the team's final score. If he scored 18 points, what was the team score?

11. One-third of a certain number increased by 12 is equal to 18. Find the number.

12. The larger of two numbers is 7 times the smaller. If n represents the smaller, then:

    a. Represent the larger in terms of n.

    b. If the sum of the two numbers is 120, write an equation expressing this relation.

    c. Solve this equation for n.

    d. Write both numbers and check.

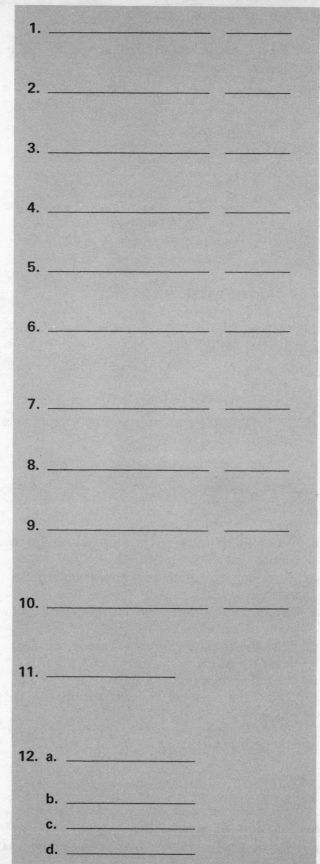

1. _____ _____

2. _____ _____

3. _____ _____

4. _____ _____

5. _____ _____

6. _____ _____

7. _____ _____

8. _____ _____

9. _____ _____

10. _____ _____

11. _____

12. a. _____

    b. _____

    c. _____

    d. _____

13. A board which is 80 inches long is cut into two pieces so that one piece is four times as long as the other. If y is the length in inches of the smaller piece, then:

a. Represent the larger piece in terms of y.

b. Write an equation to find y.

c. Solve the equation and check.

14. What number increased by $\frac{1}{4}$ of itself is equal to 30?

15. A boy has three times as much as his sister. Together they have $60. How much does each have?

16. A man paid for a TV set in 12 equal payments. If the set cost $240, how much did he pay each month?

17. One number is four times another. The difference between the larger number and the smaller number is 48. Find the two numbers.

18. Mary and Nancy saved $30 together. In dividing it between them, Mary got $4 more than Nancy. How much did each receive?

19. Separate 180 into two parts so that one part will be 5 times the other.

20. A girl earned $20 more than twice as much as her brother. Together, they earned $80. How much did each earn?

3. Consecutive number problems

When a whole number is increased by 1, the resulting number is the *consecutive* number of the first. Thus 8 is consecutive to 7. If 11 is the first of three consecutive numbers, what are the other two?

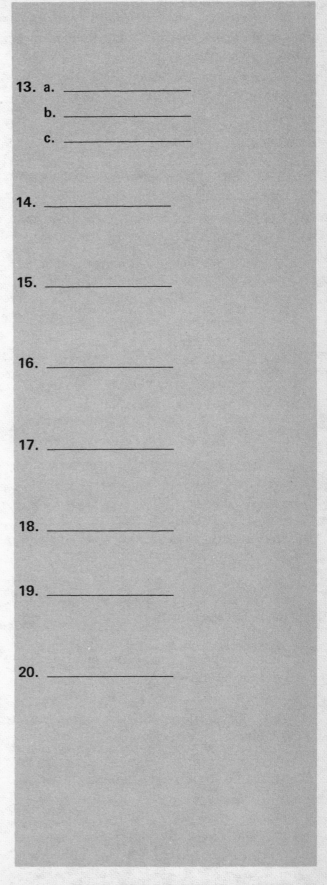

13. a. _____

    b. _____

    c. _____

14. _____

15. _____

16. _____

17. _____

18. _____

19. _____

20. _____

ILLUSTRATIVE PROBLEM 1

What is the sum of 8 and its next higher consecutive number?

Solution: $8 + 9 = 17$

ILLUSTRATIVE PROBLEM 2

The sum of two consecutive numbers is 43. Find the numbers.

Solution:

Let n = the first number.
Then $n + 1$ = the next consecutive number.
$n + n + 1 = 43$ (sum of the numbers)

$$2n + 1 = 43$$
$$\underline{-1 \quad -1}$$
$$2n \quad\; = 42$$

$n = 21$ (first number)
$n + 1 = 22$ (next number)

The numbers are 21 and 22.

Check: $21 + 22 = 43$ ✓

Exercises

1. The first of three consecutive numbers is 15. Write the other two.

1. _____

2. The first of three consecutive numbers is p. Represent the other two.

2. _____

3. The sum of two consecutive numbers is 61. Find the numbers.

3. _____

4. The sum of three consecutive numbers is 69. Find the numbers.

4. _____

5. Name the three greatest consecutive 2-digit integers.

5. _____

6. The sum of the first and third of three consecutive numbers is 34. What are the numbers?

6. _____

7. Numbers such as 6, 8, 10 are called consecutive *even* integers.

    a. Starting with 12, what are the next two consecutive *even* integers?

    b. If x is an *even* integer, represent the next two consecutive *even* integers.

8. The sum of two consecutive even integers is 86. Find them.

9. Numbers such as 13, 15, 17 are called consecutive *odd* integers.

    a. Starting with 23, name the next two odd integers.

    b. If t is an odd number, represent the next two consecutive odd integers.

10. Let r be an odd integer.

    a. Is $(r + 1)$ an even or an odd integer?

    b. Is $(r + 2)$ an even or an odd integer?

11. The sum of two consecutive *odd* integers is 72. Find the numbers.

12. The sum of three consecutive odd integers is 99. Find them.

7. a. _____

   b. _____

8. _____

9. a. _____

   b. _____

10. a. _____

    b. _____

11. _____

12. _____

4. Coin problems

ILLUSTRATIVE PROBLEM

Bill has 5 more pennies than dimes. He has 71¢ altogether. How many of each coin does he have?

Solution:

Let d = the number of dimes.
Then $d + 5$ = the number of pennies.
And $10d$ = the value of the *dimes* in cents.
$10d + d + 5 = 71$ (value of dime and pennies in cents)

$$11d + 5 = 71$$
$$\underline{\quad\; -5 \quad -5 \quad}$$
$$11d \quad\;\; = 66$$

$$d = 6 \quad \text{(number of dimes)}$$
$$d + 5 = 11 \quad \text{(number of pennies)}$$

Check: The value of 6 dimes = 60¢
The value of 11 pennies = 11¢
Total value = $\overline{71¢}$ ✓

Exercises

1. What is the value in cents of:

   a. 3 dimes?   **b.** 6 dimes?   **c.** *n* dimes?

   1. a. _____ b. _____ c. _____

2. Bill has *y* dimes. What is their value in cents?

   2. _____

3. What is the value in cents of:

   a. 3 dimes and 4 pennies

   b. 5 dimes and 7 pennies

   c. *n* dimes and 3 pennies?

   3. a. _____

      b. _____

      c. _____

4. Anne has *d* dimes.

   a. What is their value in cents?

   b. If she has 4 more pennies than dimes, represent the number of pennies she has.

   c. Express in terms of *d* the total value in cents of her coins.

   4. a. _____

      b. _____

      c. _____

5. A man has 5 more pennies than dimes. If he has 93¢ altogether, how many coins of each kind does he have?

   5. _____

6. What is the value in cents of:

   a. 3 quarters?   **b.** *n* quarters?

   c. 3 quarters and 2 dimes?

   d. *n* quarters and 4 dimes?

   6. a. _____ b. _____

      c. _____

      d. _____

7. A toy bank contains twice as many pennies as quarters. If it contains \$1.35, how many of each coin does it have?

   7. _____

8. What is the value in cents of:

   a. 8 nickels?   **b.** *n* nickels?

   8. a. _____ b. _____

c. *y* nickels and 7 pennies?

9. Represent the total value in cents of *q* quarters, *d* dimes, and *n* nickels.

10. Bill saved only quarters and nickels in a toy bank. When the number of quarters and nickels were equal, he had $2.70. How many of each coin did he have?

c. _____

9. _____

10. _____

5. Geometric problems

ILLUSTRATIVE PROBLEM 1

The length of a rectangular table is twice its width. If the perimeter is 84 inches, find the length and width of the table.

Solution: Let W = width in inches.

And $2W$ = length in inches.

Make a diagram, as shown at the right.

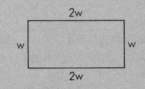

$W + 2W + W + 2W = 84$ (perimeter)

$6W = 84$ (combine like terms)

$W = 14$ (divide both members by 6)

$2W = 28$ (length)

Answer: The table is 14 inches wide and 28 inches long.

Check: The perimeter is:

$$14 + 28 + 14 + 28 = 84 \ \checkmark$$

ILLUSTRATIVE PROBLEM 2

In a triangle, two angles are equal and the third angle is twice as large as each of the others. Find the angles. (Recall that the sum of the angles of a triangle is $180°$.)

Solution:

Let x = number of degrees in each of the smaller angles.

And $2x$ = number of degrees in the larger angle.

Make a diagram, as shown at the right.

$2x + x + x = 180$ (sum of angles is $180°$)

$\qquad 4x = 180$ (combine like terms)

$\qquad x = 45$ (divide both sides by 4)

$\qquad 2x = 90$ (larger angle)

Answer: The angles are $45°$, $45°$, and $90°$.

Check: $45° + 45° + 90° = 180°$ ✓

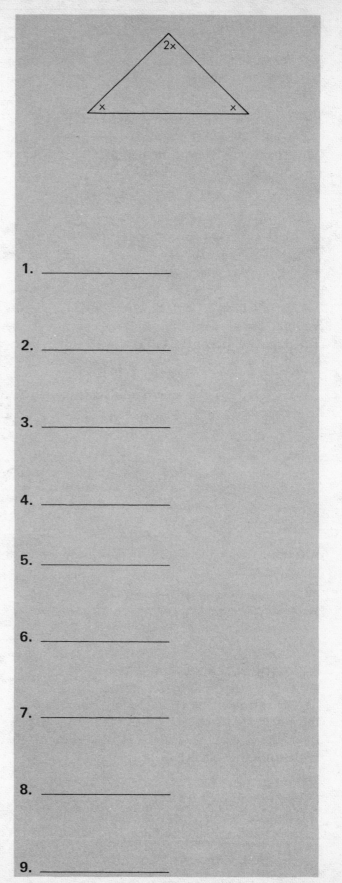

Exercises

1. Find the side of a square whose perimeter is 84 feet.

1. _____

2. The length of a rectangle is 3 times its width. If the perimeter is 96 inches, find the length and width.

2. _____

3. If the three angles of a triangle are equal to one another, find the number of degrees in each angle.

3. _____

4. In a triangle, one angle is twice the other and the third is three times as large as the smallest. Find the number of degrees in each angle.

4. _____

5. The perimeter of an equilateral triangle is 69 inches. Find each side.

5. _____

6. The length of a rectangle is 4 inches more than the width. If the perimeter is 56, find the length and width.

6. _____

7. If each of the equal angles of an isosceles triangle is $38°$, how many degrees is the third angle?

7. _____

8. The length of a rectangle is 3 more than twice the width. If the perimeter is 72 inches, find the length and width.

8. _____

9. The width of a rectangle is one-half of its length. If the perimeter is 93 inches, find the length and width.

9. _____

6. Using equations with formulas

In Chapter 1, we learned something about the use of formulas. With our new knowledge of how to solve equations, we can now extend our use of formulas.

ILLUSTRATIVE PROBLEM

The perimeter of a square is given by the formula $p = 4s$, where s is the length of a side. If p is 92 inches, find s.

Solution:

$p = 4s$ (perimeter formula)

$92 = 4s$ (substitute 92 for p)

$23 = s$ (divide both sides by 4)

$s = 23$ inches   (*answer*)

Exercises

1. The perimeter of a square is 72 inches. Using the formula $p = 4s$, find s.

    1. _____

2. The formula for the perimeter of an equilateral triangle of side s is $p = 3s$. If the perimeter of an equilateral triangle is 70 inches, find the length of each side.

    2. _____

3. The formula for the number of feet f in y yards is $f = 3y$. Find the number of yards in 96 feet.

    3. _____

4. In the formula $S = C + P$, S is the selling price of an article, C its cost, and P the profit. If $S = \$32.50$ and $C = \$21.25$, find P.

    4. _____

5. The formula $P = 2g + f$ gives the total number of points P scored by a basketball team making g field goals and f foul shots. If $P = 68$ and $f = 26$, find the number of field goals.

    5. _____

Ex. 6.

6. The perimeter of the isosceles triangle is given by $p = 2a + b$. If $p = 38''$ and $b = 15''$, find a.

6. _____

7. The formula $F = \frac{9}{5}C + 32$ converts Centigrade (or Celsius) temperatures to the Fahrenheit scale. If $F = 68°$, find C.

7. _____

8. The formula $d = rt$ gives the distance d (in miles) covered by an object moving at r miles per hour for t hours. Find the rate r for a car that travels 215 miles in 5 hours.

8. _____

9. Using the formula $d = rt$, find how many hours it takes for a train to travel 288 miles at 64 miles per hour.

9. _____

10. The formula $C = 40 + 8n$ gives the cost, in cents, of developing and printing n films. If a man pays $1.52 to develop and print some films, find the number of them.

10. _____

Chapter review exercises

1. Tom is t years old.

   a. Represent his age 7 years ago.

   b. Represent his age 3 years from now.

1. a. _____

   b. _____

2. Bill has n nickels and Mary has 3 more than Bill.

   a. Represent the number Mary has.

   b. Represent the value in cents of Mary's nickels.

   c. Represent the number of nickels they both have.

   d. Represent the value in cents of the nickels they both have.

2. a. _____

   b. _____

   c. _____

   d. _____

3. a. If the smallest of 3 consecutive numbers is p, represent the other two.

   b. Represent the sum of all three.

3. a. _____

   b. _____

4. Six times a number is increased by 4. The result is 68. Find the number.

4. _____

5. The sum of two angles is 120°. If one angle is 4 times as large as the other, how many degrees are there in each angle?

5. _____

6. The sum of two consecutive numbers is 85. What are the numbers?

6. _____

7. Paul has three times as many dimes as pennies. The total he has is $1.24. How many of each coin does he have?

7. _____

8. There are three consecutive numbers such that the sum of the first and third is 86. Find them.

8. _____

9. In a ninth grade class of 420 pupils, there are twice as many girls as boys. How many of each are there?

9. _____

10. A girl is paid $1.25 per hour for baby-sitting plus 70 cents for carfare. If she receives $6.95 one evening, how many hours did she baby-sit?

10. _____

11. A bottle and a cork cost $2.20. If the bottle costs $2.00 more than the cork, how much does each cost?

11. _____

12. The length of a rectangle is 4 times its width. If the perimeter is 75 inches, find the length and width.

12. _____

13. The average of three numbers p, q, and r is given by the formula $A = \dfrac{p + q + r}{3}$. If a boy gets 81 and 84 on two tests, what must he get on a third test to average 85?

13. _____

14. Frank had $32.50. He worked for 15 hours and then had $70 altogether. How much did he earn per hour?

14. _____

15. In a triangle one angle is twice another and the third angle is 20° more than the smallest angle. Find the three angles.

15. _____

Check your arithmetic skills

1. Subtract:

    a. 639   **b.** 400   **c.** 3457
          378   238   2498

    d. 7005   **e.** 7928
        487   5349

1. a. _____ **b.** _____ **c.** _____

    d. _____ **e.** _____

2. Find the value of each of the following:

    a. 14×0 **b.** 154×100

    c. $\frac{860}{10}$ **d.** $26{,}000 \div 1000$

2. a. _____ **b.** _____
    c. _____ **d.** _____

3. Multiply:

    a. 52   **b.** 37   **c.** 940
        ×18   ×34   ×20

    d. 694   **e.** 805   **f.** 6458
        ×83   ×306   ×82

3. a. _____ **b.** _____ **c.** _____

    d. _____ **e.** _____ **f.** _____

4. Divide:

    a. $549 \div 9$ **b.** $8\overline{)248}$ **c.** $\frac{289}{4}$

    d. $363 \div 4$ **e.** $\frac{304}{4}$ **f.** $7\overline{)503}$

    g. $\frac{170}{33}$ **h.** $38\overline{)250}$ **i.** $25\overline{)2300}$

4. a. _____ **b.** _____ **c.** _____
    d. _____ **e.** _____ **f.** _____
    g. _____ **h.** _____ **i.** _____

5. A man receives $32 per day. How much does he receive for 25 workdays?

5. _____

6. A certain job requires 1144 hours for completion. If the work is divided equally among 26 men, how many hours must each man work?

6. _____

7. In a class of 28 students, 52¢ is collected from each child. What is the total amount collected?

7. _____

COMMON FRACTIONS
AND SIMPLE
FRACTIONAL
EQUATIONS

4

1. Meaning of a fraction

In this chapter, we shall review some of the basic ideas and skills relating to *common fractions*.

On the number line above, the space between 0 and 1 has been divided into four equal parts. Each part is then called one-fourth of the distance from 0 to 1. If this distance from 0 to 1 is 1 inch then the first fractional part represents one-fourth of an inch; this fraction is written $\frac{1}{4}$. If we take 3 of these smaller units, the distance from 0 is then three-fourths of an inch, written $\frac{3}{4}$. The number below the fraction line tells us into how many equal parts the inch has been divided; this is the **denominator** of the fraction. The number above the fraction line tells us how many of these fractional parts to take; this is called the **numerator** of the fraction.

The numerator and denominator are called **terms** of a fraction. The fraction $\frac{5}{8}$ is read "five-eighths" and means that five of eight equal parts are being taken, as shown in the figure. When the terms of a fraction are whole numbers, we refer to the fraction as a **common fraction** or a **rational number**.

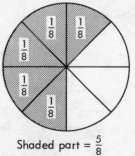

Shaded part = $\frac{5}{8}$

On the number line above, we can see that the fraction $\frac{4}{4}$ brings us to 1. If we continue the division of the space from 1 to 2 into quarters, we will then have lengths of $\frac{5}{4}, \frac{6}{4}, \frac{7}{4}, \frac{8}{4}$.

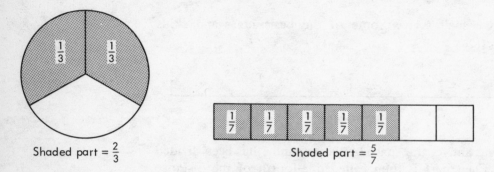

Note that $\frac{8}{4}$ will bring us to 2, or $8 \div 4$. Thus the fraction line behaves like a division sign, so that a common fraction is the indicated *division* of one whole number by another whole number.

A *proper fraction* is one in which the numerator is less than the denominator. Thus $\frac{1}{7}$, $\frac{2}{5}$, and $\frac{5}{8}$ are proper fractions. The value of a proper fraction is always less than 1.

The following figures represent proper fractions as shown:

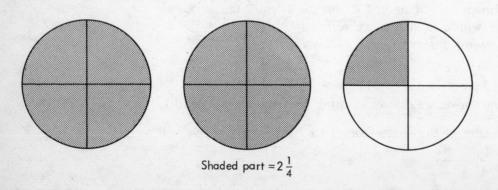

Shaded part = $\frac{2}{3}$

Shaded part = $\frac{5}{7}$

An *improper fraction* is one in which the numerator is greater than or equal to the denominator. Thus $\frac{3}{2}$, $\frac{8}{5}$, and $\frac{7}{7}$ are improper fractions. The value of an improper fraction is always greater than or equal to 1. $\frac{5}{1}$ is an improper fraction equal to 5.

A *mixed number* consists of a whole number and a fraction. Thus $4\frac{1}{2}$, $7\frac{2}{3}$, and $5\frac{7}{8}$ are mixed numbers.

The mixed number $2\frac{1}{4}$ means $2 + \frac{1}{4}$, or 2 and $\frac{1}{4}$, as shown in the following figure:

Shaded part = $2\frac{1}{4}$

Exercises

1. From the following fractions, choose:

   a. the proper fractions

   b. the improper fractions

   c. the mixed numbers

   $$\frac{4}{7} \quad \frac{9}{13} \quad \frac{17}{12} \quad 3\frac{1}{2} \quad \frac{5}{3} \quad \frac{5}{8} \quad \frac{99}{100} \quad \frac{6}{3} \quad \frac{7}{1} \quad \frac{1}{7}$$

   d. Locate on a number line: $3\frac{1}{2}, \frac{5}{8}, \frac{6}{3}$

2. a. Into how many equal parts is the circle divided?

   b. What fractional part of the circle is each of the equal parts?

   c. What fractional part of the circle is shaded?

   d. What fractional part of the circle is unshaded?

   e. If one of the un-shaded portions were to be cut in half, what part of the circle would each of the new pieces be?

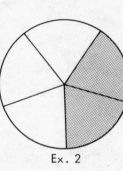

Ex. 2

3. Using the numbers 3, 4, 5, write:

   a. a proper fraction

   b. an improper fraction

   c. a mixed number

4. For each part of this exercise, use the diagram in the right-hand column.

   a. In the figure, shade $\frac{3}{4}$.

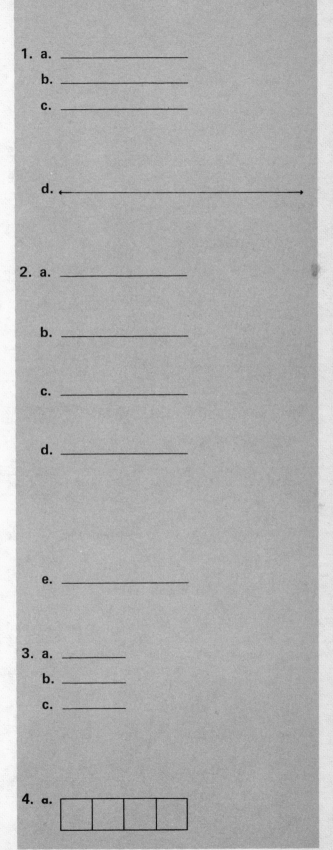

1. a. _____

   b. _____

   c. _____

   d. ⟵_____⟶

2. a. _____

   b. _____

   c. _____

   d. _____

   e. _____

3. a. _____

   b. _____

   c. _____

4. a.

b. In the figure, shade $\frac{5}{6}$.

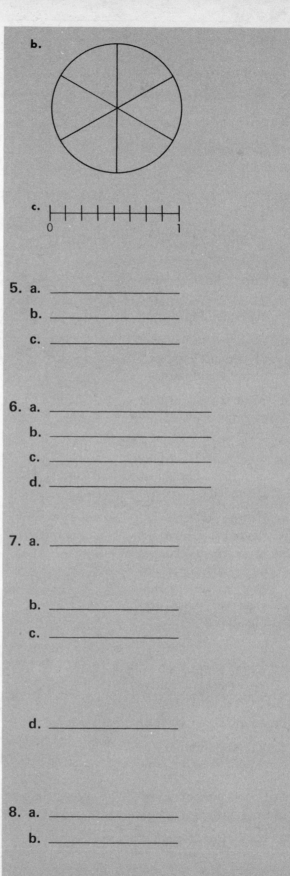

c. In the figure, darken the line segment for $\frac{5}{8}$.

5. a. A quarter is what fractional part of a dollar?

b. A dime is what fractional part of a dollar?

c. A nickel is what part of a dollar?

5. a. _____

   b. _____

   c. _____

6. What do we call each of the following?

a. top number of a fraction

b. bottom number of a fraction

c. a whole number and a fraction

d. a fraction less than 1 in value

6. a. _____

   b. _____

   c. _____

   d. _____

7. a. What is the value of a fraction whose numerator and denominator are equal?

b. What is the value of $\frac{n}{1}$ where n is a whole number?

c. If $\frac{x}{12} = 1$, what is the value of x?

d. If you divide a pie into 10 equal parts and take $\frac{7}{10}$ away, what fractional part of the pie remains?

7. a. _____

   b. _____

   c. _____

   d. _____

8. Given the fractions $\frac{1}{3}, \frac{1}{4}, \frac{1}{5}$.

a. Which is the smallest fraction?

b. Which is the largest fraction?

8. a. _____

   b. _____

2. Reducing fractions to lowest terms

The figures at the right indicate that $\frac{6}{8}$ of a circle has the same value as $\frac{3}{4}$ of a circle. We refer to $\frac{6}{8}$ and $\frac{3}{4}$ as *equivalent fractions* and write $\frac{6}{8} = \frac{3}{4}$. Note that, if we divide both 6 and 8 by 2 in the first fraction, we obtain the second fraction, $\frac{3}{4}$. We say that we have *reduced* the first fraction to *lower terms*. In this example, we say that $\frac{3}{4}$ is in *lowest terms* because the 3 and 4 have no common factor other than 1, and thus the fraction cannot be reduced further.

The fraction $\frac{12}{18}$ may be reduced as follows:

$$\frac{12}{18} = \frac{12 \div 3}{18 \div 3} = \frac{4}{6} = \frac{4 \div 2}{6 \div 2} = \frac{2}{3}$$

Thus, $\frac{12}{18} = \frac{4}{6} = \frac{2}{3}$. We say $\frac{4}{6}$ is in *lower* terms and $\frac{2}{3}$ is in *lowest* terms.

Rule: The numerator and denominator of a fraction may both be *divided* by the same number without changing the value of the fraction.

Just as we can *reduce* a fraction to *lower* terms, we may also *raise* a fraction to *higher terms*. We frequently find it convenient to change a fraction to an equivalent fraction with a larger denominator. Thus, we can change $\frac{2}{3}$ to $\frac{6}{9}$ by multiplying both terms of the fraction by 3.

Rule: The numerator and denominator of a fraction may both be *multiplied* by the same number without changing the value of the fraction.

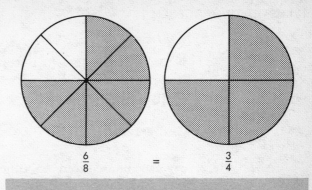

$$\frac{6}{8} = \frac{3}{4}$$

ILLUSTRATIVE PROBLEM 1

Reduce $\dfrac{18}{30}$ to lowest terms.

Solution: 18 and 30 are both divisible by 6.

$$\frac{18 \div 6}{30 \div 6} = \frac{3}{5} \quad (answer)$$

Note: Here, $\dfrac{18}{30}$ can be reduced to other fractions $\left(\dfrac{9}{15}, \dfrac{6}{10}\right)$, but $\dfrac{3}{5}$ is the fraction in *lowest* terms.

ILLUSTRATIVE PROBLEM 2

Write $\dfrac{2}{5}$ as an equivalent fraction with 20 as a denominator.

Solution:

$$\frac{2}{5} = \frac{?}{20}$$

To change the denominator 5 to 20, we must multiply it by 4. Hence, we must also multiply the numerator 2 by 4.

$$\frac{2}{5} = \frac{2 \times 4}{5 \times 4} = \frac{8}{20} \quad (answer)$$

Exercises

In 1 to 15, reduce each fraction to lowest terms.

1. $\dfrac{15}{20}$ 2. $\dfrac{24}{60}$ 3. $\dfrac{18}{48}$

4. $\dfrac{35}{56}$ 5. $\dfrac{18}{24}$ 6. $\dfrac{9}{144}$

7. $\dfrac{45}{70}$ 8. $\dfrac{8}{14}$ 9. $\dfrac{45}{180}$

10. $\dfrac{21}{28}$ 11. $\dfrac{80}{120}$ 12. $\dfrac{23}{69}$

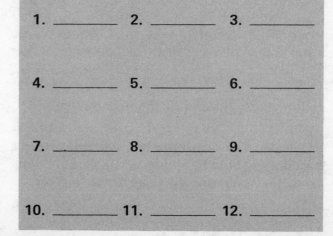

1. _____ 2. _____ 3. _____

4. _____ 5. _____ 6. _____

7. _____ 8. _____ 9. _____

10. _____ 11. _____ 12. _____

13. $\dfrac{45}{54}$ **14.** $\dfrac{150}{200}$ **15.** $\dfrac{104}{108}$

In 16 to 24, raise each fraction to higher terms.

16. $\dfrac{3}{5} = \dfrac{?}{25}$ **17.** $\dfrac{3}{4} = \dfrac{?}{16}$ **18.** $\dfrac{3}{7} = \dfrac{?}{14}$

19. $\dfrac{7}{8} = \dfrac{?}{16}$ **20.** $\dfrac{4}{15} = \dfrac{?}{30}$ **21.** $\dfrac{5}{16} = \dfrac{?}{64}$

22. $\dfrac{9}{10} = \dfrac{?}{50}$ **23.** $\dfrac{7}{2} = \dfrac{?}{10}$ **24.** $\dfrac{5}{3} = \dfrac{?}{12}$

25. How many sixteenths of an inch are in $\dfrac{3}{4}$ of an inch?

26. How many sixteenths of a pound (ounces) are in one-half of a pound?

27. How many twelfths of a foot (inches) are in $\dfrac{2}{3}$ of a foot?

3. Equivalence of mixed numbers and improper fractions

It is frequently desirable to change an improper fraction to a mixed number. A recipe might call for $1\dfrac{1}{2}$ cups of flour but would not call for $\dfrac{3}{2}$ cups.

Since a fraction is an indicated division, a method is already suggested for reducing an improper fraction to a mixed number. For example, $\dfrac{7}{3}$ may be written as $7 \div 3$. Thus:

$$\begin{array}{r} 2\frac{1}{3} \\ 3\overline{)7} \\ \underline{6} \\ 1 \end{array}$$

We see that $\dfrac{7}{3} = 2\dfrac{1}{3}$.

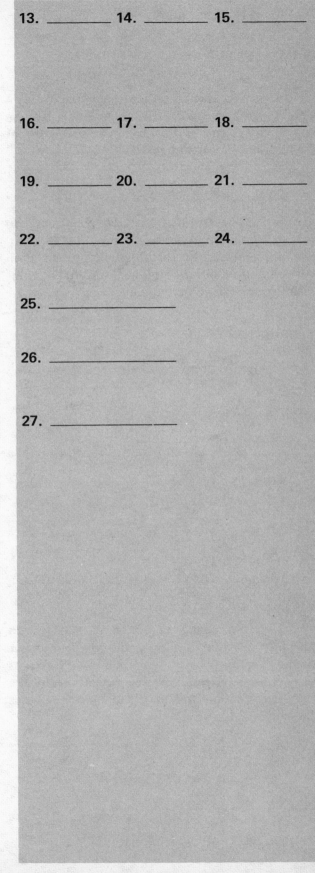

13. _____ **14.** _____ **15.** _____

16. _____ **17.** _____ **18.** _____

19. _____ **20.** _____ **21.** _____

22. _____ **23.** _____ **24.** _____

25. _____

26. _____

27. _____

We may *check* this by noting that, if $1 = \dfrac{3}{3}$,

then $2 = \dfrac{6}{3}$ and $2\dfrac{1}{3} = 2 + \dfrac{1}{3} = \dfrac{6}{3} + \dfrac{1}{3} = \dfrac{7}{3}$.

Rule: To change an improper fraction to a mixed number, divide the numerator by the denominator and write the fractional part of the quotient in lowest terms.

Thus, $\dfrac{65}{10} = 6\dfrac{5}{10} = 6\dfrac{1}{2}$.

In computation, it is often convenient to change a mixed number to an improper fraction. The problem can be solved by finding an equivalent fraction and a simple addition of fractions with the same denominators.

ILLUSTRATIVE PROBLEM 1

Change $3\dfrac{1}{5}$ to an improper fraction.

Solution: $3\dfrac{1}{5} = 3 + \dfrac{1}{5}$

Write 3 as an equivalent fraction with a denominator of 5:

$$\dfrac{3}{1} = \dfrac{3 \times 5}{1 \times 5} = \dfrac{15}{5}$$

Then: $3\dfrac{1}{5} = 3 + \dfrac{1}{5} = \dfrac{15}{5} + \dfrac{1}{5} = \dfrac{16}{5}$ *(answer)*

The process may be summarized in the following rule:

Rule: To change a mixed number to an improper fraction, multiply the whole number by the denominator of the fraction and add its numerator. The result is the numerator of the improper fraction and the denominator remains the same.

Thus, $3\dfrac{1}{5} = \dfrac{3 \times 5 + 1}{5} = \dfrac{15 + 1}{5} = \dfrac{16}{5}$.

ILLUSTRATIVE PROBLEM 2

Change $3\dfrac{4}{7}$ to an improper fraction.

Solution: $3\dfrac{4}{7} = \dfrac{3 \times 7 + 4}{7} = \dfrac{21 + 4}{7} = \dfrac{25}{7}$

ILLUSTRATIVE PROBLEM 3

Change 7 into an equivalent fraction having 3 as the denominator.

Solution: $7 = \dfrac{7}{1} = \dfrac{7 \times 3}{1 \times 3} = \dfrac{21}{3}$

Exercises

In 1 to 12, change each improper fraction to a mixed number or a whole number.

1. $\dfrac{15}{6}$ 2. $\dfrac{31}{20}$ 3. $\dfrac{65}{20}$

4. $\dfrac{48}{4}$ 5. $\dfrac{28}{3}$ 6. $\dfrac{150}{10}$

7. $\dfrac{35}{9}$ 8. $\dfrac{34}{6}$ 9. $\dfrac{18}{4}$

10. $\dfrac{27}{27}$ 11. $\dfrac{7}{6}$ 12. $\dfrac{88}{11}$

In 13 to 18, change the following whole numbers into improper fractions as indicated.

13. $3 = \dfrac{?}{8}$ 14. $5 = \dfrac{?}{7}$ 15. $12 = \dfrac{?}{8}$

16. $14 = \dfrac{?}{3}$ 17. $20 = \dfrac{?}{100}$ 18. $15 = \dfrac{?}{4}$

In 19 to 26, write each of the following mixed numbers as improper fractions.

19. $3\dfrac{2}{7}$ 20. $5\dfrac{1}{2}$ 21. $1\dfrac{1}{6}$

22. $7\dfrac{8}{15}$ 23. $7\dfrac{3}{10}$ 24. $8\dfrac{1}{6}$

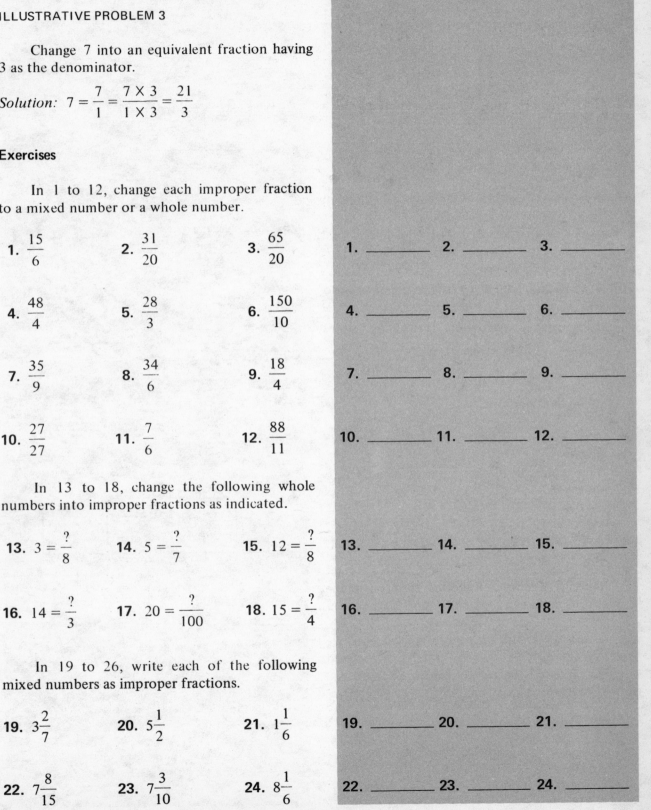

1. _____ 2. _____ 3. _____

4. _____ 5. _____ 6. _____

7. _____ 8. _____ 9. _____

10. _____ 11. _____ 12. _____

13. _____ 14. _____ 15. _____

16. _____ 17. _____ 18. _____

19. _____ 20. _____ 21. _____

22. _____ 23. _____ 24. _____

25. $1\dfrac{5}{24}$ **26.** $3\dfrac{11}{20}$

25. _____ **26.** _____

27. How many $\dfrac{1}{4}$-inch parts are there in $3\dfrac{1}{4}$ inches?

27. _____

28. How many $\dfrac{1}{2}$-cups of milk are there in a container holding $4\dfrac{1}{2}$ cups?

28. _____

29. How many eighths of an inch are there in $4\dfrac{3}{8}$ inches?

29. _____

30. A carpenter cuts $5\dfrac{2}{3}$ yards of molding into strips each $\dfrac{1}{3}$ yard long. How many strips does he obtain?

30. _____

4. Adding like fractions

Like fractions are fractions having the same denominator.

The rectangle in the figure is divided into seven equal parts, so that each is $\dfrac{1}{7}$ of the rectangle.

Note that $\dfrac{2}{7} + \dfrac{3}{7} = \dfrac{5}{7}$ and that $\dfrac{4}{7} + \dfrac{3}{7} = \dfrac{7}{7} = 1$.

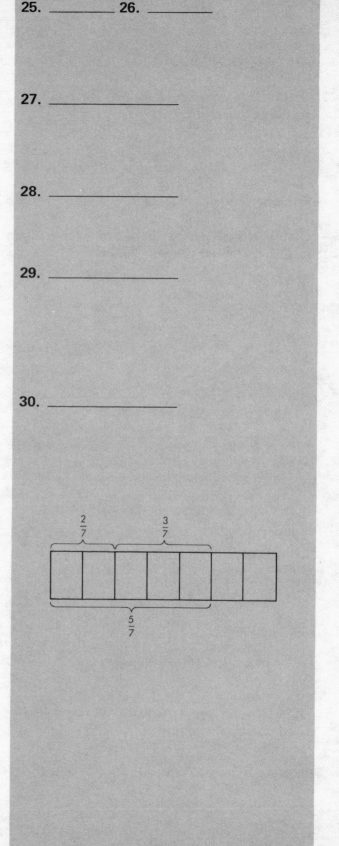

Rule: To add like fractions, simply add the numerators and keep the same denominator.

When the result is an improper fraction, we usually reduce it to a whole number or a mixed number. It is customary to reduce all fractional results to lowest terms.

ILLUSTRATIVE PROBLEM 1

Add $\dfrac{4}{9}$ and $\dfrac{2}{9}$.

Solution: $\dfrac{4}{9} + \dfrac{2}{9} = \dfrac{6}{9} = \dfrac{6 \div 3}{9 \div 3} = \dfrac{2}{3}$

ILLUSTRATIVE PROBLEM 2

Add $\dfrac{3}{11}$, $\dfrac{5}{11}$, and $\dfrac{6}{11}$.

Solution: $\dfrac{3}{11} + \dfrac{5}{11} + \dfrac{6}{11} = \dfrac{14}{11} = 1\dfrac{3}{11}$

ILLUSTRATIVE PROBLEM 3

Add $3\dfrac{3}{8}$ and $4\dfrac{7}{8}$.

Solution:
$$3\dfrac{3}{8}$$
$$+4\dfrac{7}{8}$$
$$\overline{7\dfrac{10}{8}}$$

Change $\dfrac{10}{8}$ to $1\dfrac{2}{8} = 1\dfrac{1}{4}$. Thus,

$$7\dfrac{10}{8} = 7 + \dfrac{10}{8} = 7 + 1\dfrac{1}{4} = 8\dfrac{1}{4} \quad (answer)$$

Exercises

Add the following fractions and reduce all results to lowest terms.

1. $\dfrac{3}{8} + \dfrac{2}{8}$ **2.** $\dfrac{15}{19} + \dfrac{2}{19}$ **3.** $\dfrac{7}{24} + \dfrac{13}{24}$

4. $\dfrac{8}{11} + \dfrac{3}{11}$ **5.** $2\dfrac{1}{3} + 3\dfrac{1}{3}$ **6.** $4\dfrac{5}{7} + 6\dfrac{3}{7}$

7. $\dfrac{3}{10} + \dfrac{2}{10}$ **8.** $\dfrac{8}{15} + \dfrac{9}{15}$ **9.** $\begin{array}{r} 5\dfrac{2}{9} \\ +7\dfrac{4}{9} \\ \hline \end{array}$

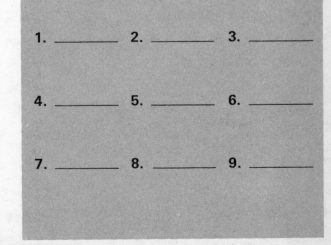

1. _____   2. _____   3. _____

4. _____   5. _____   6. _____

7. _____   8. _____   9. _____

10. $3\dfrac{2}{11}$ **11.** $2\dfrac{5}{18}$ **12.** $\dfrac{2}{13} + \dfrac{3}{13} + \dfrac{6}{13}$

$+4\dfrac{9}{11}$ $3\dfrac{7}{18}$

$5\dfrac{11}{18}$

13. $\dfrac{8}{25} + \dfrac{9}{25} + \dfrac{7}{25} + \dfrac{11}{25}$

10. _____ **11.** _____ **12.** _____

13. _____

5. Adding fractions with different denominators

Fractions having different denominators are called **unlike fractions**. Suppose we wish to add two unlike fractions such as $\dfrac{1}{2}$ and $\dfrac{3}{5}$. We must first change these two fractions to equivalent fractions with the same denominator. This **least common denominator** (L.C.D.) is the smallest number that both denominators divide into evenly. In this case, the L.C.D. is 10 (2 × 5), so that

$$\frac{1}{2} = \frac{1 \times 5}{2 \times 5} = \frac{5}{10} \quad \text{and} \quad \frac{3}{5} = \frac{3 \times 2}{5 \times 2} = \frac{6}{10}$$

Thus, $\dfrac{1}{2} + \dfrac{3}{5} = \dfrac{5}{10} + \dfrac{6}{10} = \dfrac{11}{10} = 1\dfrac{1}{10}$.

Rule: To add unlike fractions, the fractions must be changed to equivalent fractions which have the same denominator, known as the *common denominator.*

ILLUSTRATIVE PROBLEM 1

Add $\dfrac{1}{2}$ and $\dfrac{2}{3}$.

Solution: The L.C.D. is 6.

$$\frac{1}{2} = \frac{1 \times 3}{2 \times 3} = \frac{3}{6}$$

$$\frac{2}{3} = \frac{2 \times 2}{3 \times 2} = \frac{4}{6}$$

$$\frac{3}{6} + \frac{4}{6} = \frac{7}{6} = 1\frac{1}{6} \quad (answer)$$

Note that, if we had used 12 for the common denominator, then:

$$\frac{1}{2} = \frac{1 \times 6}{2 \times 6} = \frac{6}{12} \quad \text{and} \quad \frac{2}{3} = \frac{2 \times 4}{3 \times 4} = \frac{8}{12}$$

$$\frac{6}{12} + \frac{8}{12} = \frac{14}{12} = \frac{14 \div 2}{12 \div 2} = \frac{7}{6} = 1\frac{1}{6}$$

The result is the same, but it is simpler to use the *least* common denominator (L.C.D.).

When there are two or more fractions, it is sometimes difficult to find the L.C.D. One procedure is to take the largest denominator and consider its multiples. That is, multiply the denominator by 2, 3, 4, 5, 6, etc., until a product is found that is divisible by all denominators.

ILLUSTRATIVE PROBLEM 2

$$\frac{1}{8} + \frac{1}{4} + \frac{2}{5} = ?$$

Solution: Consider the multiples of 8:

$$8 \times 2 = 16$$

$$8 \times 3 = 24$$

$$8 \times 4 = 32$$

$$8 \times 5 = 40$$

The first product we reach that is also divisible by 4 and 5 is 40. This is the L.C.D. Thus,

$$\frac{1}{8} = \frac{1 \times 5}{8 \times 5} = \frac{5}{40}$$

$$\frac{1}{4} = \frac{1 \times 10}{4 \times 10} = \frac{10}{40}$$

$$\frac{2}{5} = \frac{2 \times 8}{5 \times 8} = \frac{16}{40}$$

$$\frac{31}{40} \quad (answer)$$

To add mixed numbers with unlike fractions, we may arrange the work as shown in Illustrative Problem 3.

ILLUSTRATIVE PROBLEM 3

$$3\frac{3}{4} + 5\frac{2}{3} = ?$$

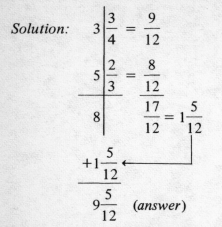

Solution:

$$3\frac{3}{4} = \frac{9}{12}$$

$$5\frac{2}{3} = \frac{8}{12}$$

$$8 \quad \frac{17}{12} = 1\frac{5}{12}$$

$$+1\frac{5}{12} \longleftarrow$$

$$9\frac{5}{12} \quad (answer)$$

Here, we are adding the fractional parts of the mixed numbers and then adding this sum to the sum of the whole numbers.

Exercises

In 1 to 15, add the fractions and reduce each answer to *simplest form* (lowest terms for proper fractions; change improper fractions to whole numbers or mixed numbers).

1. $\dfrac{1}{3} + \dfrac{1}{6}$

2. $\dfrac{1}{2} + \dfrac{1}{3} + \dfrac{1}{4}$

3. $\dfrac{5}{12} + \dfrac{2}{3}$

4. $\dfrac{1}{6} + \dfrac{3}{10} + \dfrac{2}{5}$

5. $\dfrac{5}{9} + \dfrac{2}{3} + \dfrac{1}{6}$

6. $\dfrac{3}{4} + \dfrac{7}{16}$

7. $4\dfrac{5}{8}$
   $3\dfrac{1}{2}$
   $5\dfrac{1}{4}$

8. $2\dfrac{1}{7}$
   $1\dfrac{3}{4}$

9. $3\dfrac{5}{8}$
   $7\dfrac{3}{20}$

10. $4\dfrac{3}{4}$
    $6\dfrac{5}{12}$

11. $\dfrac{1}{2}$
    $7\dfrac{11}{12}$

12. $12\dfrac{4}{5}$
    $11\dfrac{3}{4}$

1. _____ 2. _____ 3. _____

4. _____ 5. _____ 6. _____

7. _____ 8. _____ 9. _____

10. _____ 11. _____ 12. _____

13. $18\dfrac{1}{6}$

$9\dfrac{2}{3}$

$5\dfrac{1}{2}$

14. $5\dfrac{3}{4}$

$7\dfrac{3}{8}$

$2\dfrac{5}{16}$

15. $9\dfrac{7}{8}$

$4\dfrac{5}{12}$

$8\dfrac{1}{6}$

16. A girl needs $5\dfrac{1}{3}$ yards of pink ribbon, $4\dfrac{3}{4}$ yards of blue ribbon, and $3\dfrac{1}{2}$ yards of yellow ribbon. How many yards of ribbon does she need in all?

17. A carpenter adds an extension of $22\dfrac{7}{8}$ inches to a shelf that is $35\dfrac{3}{4}$ inches. How long is the new shelf?

18. What is the total weight of a can of soup if the soup weighs $12\dfrac{2}{3}$ ounces and the can weighs $4\dfrac{4}{5}$ ounces?

6. Subtracting fractions

The subtraction of fractions is very similar to the addition of fractions.

Thus, $\dfrac{5}{7} - \dfrac{2}{7} = \dfrac{3}{7}$.

Rule: To subtract like fractions, subtract the numerators and write the difference over the common denominator.

To subtract unlike fractions, we raise each fraction to an equivalent fraction with the same common denominator.

ILLUSTRATIVE PROBLEM 1

$\dfrac{7}{8} - \dfrac{2}{5} = ?$

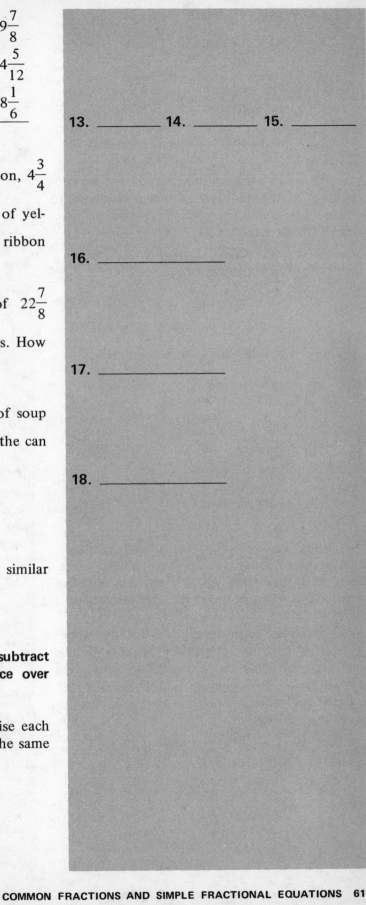

13. _____ 14. _____ 15. _____

16. _____

17. _____

18. _____

Solution: The L.C.D. is 40. Thus,

$$\frac{7}{8} = \frac{7 \times 5}{8 \times 5} = \frac{35}{40}$$

$$\frac{2}{5} = \frac{2 \times 8}{5 \times 8} = \frac{16}{40}$$

$$\frac{7}{8} - \frac{2}{5} = \frac{35}{40} - \frac{16}{40} = \frac{35 - 16}{40} = \frac{19}{40} \quad (answer)$$

When we subtract mixed numbers, we proceed, as in the addition of mixed numbers, to change the fractional parts to equivalent fractions with the same L.C.D.

ILLUSTRATIVE PROBLEM 2

$$6\frac{3}{4} - 1\frac{2}{3} = ?$$

Solution: The following form is suggested:

$$
\begin{array}{r|c}
6 & \dfrac{3}{4} = \dfrac{9}{12} \\
-1 & \dfrac{2}{3} = \dfrac{8}{12} \\
\hline
5 & \dfrac{1}{12}
\end{array}
$$

Answer: The difference is $5\frac{1}{12}$.

Rule: To subtract two mixed numbers, change the fractional parts to equivalent fractions with the same L.C.D., subtract the like fractions, and then subtract the whole numbers.

An added problem arises when the upper fraction is less than the lower fraction. In this case, we overcome the difficulty by borrowing 1 from the whole number in the upper mixed number and adding it to the upper fraction to make it improper.

ILLUSTRATIVE PROBLEM 3

$$5\frac{2}{3} - 2\frac{11}{12} = ?$$

Solution:

$$5\,\Big|\,\frac{2}{3} = \frac{8}{12}$$
$$-2\,\Big|\,\frac{11}{12} = \frac{11}{12}$$

Now, since we cannot subtract $\frac{11}{12}$ from $\frac{8}{12}$, we borrow 1 from the 5, change the 1 to $\frac{12}{12}$, and add $\frac{12}{12}$ to $\frac{8}{12}$. Thus,

$$\overset{4}{\cancel{5}}\,\Big|\,\frac{8}{12} + \frac{12}{12} = \frac{20}{12}$$
$$-2\,\Big|\,\frac{11}{12} \phantom{+ \frac{12}{12}} = \frac{11}{12}$$
$$\overline{2\,\Big|\phantom{\frac{11}{12} + \frac{12}{12}} \quad \frac{9}{12}}$$

Answer: The difference is $2\frac{9}{12} = 2\frac{3}{4}$.

Exercises

In 1 to 15, subtract. Reduce the answer to lowest terms.

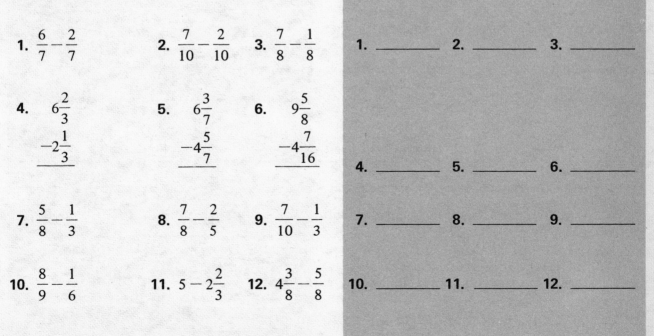

1. $\dfrac{6}{7} - \dfrac{2}{7}$　　2. $\dfrac{7}{10} - \dfrac{2}{10}$　3. $\dfrac{7}{8} - \dfrac{1}{8}$

4. $\begin{array}{r} 6\frac{2}{3} \\ -2\frac{1}{3} \\ \hline \end{array}$　　5. $\begin{array}{r} 6\frac{3}{7} \\ -4\frac{5}{7} \\ \hline \end{array}$　　6. $\begin{array}{r} 9\frac{5}{8} \\ -4\frac{7}{16} \\ \hline \end{array}$

7. $\dfrac{5}{8} - \dfrac{1}{3}$　　8. $\dfrac{7}{8} - \dfrac{2}{5}$　　9. $\dfrac{7}{10} - \dfrac{1}{3}$

10. $\dfrac{8}{9} - \dfrac{1}{6}$　　11. $5 - 2\frac{2}{3}$　　12. $4\frac{3}{8} - \dfrac{5}{8}$

1. _____　2. _____　3. _____

4. _____　5. _____　6. _____

7. _____　8. _____　9. _____

10. _____　11. _____　12. _____

13. $5\dfrac{1}{2}$
$-\dfrac{3}{4}$

14. $7\dfrac{5}{6}$
$-2\dfrac{4}{9}$

15. 17
$-5\dfrac{3}{7}$

In 16 to 19, do the indicated adding and subtracting. Reduce the answer to lowest terms.

16. $6 + 3\dfrac{5}{8} - 2\dfrac{1}{4}$ **17.** $5\dfrac{1}{3} + 2\dfrac{5}{9} - 4\dfrac{5}{6}$

18. $7\dfrac{1}{4} + 3\dfrac{1}{8} - 4\dfrac{2}{3}$ **19.** $\dfrac{7}{8} - \dfrac{3}{16} + \dfrac{1}{4}$

20. Mrs. Smith borrowed $\dfrac{3}{4}$ of a cup of flour and returned $\dfrac{1}{2}$ of a cup. How much does she still owe?

21. A boy had a board $6\dfrac{5}{8}$ feet long. He cut off a piece $3\dfrac{2}{3}$ feet long. How many feet were left?

22. A roast beef weighed $8\dfrac{2}{5}$ pounds. In the roasting, it lost $2\dfrac{3}{4}$ pounds. How many pounds remained?

23. Bill lives $4\dfrac{5}{8}$ miles from school. Tom lives $2\dfrac{1}{3}$ miles from school along the same straight road as Bill. How much nearer to school does Tom live?

24. A girl has $8\dfrac{1}{2}$ yards of ribbon and cuts off $3\dfrac{4}{5}$ yards. How many yards are left?

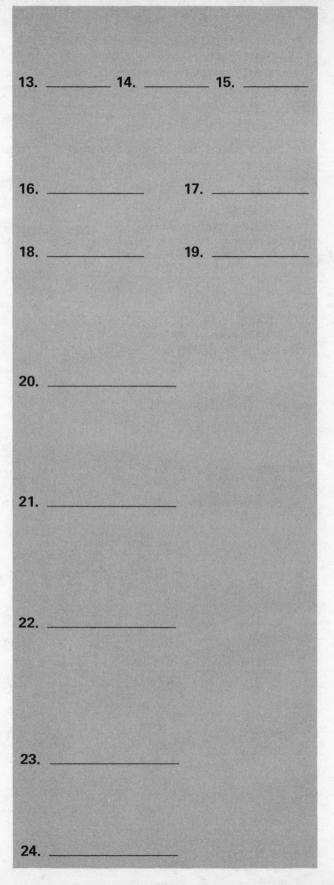

13. _____ **14.** _____ **15.** _____

16. _____   **17.** _____

18. _____   **19.** _____

20. _____

21. _____

22. _____

23. _____

24. _____

25. The Dugans put in $3\frac{1}{2}$ tons of coal in the fall. They use up $1\frac{5}{16}$ tons over the winter. How many tons are left?

25. _____

7. Multiplying fractions

Just as the product 4×3 means 3 added to itself 4 times, the product $4 \times \frac{2}{3}$ means the fraction $\frac{2}{3}$ added to itself 4 times. Thus, $4 \times \frac{2}{3} = \frac{2}{3} + \frac{2}{3} + \frac{2}{3} + \frac{2}{3} = \frac{8}{3} = 2\frac{2}{3}$. The same result can be obtained by multiplying the whole number by the numerator of the fraction:

$$4 \times \frac{2}{3} = \frac{4}{1} \times \frac{2}{3} = \frac{4 \times 2}{1 \times 3} = \frac{8}{3} = 2\frac{2}{3}$$

When we multiply whole numbers, the order of multiplication does not matter. Thus $5 \times 7 = 7 \times 5$. This law of order is known as the **commutative law,** and we apply it to fractions as well. Thus,

$$4 \times \frac{2}{3} = \frac{2}{3} \times 4 = 2\frac{2}{3}$$

Note that, in the above example, we were able to obtain the product of the two fractions by multiplying the two numerators and multiplying the two denominators to give us the numerator and denominator of the product. It can be shown that this gives us a method for multiplying any two or more fractions.

ILLUSTRATIVE PROBLEM 1

$$\frac{3}{4} \times \frac{5}{7} = ?$$

Solution: $\frac{3}{4} \times \frac{5}{7} = \frac{3 \times 5}{4 \times 7} = \frac{15}{28}$

ILLUSTRATIVE PROBLEM 2

$$2\frac{1}{2} \times 3\frac{2}{3} = ?$$

Solution: $\dfrac{5}{2} \times \dfrac{11}{3} = \dfrac{55}{6} = 9\dfrac{1}{6}$

As usual, we reduce fractional results to lowest terms. However, to avoid working with larger numbers, it is possible to start this reduction *before* multiplying by dividing out ("cancelling") common factors in numerators and denominators. This process is illustrated in the following problem:

ILLUSTRATIVE PROBLEM 3

$\dfrac{2}{3} \times \dfrac{3}{7} = ?$

Solution: $\dfrac{2}{3} \times \dfrac{3}{7} = \dfrac{6}{21} = \dfrac{2 \times 3}{7 \times 3} = \dfrac{2}{7}$ (*answer*)

Note that we divide the numerator and denominator of $\dfrac{6}{21}$ by 3, so as to reduce the fraction. We could have done this at the very beginning, like this:

$\dfrac{2}{\overset{}{\underset{1}{\cancel{3}}}} \times \dfrac{\overset{1}{\cancel{3}}}{7} = \dfrac{2 \times 1}{1 \times 7} = \dfrac{2}{7}$

Whenever any number divides evenly into both a numerator and denominator, you may simplify by dividing before multiplying the numerators and denominators. This is further illustrated in the following:

ILLUSTRATIVE PROBLEM 4

$\dfrac{3}{4} \times \dfrac{8}{9} = ?$

Solution: $\dfrac{\overset{1}{\cancel{3}}}{\underset{1}{\cancel{4}}} \times \dfrac{\overset{2}{\cancel{8}}}{\underset{3}{\cancel{9}}} = \dfrac{2}{3}$ (*answer*)

Here, we have divided by 4 the denominator of the first fraction and the numerator of the second fraction. We have also divided by 3 the numerator of the first fraction and the denominator of the second. Thus, the product is already in lowest terms. The same procedure can be applied to three or more fractions.

ILLUSTRATIVE PROBLEM 5

$$\frac{1}{3} \times \frac{2}{5} \times \frac{3}{2} = ?$$

Solution: $\dfrac{1}{\cancel{3}_1} \times \dfrac{\cancel{2}^1}{5} \times \dfrac{\cancel{3}^1}{\cancel{2}_1} = \dfrac{1}{5}$

Exercises

In 1 to 16, find the products. Reduce to lowest terms by cancellation wherever possible.

1. $12 \times \dfrac{5}{8}$　　　**2.** $\dfrac{4}{9} \times 5$　　　**3.** $\dfrac{1}{5} \times \dfrac{2}{3}$

4. $\dfrac{1}{2} \times \dfrac{2}{5} \times \dfrac{1}{3}$　　**5.** $6 \times \dfrac{3}{4}$　　　**6.** $\dfrac{1}{6} \times \dfrac{4}{3}$

7. $\dfrac{2}{3} \times 6$　　　**8.** $3\dfrac{1}{3} \times 10\dfrac{1}{2}$　　**9.** $12 \times 1\dfrac{5}{6}$

10. $\dfrac{2}{5} \times 8\dfrac{3}{4}$　　**11.** $\dfrac{3}{5} \times \dfrac{7}{12}$　　**12.** $4\dfrac{1}{2} \times \dfrac{5}{8}$

13. $3\dfrac{1}{3} \times 2\dfrac{1}{4}$　　**14.** $\dfrac{1}{3}$ of $\dfrac{6}{7}$　　**15.** $\dfrac{2}{5}$ of $\dfrac{1}{2}$

16. $24 \times 6\dfrac{2}{3}$

1. _____	2. _____	3. _____
4. _____	5. _____	6. _____
7. _____	8. _____	9. _____
10. _____	11. _____	12. _____
13. _____	14. _____	15. _____
16. _____		

Note: An alternate solution to exercise 16 is to multiply 24 by 6, multiply 24 by $\dfrac{2}{3}$, and add the two partial products:

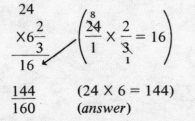

$$\begin{array}{r} 24 \\ \times 6\frac{2}{3} \\ \hline 16 \\ \hline 144 \\ \hline 160 \end{array}$$

$\left(\dfrac{\cancel{24}^8}{1} \times \dfrac{2}{\cancel{3}_1} = 16 \right)$

(24 × 6 = 144)

(*answer*)

This method is convenient when the whole number is a large number. Use this method to find the products in 17 to 19.

17. $48 \times 3\frac{5}{8}$ **18.** $45 \times 4\frac{2}{5}$ **19.** $54 \times 12\frac{5}{9}$

17. _____ **18.** _____ **19.** _____

20. How many feet of lumber are needed to make 15 shelves each $5\frac{2}{3}$ feet long?

20. _____

21. John's mother buys $\frac{1}{2}$ gallon of milk. They drink $\frac{2}{3}$ of it. What fraction of a gallon do they drink?

21. _____

22. Tom rides his bike at $6\frac{1}{4}$ miles per hour. How many miles does he travel in $2\frac{1}{5}$ hours?

22. _____

23. An inch is $\frac{1}{12}$ of a foot. What fractional part of a foot is $\frac{3}{5}$ of an inch?

23. _____

24. A *furlong* is a distance that is about $\frac{1}{8}$ of a mile. What fractional part of a mile is:

   a. 2 furlongs?   **b.** $\frac{2}{3}$ of a furlong?

24. a. _____ **b.** _____

25. What is the total weight of a dozen chickens, each weighing $4\frac{3}{4}$ pounds?

25. _____

8. Dividing fractions

How many $\frac{1}{4}$-inch line segments are there in $2\frac{1}{2}$ inches? This problem is equivalent to dividing $2\frac{1}{2}$ by $\frac{1}{4}$.

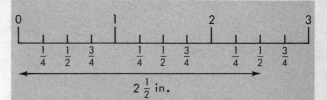

If we look at the $2\frac{1}{2}$-inch line segment in the figure and count the quarter-inch segments that make it up, we see that there are 10 such smaller segments. Thus, $2\frac{1}{2} \div \frac{1}{4} = 10$ or $\frac{5}{2} \div \frac{1}{4} = 10$. Note that this result can also be obtained by *inverting* the divisor (turning the second fraction upside down) and multiplying the result by the dividend (the first fraction). Thus,

$$\frac{5}{2} \div \frac{1}{4} = \frac{5}{2} \times \frac{4}{1} = \frac{5}{\underset{1}{2}} \times \frac{\overset{2}{4}}{1} = \frac{10}{1} = 10$$

When we invert a fraction, we call the resulting fraction the *reciprocal* of the original fraction. The reciprocal of $\frac{2}{3}$ is $\frac{3}{2}$; the reciprocal of $\frac{5}{1}$ is $\frac{1}{5}$. Note that the product of any fraction and its reciprocal is always 1. For example, $\frac{2}{3} \times \frac{3}{2} = 1$ and $\frac{5}{1} \times \frac{1}{5} = 1$.

We may now state the following rule:

Rule: To divide one fraction by another, *invert* the divisor (the fraction after the division sign) and *multiply*.

Thus, division by a fraction is equivalent to multiplication by the reciprocal of the fraction.

ILLUSTRATIVE PROBLEM 1

Divide 18 by $\frac{3}{5}$.

Solution: $\frac{18}{1} \div \frac{3}{5} = \frac{\overset{6}{18}}{1} \times \frac{5}{\underset{1}{3}} = \frac{30}{1} = 30$

ILLUSTRATIVE PROBLEM 2

$\frac{9}{16} \div \frac{3}{10} = ?$

Solution: $\frac{9}{16} \div \frac{3}{10} = \frac{\overset{3}{9}}{\underset{8}{16}} \times \frac{\overset{5}{10}}{\underset{1}{3}} = \frac{15}{8} = 1\frac{7}{8}$

ILLUSTRATIVE PROBLEM 3

$$10 \div 5\frac{3}{4} = ?$$

Solution: $\dfrac{10}{1} \div \dfrac{23}{4} = \dfrac{10}{1} \times \dfrac{4}{23} = \dfrac{40}{23} = 1\dfrac{17}{23}$

ILLUSTRATIVE PROBLEM 4

$$2\frac{2}{5} \div 8 = ?$$

Solution: $\dfrac{12}{5} \div \dfrac{8}{1} = \dfrac{\overset{3}{\cancel{12}}}{5} \times \dfrac{1}{\underset{2}{\cancel{8}}} = \dfrac{3}{10}$

Exercises

In 1 to 9, perform the indicated operations.

1. $\dfrac{3}{8} \div \dfrac{3}{2}$ 2. $\dfrac{1}{3} \div \dfrac{4}{6}$ 3. $14 \div \dfrac{7}{10}$

4. $3\dfrac{3}{4} \div \dfrac{5}{8}$ 5. $\dfrac{3}{20} \div 6$ 6. $4\dfrac{2}{3} \div 2\dfrac{4}{5}$

7. $2\dfrac{1}{6} \div 2\dfrac{2}{3}$ 8. $8 \div \dfrac{4}{9}$ 9. $\dfrac{4}{9} \div \dfrac{1}{6}$

10. A $3\dfrac{3}{4}$-foot length of molding is cut into $\dfrac{3}{4}$-foot strips. How many strips are there?

11. A man drove 90 miles in $2\dfrac{1}{4}$ hours. How many miles did he drive in one hour?

12. A board $9\dfrac{3}{4}$ feet long is cut into 13 equal pieces. How many feet long is each such piece?

1. _____ 2. _____ 3. _____

4. _____ 5. _____ 6. _____

7. _____ 8. _____ 9. _____

10. _____

11. _____

12. _____

13. If a suit requires $4\frac{1}{5}$ yards of fabric, how many suits can be made with 42 yards of fabric?

13. _____

14. A man pours $4\frac{1}{2}$ quarts of milk into containers holding $1\frac{1}{2}$ quarts each. How many containers does he fill?

14. _____

9. Finding fractional parts

In a class of 30 students, 25 are present. What fractional part of the class is present? Here, we are asking the question "25 is what fractional part of 30?" We can write a fraction with the *total amount* as the *denominator* and the *fractional part* as the *numerator*. Thus,

$$\frac{25}{30} = \frac{25 \div 5}{30 \div 5} = \frac{5}{6}$$

$\frac{5}{6}$ of the class is present.

Check: Does $\frac{5}{6}$ of 30 equal 25?

$$\frac{5}{\overset{6}{\underset{1}{\cancel{6}}}} \times \frac{\overset{5}{\cancel{30}}}{1} = \frac{25}{1} = 25 \ \checkmark$$

A useful memory device here is to remember that the number going with the word "is" becomes the numerator and the number going with the word "of" becomes the denominator.

ILLUSTRATIVE PROBLEM 1

18 is what part of 24?

Solution: $\dfrac{\text{is}}{\text{of}} = \dfrac{18}{24} = \dfrac{18 \div 6}{24 \div 6} = \dfrac{3}{4}$

ILLUSTRATIVE PROBLEM 2

What part of 80 is 50?

Solution: $\dfrac{\text{is}}{\text{of}} = \dfrac{50}{80} = \dfrac{50 \div 10}{80 \div 10} = \dfrac{5}{8}$

Exercises

1. 7 is what part of 28?

2. 18 is what part of 20?

3. 16 is what part of 20?

4. What part of 90 is 60?

5. What part of 100 is 73?

6. What part of 72 is 30?

7. What part of 23 is 18?

8. What part of 150 is 100?

9. In a class of 28 students, 8 receive A's. What part of the class receives A?

10. In a spelling test of 25 words, Nancy spells 20 correctly. What part of all the words does Nancy spell correctly?

11. In traveling 800 miles, a man does 600 miles by train and 200 miles by car.

   a. What part of the trip does he do by train?

   b. What part of the trip does he drive?

12. In a class of 32 students, 6 are absent.

   a. What part of the class is absent?

   b. What part of the class is present?

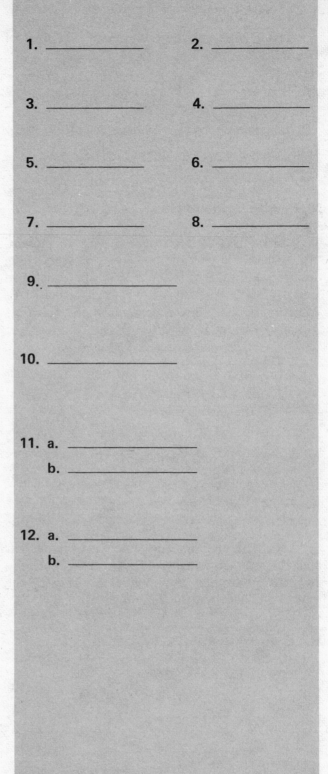

1. _____ 2. _____

3. _____ 4. _____

5. _____ 6. _____

7. _____ 8. _____

9. _____

10. _____

11. a. _____

   b. _____

12. a. _____

   b. _____

10. Finding a number given a fractional part of it

ILLUSTRATIVE PROBLEM

$\dfrac{5}{8}$ of what number is 60?

Solution: In problems of this type, it is convenient to use the equation method we learned in Chapter 3.

     Let n = the number.

Then $\dfrac{5}{8}$ of n = 60, or

$$\frac{5}{8}n = 60$$

Now, divide both sides of the equation by $\frac{5}{8}$

$$\frac{\frac{5}{8}n}{\frac{5}{8}} = \frac{60}{\frac{5}{8}}$$

$$n = 60 \div \frac{5}{8}$$

$$n = \frac{\overset{12}{\cancel{60}}}{1} \times \frac{8}{\cancel{5}_1}$$

$$n = 96 \quad (answer)$$

Check: Does $\frac{5}{8}$ of 96 equal 60?

$$\frac{5}{\cancel{8}_1} \times \frac{\overset{12}{\cancel{96}}}{1} = \frac{60}{1} = 60 \; \checkmark$$

Alternate Solution: Another way of solving the fractional equation above is to multiply both sides by the reciprocal of $\frac{5}{8}$, which is $\frac{8}{5}$. Remember that the product of a number and its reciprocal is 1. Thus,

$$\frac{5}{8}n = 60$$

$$\frac{\overset{1}{\cancel{8}}}{\cancel{5}_1} \times \frac{\overset{1}{\cancel{5}}}{\cancel{8}_1}n = \frac{\overset{12}{\cancel{60}}}{1} \times \frac{8}{\cancel{5}_1}$$

$$n = 12 \times 8 = 96 \quad (answer)$$

Exercises

1. Solve: $\frac{3}{4}x = 30$ 2. Solve: $\frac{1}{8}y = 14$

1. _____   2. _____

3. Solve: $\frac{7}{5}n = 140$ 4. Solve: $180 = \frac{6}{7}p$

3. _____   4. _____

5. $\frac{5}{8}$ of what number is 35?

5. _____

6. 80 is $\frac{2}{3}$ of what number?

6. _____

7. If $\frac{3}{16}$ of a number is 24, find the number.

7. _____

8. 31 is $\frac{1}{5}$ of what number?

8. _____

9. Jane gets $\frac{4}{5}$ of the problems right on a test. If she gets 24 right, how many problems were there on the test?

9. _____

10. Tom scored 27 points in a basketball game. This was $\frac{3}{8}$ of the total scored by the team. How many points did the team make?

10. _____

11. Jim delivered $\frac{5}{6}$ of the newspapers he received. If he delivered 40 newspapers, how many did he receive?

11. _____

12. Solve the equation: $\frac{3}{4} x = \frac{3}{2}$

12. _____

11. Simplifying complex fractions

A *complex* fraction is one that has a fraction in one or both of its terms. Thus,

$$\frac{\frac{3}{5}}{2}, \frac{4}{\frac{5}{8}}, \text{ and } \frac{3\frac{1}{3}}{2\frac{1}{2}}$$

are all complex fractions. These are easily simplified if we remember that the fraction line is equivalent to a division sign. Thus,

$$\frac{\frac{3}{5}}{\frac{3}{4}}$$

may be written

$$\frac{3}{5} \div \frac{3}{4} = \frac{\overset{1}{\cancel{3}}}{5} \times \frac{4}{\cancel{3}_{1}} = \frac{4}{5}$$

Rule: To simplify a complex fraction, divide the numerator by the denominator and proceed as in the division of fractions.

Exercises

Simplify the following complex fractions:

1. $\dfrac{\dfrac{1}{7}}{\dfrac{7}{8}}$ 2. $\dfrac{\dfrac{1}{3}}{\dfrac{8}{}}$ 3. $\dfrac{\dfrac{4}{5}}{8}$

4. $\dfrac{3\dfrac{1}{2}}{7}$ 5. $\dfrac{3\dfrac{1}{3}}{2\dfrac{1}{2}}$ 6. $\dfrac{4\dfrac{2}{5}}{7\dfrac{1}{3}}$

7. $\dfrac{3\dfrac{2}{3}}{2\dfrac{2}{5}}$ 8. $\dfrac{16\dfrac{2}{3}}{100}$ 9. $\dfrac{\dfrac{7}{8}}{\dfrac{5}{16}}$

10. $\dfrac{62\dfrac{1}{2}}{100}$ 11. $\dfrac{1\dfrac{2}{3}}{4\dfrac{1}{3}}$ 12. $\dfrac{83\dfrac{1}{3}}{50}$

Chapter review exercises

In 1 to 12, perform the operations indicated.

1. $\dfrac{2}{3} \times \dfrac{1}{2}$ 2. $\dfrac{3}{4} - \dfrac{1}{3}$ 3. $1\dfrac{1}{4} + 3\dfrac{2}{3}$

4. $\begin{array}{r} 6\dfrac{1}{5} \\ -3\dfrac{5}{6} \\ \hline \end{array}$ 5. Add: $\begin{array}{r} 6\dfrac{1}{2} \\ 5\dfrac{1}{3} \\ 7\dfrac{3}{8} \\ \hline \end{array}$ 6. $\dfrac{3}{8} \div \dfrac{2}{3}$

1. _____ 2. _____ 3. _____

4. _____ 5. _____ 6. _____

7. _____ 8. _____ 9. _____

10. _____ 11. _____ 12. _____

1. _____ 2. _____ 3. _____

4. _____ 5. _____ 6. _____

7. $\dfrac{5}{6} \times 1\dfrac{2}{3}$ **8.** $3\dfrac{1}{8} \div 2\dfrac{1}{2}$ **9.** $\dfrac{3}{4} \times 1\dfrac{1}{8}$

10. $2\dfrac{3}{4} \times 3\dfrac{1}{7}$ **11.** $5 \div \dfrac{5}{3}$ **12.** $8 - 1\dfrac{5}{6}$

13. 25 is what part of 35?

14. $4\dfrac{1}{2} + 1\dfrac{2}{3} - 3\dfrac{1}{4} = ?$

15. 65 is $\dfrac{5}{8}$ of what number?

16. How many $\dfrac{3}{4}$-pound bags can be filled from 15 pounds of sugar?

17. 21 is $\dfrac{3}{4}$ of what number?

18. A carpenter planes down the thickness of a board from $\dfrac{7}{8}$ of an inch to $\dfrac{11}{16}$ of an inch. What was the thickness of the wood removed?

19. Find the sum of $3\dfrac{3}{32}$, $8\dfrac{1}{16}$, $7\dfrac{5}{64}$.

20. A drain pipe can empty $\dfrac{1}{3}$ of an oil tank every hour. Another can empty $\dfrac{1}{2}$ of it in the same time.
   a. What part of the tank will both pipes empty in an hour?
   b. What part will remain in the tank?

21. How much greater is a wire $\dfrac{3}{8}$ of an inch in diameter than one $\dfrac{5}{16}$ of an inch in diameter?

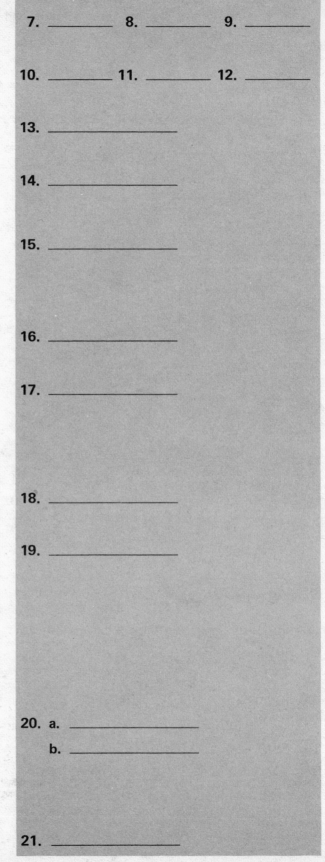

7. _____ **8.** _____ **9.** _____

10. _____ **11.** _____ **12.** _____

13. _____

14. _____

15. _____

16. _____

17. _____

18. _____

19. _____

20. a. _____
   b. _____

21. _____

22. How many sheets of tin, each $\frac{1}{32}$ of an inch thick, are there in a pile $12\frac{1}{4}$ inches high?

22. _____

23. Simplify: $\dfrac{5\frac{5}{8}}{10}$

23. _____

24. Find the average of $8\frac{3}{4}$, $7\frac{1}{2}$, and $4\frac{5}{8}$.

24. _____

25. Solve the equation: $\frac{3}{4}\,t = \frac{7}{8}$

25. _____

DECIMAL FRACTIONS AND SIMPLE DECIMAL EQUATIONS

1. Meaning of decimal fractions

A *decimal fraction* is simply a fraction whose denominator is 10 or some power of 10, such as 100, 1000, 10,000, etc. Thus, $\frac{9}{10}$, $\frac{17}{100}$, and $\frac{375}{1000}$ are decimal fractions. Since we use a number system to base 10, we find that decimal fractions often make computation simpler than other fractions.

Instead of writing these denominators in decimal fractions, we often write the numbers with a *decimal point*. Thus,

$$\frac{9}{10} \text{ becomes .9}$$

$$\frac{17}{100} \text{ becomes .17}$$

$$\frac{375}{1000} \text{ becomes .375}$$

Decimal fractions are often just called *decimals* when written in the *shortened* form with the decimal point. A simple rule for writing a decimal fraction in the shortened form is the following:

Rule: Begin at the right-hand digit of the numerator, count off as many places to the left as there are zeros in the denominator, and place the decimal point to the left of the last digit counted.

Thus, applying the rule to the decimal fraction $\frac{16}{100}$, we start at the 6, count off two places to the left, and get .16. $\frac{193}{1000}$ would become .193.

Note that, in some cases, we must write place-holding zeros to the left of the left-hand digit in the numerator.

$$\frac{78}{10,000} = .0078$$

Beginning with the digit 8, we count off four places to the left, adding two zeros as we count, and place the decimal point to the extreme left. Either form is read "seventy-eight ten-thousandths."

Each decimal place in a given decimal is given a name. Thus, for the number .37589, we indicate the value of each digit as follows:

TENTHS	HUNDREDTHS	THOUSANDTHS	TEN-THOUSANDTHS	HUNDRED-THOUSANDTHS
.3	7	5	8	9

In the number .777, each digit is multiplied by $\frac{1}{10}$ as we move to the right. (The "*place value*" of each 7 is divided by 10. See Appendix I, page 276.)

$$\text{The first 7 means 7 tenths} \quad = \frac{7}{10} = .7$$

$$\text{The second 7 means 7 hundredths} = \frac{7}{100} = .07$$

$$\text{The third 7 means 7 thousandths} = \frac{7}{1000} = .007$$

If we add these fractions by changing to a common denominator, we obtain

$$\frac{7}{10} = \frac{700}{1000} = .700$$

$$\frac{7}{100} = \frac{70}{1000} = .070$$

$$\frac{7}{1000} = \frac{7}{1000} = .007$$

$$\textit{Sum:} \quad \frac{777}{1000} = .777$$

Note that the sum in the shortened decimal form can be obtained by simply adding up the digit columns of the addends. This indicates one of the advantages of using the shortened decimal form.

From the above example, note that the value of a decimal is not changed by placing zeros after the extreme right-hand digit. Thus, .7, .70, and .700 all have the same value. However, this is not true when zeros are placed between the decimal point and the extreme left digit. Thus, .7, .07, and .007 have different values.

To read a decimal fraction in full, we read both its numerator and denominator. To read .513, we read "five hundred thirteen" (numerator) "thousandths" (denominator). The denominator is always 1 followed by as many zeros as decimal places.

A number such as 23.754, which is made up of a whole number and a decimal, is called a *mixed decimal*. Mixed decimals are read the same as mixed numbers. Thus, 112.73 is read "one hundred twelve *and* seventy-three hundredths."

When the decimal point is not shown in a number, it is always considered to be to the right of the extreme right-hand digit. In the number 237, the decimal point is considered to be to the right of the 7.

Exercises

1. Write the following fractions as decimals:

a. $\dfrac{27}{100}$　　**b.** $\dfrac{7}{10}$　　**c.** $\dfrac{64}{100}$

d. $\dfrac{6}{100}$　　**e.** $\dfrac{76}{1000}$　　**f.** $\dfrac{9}{1000}$

g. $\dfrac{23}{1000}$　　**h.** $\dfrac{17}{100}$　　**i.** $\dfrac{47}{10,000}$

2. Write the following numbers as figures in decimal form:

a. seven hundredths

b. six thousandths

c. five hundred eighteen thousandths

d. four hundred eleven ten-thousandths

e. fifty-four ten-thousandths

3. In exercise **2,** write each decimal as a common fraction.

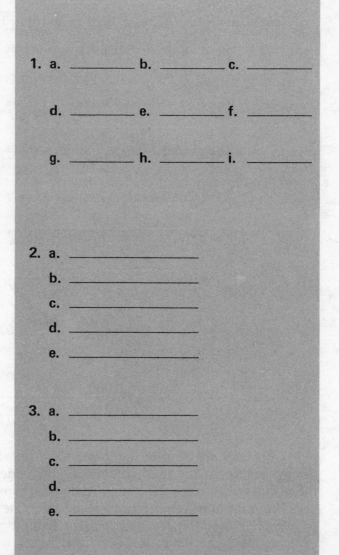

1. a. _____ b. _____ c. _____

   d. _____ e. _____ f. _____

   g. _____ h. _____ i. _____

2. a. _____

   b. _____

   c. _____

   d. _____

   e. _____

3. a. _____

   b. _____

   c. _____

   d. _____

   e. _____

4. The circle has been divided into 10 equal parts. Write as a decimal the part of the circle that is shaded.

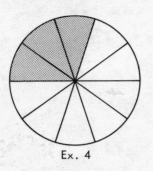

Ex. 4

5. The ruler shown is a centimeter ruler (enlarged). Each centimeter is divided into 10 equal parts. Give the number of centimeters at *a*, *b*, *c*, *d* as a decimal.

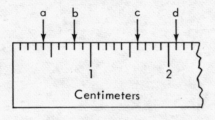

Centimeters

Ex. 5

6. Read each of the following numbers:

a. 30.2

b. 23.0

c. 27.18

d. 6.66

e. 130.03

f. .0804

g. 3.007

h. .00008

7. In the number 92.09, the first nine has a place value which is how many times greater than the second nine?

8. A boy is running a 1000-meter race. When he has run 675 meters, write as a decimal the part of the distance he has already run.

4. _____

5. _____

6. a. _____

b. _____

c. _____

d. _____

e. _____

f. _____

g. _____

h. _____

7. _____

8. _____

9. A girl receives 100 envelopes in a box. She uses 23 of them. Write as a decimal the part of the box of envelopes she has left.

10. A typist receives a 1000-sheet package of typing paper. He uses 372 of the sheets. Write as a decimal the part of the package that remains.

9. _____

10. _____

2. Comparing decimals

Which is larger, .79 or .8?

To compare two such decimals, we treat them as we do fractions; that is, we change them to equivalent fractions with the same denominators. Thus,

$$.79 = \frac{79}{100}$$

$$.8 = .80 = \frac{80}{100}$$

Now $\frac{80}{100}$ is greater than $\frac{79}{100}$, so that .80 or .8 is greater than .79.

We can use here the fact that writing zeros to the right of the extreme right-hand digit in a decimal does not change its value.

Rule: To compare decimals, change them to equivalent decimals by writing zeros to the right until all of them have the same number of decimal places. Then compare the resulting numbers.

ILLUSTRATIVE PROBLEM

Arrange the following numbers in order of size from smallest to largest:

.6   .67   .06   .607

Solution: Change all to three-place decimals:

.6 = .600   .67 = .670   .06 = .060   .607 = .607

Arrange in order of size:

.060   .600   .607   .670

Exercises

1. Change to an equivalent fraction expressed as thousandths:

   a. .3   **b.** .9   **c.** .43

   d. .05   **e.** .98

2. In each part, choose two decimals having the same value.

   a. .700,   .07,   .70,   .007

   b. .031,   .31,   .310,   .0031

   c. 4.20,   4.02,   4.200,   4.002

3. In each pair of numbers, choose the larger.

   a. .8 or .82   **b.** .3 or .33

   c. .1 or .012   **d.** .02 or .002

   e. 2.4 or 2.38   **f.** 5.3 or 5.03

   g. .6 or .66   **h.** .162 or .17

   i. 3.7 or 3.678

4. Arrange each group of numbers in order of size with the smallest number first.

   a. 3;   .3;   .03;   .003

   b. .5;   .55;   .055;   .505

   c. .035;   .04;   .4;   .305

   d. 4.1;   .41;   .401;   4.01

   e. 1.4;   1.41;   1.414;   1.04

   f. 7.02;   7.002;   7.19;   7.019

   g. 3.2; $\frac{34}{10}$;   3.3; $3\frac{1}{10}$

   h. 2.5; $\frac{23}{10}$;   2.2; $2\frac{7}{10}$

5. Which of the following is less than 3.25?

   3.14   3.3   3.04   3.24   3.254

3. Rounding off decimal fractions

We may approximate decimals just as we do whole numbers by the process of *rounding off*.

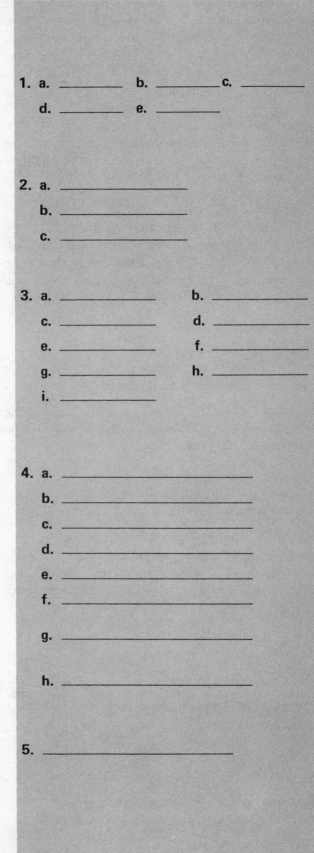

1. a. _____ b. _____ c. _____

   d. _____ e. _____

2. a. _____

   b. _____

   c. _____

3. a. _____ b. _____

   c. _____ d. _____

   e. _____ f. _____

   g. _____ h. _____

   i. _____

4. a. _____

   b. _____

   c. _____

   d. _____

   e. _____

   f. _____

   g. _____

   h. _____

5. _____

Suppose we want to write the number .257 to the nearest hundredth. Is it closer to .25 or .26? Or, put another way, is it closer to .250 or .260? The number .257 is .007 greater than .250 but .003 less than .260. Hence it is closer to .260 and we round it off as .26.

Note that, if the number were .253, it would be closer to .25. The deciding digit is the one in the thousandths place; if it is 5 or more, we agree to increase the hundredths digit by one—if it is less than 5, we drop it and leave the hundredths place unchanged.

Rule: Any decimal may be *rounded off* by first *dropping* all decimal places after the desired place. Then the last figure kept should be *increased by 1* if the next discarded figure is *5* or more. Otherwise, it should be left unchanged.

ILLUSTRATIVE PROBLEM 1

Round off .3243 to thousandths.

Solution: Keep the first three digits, .324. Now the next digit, 3, is less than 5, so drop it. The rounded-off decimal is .324 (*answer*).

ILLUSTRATIVE PROBLEM 2

Round off 3.76 to tenths.

Solution: Keep the first two digits, 3.7. Now the next digit, 6, is more than 5, so increase the digit 7 by 1. The rounded-off decimal is 3.8 (*answer*).

Exercises

1. Round off to the nearest *tenth*:

   a. .78   b. 2.33   c. 12.45

   d. .549   e. .083   f. 2.04

2. Round off to the nearest *hundredth*:

   a. .348   b. .333   c. 2.738

   d. .075   e. .388   f. 5.405

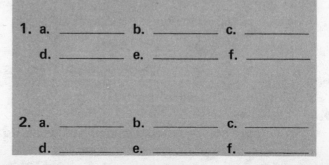

1. a. _____ b. _____ c. _____

   d. _____ e. _____ f. _____

2. a. _____ b. _____ c. _____

   d. _____ e. _____ f. _____

3. Round off to the nearest *thousandth:*

    a. .1427   **b.** .5862   **c.** .0456

    d. .00075   **e.** 3.4507   **f.** 8.0095

4. Round off the number 3.1416 to the nearest:

    a. thousandth   **b.** hundredth

    c. tenth   **d.** whole number

5. The length of a rod is 6.745 inches. Round this off to the nearest *hundredth.*

6. A high jumper leaped over a bar 5.78 feet above ground. What is this to the nearest *tenth?*

7. A boy weighs 63.4 kilograms. What is this to the nearest *whole number?*

8. The diameter of the cylinder of an engine measures 5.473 inches. What is this to the nearest *tenth?*

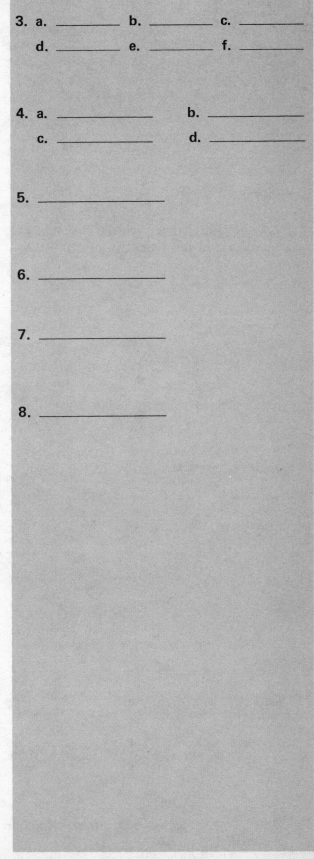

3. a. _____ b. _____ c. _____

   d. _____ e. _____ f. _____

4. a. _____ b. _____

   c. _____ d. _____

5. _____

6. _____

7. _____

8. _____

4. Changing decimals to common fractions

Any decimal may be written as a reduced common fraction. We simply write out the numerator and denominator (a power of 10) and reduce to lowest terms, if possible.

Examples

1. Write .73 as a common fraction.

$$.73 = \frac{73}{100} \quad \text{(This cannot be reduced.)}$$

2. Write .075 as a common fraction.

$$.075 = \frac{75}{1000} = \frac{25 \times 3}{25 \times 40} = \frac{3}{40}$$

3. Write 3.2 as a mixed number.

$$3.2 = 3\frac{2}{10} = 3\frac{1}{5}$$

4. Write $.07\frac{1}{2}$ as a common fraction.

$$.07\frac{1}{2} = \frac{7\frac{1}{2}}{100} = 7\frac{1}{2} \div \frac{100}{1} = \frac{15}{2} \div \frac{100}{1}$$

$$= \frac{\overset{3}{\cancel{15}}}{2} \times \frac{1}{\underset{20}{\cancel{100}}} = \frac{3}{40}$$

Exercises

In 1 to 12, change each decimal to a common fraction in lowest terms.

1. .25   **2.** .5   **3.** .37

4. .375   **5.** .15   **6.** .75

7. .80   **8.** .625   **9.** .05

10. .018   **11.** .030 **12.** .0075

In 13 to 20, change each decimal to a fraction in lowest terms.

13. $.12\frac{1}{2}$ **14.** $.33\frac{1}{3}$ **15.** $.16\frac{2}{3}$

16. $.87\frac{1}{2}$ **17.** $.37\frac{1}{2}$ **18.** $.62\frac{1}{2}$

19. $.66\frac{2}{3}$ **20.** $.83\frac{1}{3}$

21. Write 3.75 as a mixed number.

22. A sheet of tin is $.06\frac{1}{4}$ of an inch thick. Write this as a common fraction.

23. Write .4 of a second as a common fraction of a second.

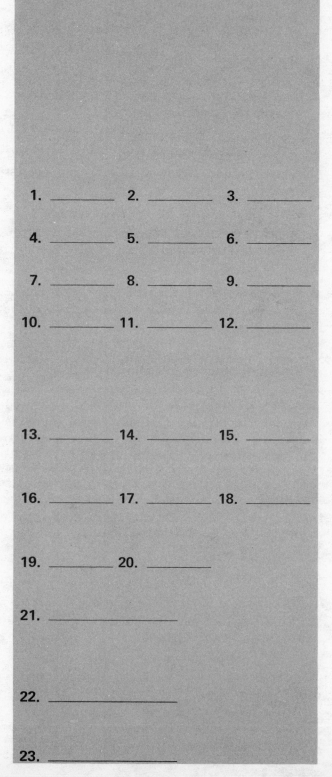

1. _____   2. _____   3. _____

4. _____   5. _____   6. _____

7. _____   8. _____   9. _____

10. _____ 11. _____ 12. _____

13. _____ 14. _____ 15. _____

16. _____ 17. _____ 18. _____

19. _____ 20. _____

21. _____

22. _____

23. _____

5. Adding and subtracting decimals

Since decimals are really fractions, we can add and subtract them in the same way we do fractions. For example,

$$.7 + .2 = \frac{7}{10} + \frac{2}{10} = \frac{9}{10} = .9$$

In the case of decimals, the common denominator for the equivalent fractions is always a power of 10. This can be accomplished easily with decimals by lining up the addends vertically, keeping the decimal points *directly under each other*.

ILLUSTRATIVE PROBLEM 1

$$2.5 + 3.57 + 1.02 = ?$$

Solution: Line up the decimal points and add:

$$
\begin{array}{r}
2.5 \\
3.57 \\
\underline{1.02} \\
7.09
\end{array}
\quad (answer)
$$

We simply bring down the decimal point and add as we do for whole numbers.

ILLUSTRATIVE PROBLEM 2

Add $4.23, $2.75, and $6.00.

Solution:
$$
\begin{array}{r}
\$4.23 \\
2.75 \\
\underline{6.00} \\
\$12.98
\end{array}
$$

The same principle also works for subtraction of decimals.

ILLUSTRATIVE PROBLEM 3

Subtract .3 from 4.1.

Solution:
$$
\begin{array}{r}
4.1 \\
\underline{-.3} \\
3.8
\end{array}
$$

ILLUSTRATIVE PROBLEM 4

Subtract .267 from 3.

Solution: Here we need to write three zeros after the decimal point following the number 3. Thus:

```
  3.000
 −.267
  2.733
```

Exercises

In 1 to 6, add the decimals.

1. .7
.5

2. .39
.04

3. 2.73
1.48

4. 2.73
3.5
2.457

5. 3.42
6.
4.2
8.53

6. 2.53
.97
4.25
1.404

7. Add: .98 + 4.35 + 35.58

8. Add: 62.2 + 928.6 + 86.4

In 9 to 14, subtract the decimals.

9. .73
.27

10. 2.87
.08

11. 73.0
14.7

12. 12.
4.23

13. 2.007
1.4

14. $23.14
8.22

15. Subtract: .08 − .032

16. From $12.34 subtract $5.88.

17. Bill went to the store with a $5.00 bill. He paid $2.37 for groceries. What change did he get from his $5.00 bill?

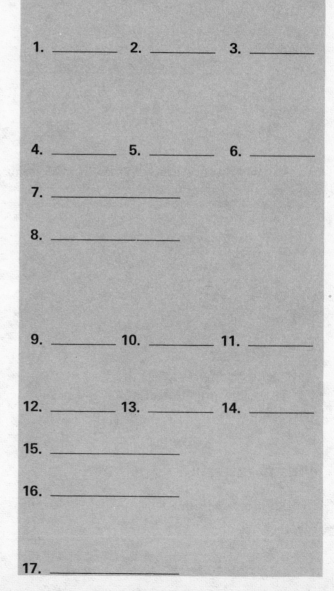

1. _____ 2. _____ 3. _____

4. _____ 5. _____ 6. _____

7. _____

8. _____

9. _____ 10. _____ 11. _____

12. _____ 13. _____ 14. _____

15. _____

16. _____

17. _____

18. A man going south drove 347.2 miles one day, 453.7 miles the next day, and 412.6 the third day. How many miles did he drive altogether?

19. One boy ran the 100-yard dash in 13.4 seconds and another in 11.9 seconds. How much longer did it take the first boy?

20. During four weeks in March, a man deposited the following amounts in the bank each week: $52.47, $83.92, $75.00, and $121.68. On March 31, he withdrew $278.47. How much money did he have left in the bank for the month of March?

18. _____

19. _____

20. _____

6. Multiplying decimals by whole numbers

If a man earns $3.75 an hour, how much does he earn in 7 hours? This requires multiplying a decimal by a whole number.

$$3.75 \times 7 = 3\frac{75}{100} \times 7 = \frac{375}{100} \times \frac{7}{1} = \frac{2625}{100}$$

$$= 26\frac{25}{100} = \$26.25$$

Note that this result can be obtained by multiplying as for whole numbers and then marking off as many decimal places in the product as in the original decimal factor.

ILLUSTRATIVE PROBLEM

$3.732 \times 8 = ?$

Solution: 3.732 (3 decimal places)
            $\underline{\times 8}$
             29.856 (3 decimal places)

Mark off 3 decimal places from the right since there are 3 such places in the factor.

Exercises

In 1 to 8, multiply.

1. .7
     $\underline{\times 8}$

2. 2.3
     $\underline{\times 6}$

3. 4.7
     $\underline{\times 14}$

1. _____ **2.** _____ **3.** _____

4. .035
   X8

5. 23.247
   X15

6. 18.26
   X23

7. $2.85
   X7

8.   23
  X.004

9. A hat store sells a dozen hats for $6.85 each. How much does it receive for the hats?

10. A sheet of tin is .18 inch thick. How thick, in inches, is a pile of 40 of these?

11. A car travels 12.4 miles on a gallon of gas. How many miles does it go on a tankful of 16 gallons?

12. What is the cost of 18 yards of moulding at $1.72 per yard?

13. A man bought a refrigerator by paying $50 down and 24 installments of $9.40 each. What was the total cost of the refrigerator?

14. Gasoline costs 53.8 cents per gallon. How much does a man pay to fill his gas tank with 15 gallons of gasoline?

7. Multiplying decimals by decimals

If we wish to multiply .21 by .7, we may think of them as fractions. Thus,

$$.21 \times .7 = \frac{21}{100} \times \frac{7}{10} = \frac{147}{1000} = .147$$

Note that there are two decimal places in the first factor, one in the second factor, and three in the product. It can thus be shown to be generally true that the number of decimal places in the product is equal to the sum of the number of decimal places in each factor.

Rule: To multiply two decimals, multiply as though they were whole numbers. Then mark off as many decimal places in the product as there are decimal places in the factors together.

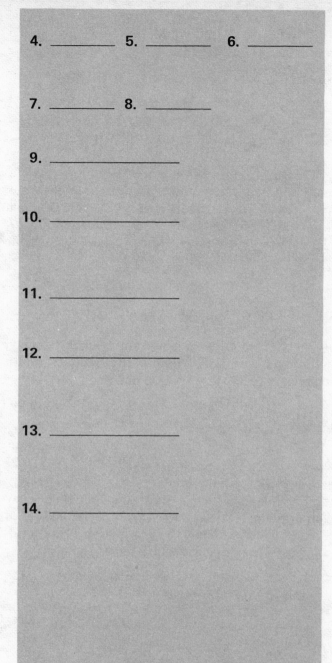

4. _____ **5.** _____ **6.** _____

7. _____ **8.** _____

9. _____

10. _____

11. _____

12. _____

13. _____

14. _____

Examples

1.   3.07 (2 decimal places)
   X.4 (1 decimal place)
  1.228 (3 decimal places)

2.   2.23 (2 decimal places)
   X.15 (2 decimal places)
  1115
  223
  .3345 (4 decimal places)

Exercises

In 1 to 12, find the products.

1. .4 × .5 **2.** 5.2 × .03 **3.** .57 × .8

4. 6.4
   X.3

5. 6.85
   X.23

6. .283
   X.06

7. .08
   X1000

8. 3.8
   X.0064

9. 5.72
   X.007

10. $3.84
   X1.2

11. $8.70
   X.04

12. $212.50
   X.07

13. What is the cost of 12.7 gallons of gasoline at 50.7 cents per gallon?

14. A cubic foot of ice weighs 57.5 pounds. What is the weight in pounds of 10.8 cubic feet of ice?

15. A car travels 20.4 miles on a gallon of gas. How many miles can it travel on 15.3 gallons?

16. A woman buys 18.6 yards of ribbon at 24 cents per yard. How much does she pay for the ribbon?

17. A plane flies at an average speed of 387.5 miles per hour. How many miles does it travel in 2.5 hours?

18. A limestone growth in a cave extends downward from the roof of a cave at the rate of .008 inch per year. How many inches does it grow in 40.5 years?

19. A gallon of milk weighs 8.7 pounds. How many pounds do 4.25 gallons weigh?

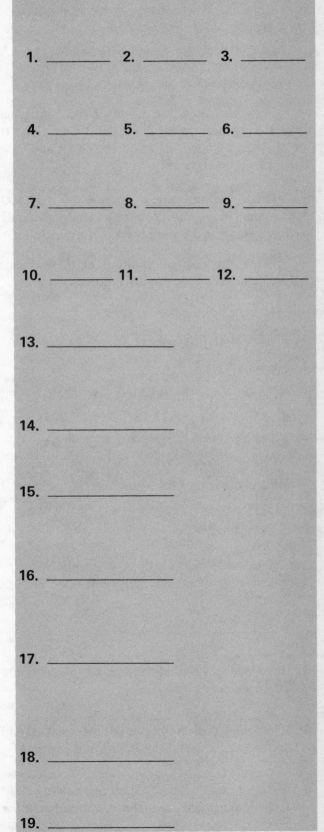

1. _____ **2.** _____ **3.** _____

4. _____ **5.** _____ **6.** _____

7. _____ **8.** _____ **9.** _____

10. _____ **11.** _____ **12.** _____

13. _____

14. _____

15. _____

16. _____

17. _____

18. _____

19. _____

8. Multiplying decimals by 10, 100, 1000, etc.

Consider the following three multiplication problems:

a.   .375   b.   375   c.   .375
     ×10   ×100   ×1000
    3.750   37.500   375.000

Note that in **a,** the effect of the multiplication is to move the decimal point one place to the right; in **b,** two places to the right; and in **c,** three places to the right.

Rule: To multiply a decimal by 10, 100, 1000, etc., move the decimal point to the right as many places as there are zeros in the multiplier.

When the decimal point is at the extreme right of a number, we usually omit it.

Examples

1. $12.48 \times 10 = 124.8$

2. $.0687 \times 1000 = 68.7$

3. $\$3.87 \times 100 = \$387$

Exercises

1. Multiply by 10:

   a. .378   b. 8.12   c. .003

   d. 83   e. $2.18   f. 2.0083

   g. .00052   h. .07   i. 23.04

2. Multiply each of the numbers in exercise **1** by 100.

3. Multiply each of the numbers in exercise **1** by 1000.

4. If a dozen eggs cost $.54, how much would 10 dozen cost?

5. If gasoline cost $.547 per gallon, what would be the cost of a 100-gallon drum of gasoline?

6. A restaurant buys 1000 doughnuts at $.07 each. How much does the restaurant pay for them?

1. a. _____   b. _____   c. _____
    d. _____   e. _____   f. _____
    g. _____   h. _____   i. _____

2. a. _____   b. _____   c. _____
    d. _____   e. _____   f. _____
    g. _____   h. _____   i. _____

3. a. _____   b. _____   c. _____
    d. _____   e. _____   f. _____
    g. _____   h. _____   i. _____

4. _____

5. _____

6. _____

9. Dividing decimals by whole numbers

Consider the examples at the right.

Note that, in each case where the division "box" ($\overline{}$) is used, the decimal point in the quotient is directly above the decimal point in the dividend. It is usually more convenient to use the division box to divide decimals than to convert decimals to improper fractions. Here is $45.75 \div 15$:

$$
\begin{array}{r}
3.05 \\
15\overline{\smash{)}45.75} \\
\underline{45} \\
75 \\
\underline{75}
\end{array}
$$

Rule: To divide a decimal by a whole number, place the decimal point in the quotient directly above the decimal point in the dividend and divide as with whole numbers.

ILLUSTRATIVE PROBLEM 1

Find, correct to the nearest tenth, $2.5 \div 3$.

Solution:
$$
\begin{array}{r}
.83 \\
3\overline{\smash{)}2.50} \\
\underline{2\,4} \\
10 \\
\underline{9} \\
1
\end{array}
$$

In this case, the quotient does not come out evenly. Hence, we write another zero to give us a quotient with one more decimal place than is required. Then we round off to the nearest tenth, so that the desired answer is .8.

ILLUSTRATIVE PROBLEM 2

Express $3 \div 4$ in decimal form with a remainder of zero.

Solution: Write enough zeros to the right of the decimal point so that the division is exact. Thus,

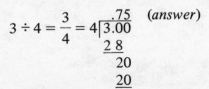

$$
3 \div 4 = \frac{3}{4} = 4\overline{\smash{)}3.00} \quad (answer)
$$

Examples

1. $.9 \div 3 = \dfrac{9}{10} \div \dfrac{3}{1} = \dfrac{\overset{3}{\cancel{9}}}{10} \times \dfrac{1}{\underset{1}{\cancel{3}}} = \dfrac{3}{10} = .3$

$$
\text{or} \quad 3\overline{\smash{)}.9}^{\,.3}
$$

2. $2.4 \div 6 = 2\dfrac{4}{10} \div \dfrac{6}{1} = \dfrac{\overset{4}{\cancel{24}}}{10} \times \dfrac{1}{\underset{1}{\cancel{6}}} = \dfrac{4}{10} = .4$

$$
\text{or} \quad 6\overline{\smash{)}2.4}^{\,.4}
$$

3. $.056 \div 8 = \dfrac{56}{1000} \div \dfrac{8}{1}$

$$
= \dfrac{\overset{7}{\cancel{56}}}{1000} \times \dfrac{1}{\underset{1}{\cancel{8}}} = \dfrac{7}{1000} = .007
$$

$$
\text{or} \quad 8\overline{\smash{)}.056}^{\,.007}
$$

Exercises

In 1 to 9, divide.

1. $3\overline{)6.9}$ **2.** $4\overline{)4.52}$ **3.** $6\overline{).24}$

4. $15\overline{)2.25}$ **5.** $35\overline{)3.605}$ **6.** $4\overline{)\$32.80}$

7. $12\overline{).96}$ **8.** $25\overline{)175.50}$ **9.** $463\overline{)41.67}$

In 10 to 15, divide. Write enough zeros after the decimal point in the dividend so that the division is exact.

10. $2\overline{).7}$ **11.** $4\overline{)2.20}$ **12.** $10\overline{)23.7}$

13. $8\overline{).0184}$ **14.** $22\overline{)57.42}$ **15.** $24\overline{)23.4}$

In 16 to 21, find each quotient to the nearest tenth.

16. $3\overline{)7.6}$ **17.** $4\overline{)5.52}$ **18.** $8\overline{)8.7}$

19. $18\overline{)292}$ **20.** $20\overline{)24.45}$ **21.** $16\overline{)4.79}$

22. Write $\dfrac{3}{5}$ as a decimal by dividing 3 by 5. (Write zeros after the decimal point in the dividend.)

23. a. Write $\dfrac{3}{8}$ as a decimal using the method of exercise **22.**

b. Write $\dfrac{5}{8}$ as a decimal.

24. Mr. Clark uses 15 gallons of gasoline to drive 247.5 miles. How many miles per gallon did he average?

25. A sporting goods store sold 14 basketballs for $137.90. What was the cost of each basketball?

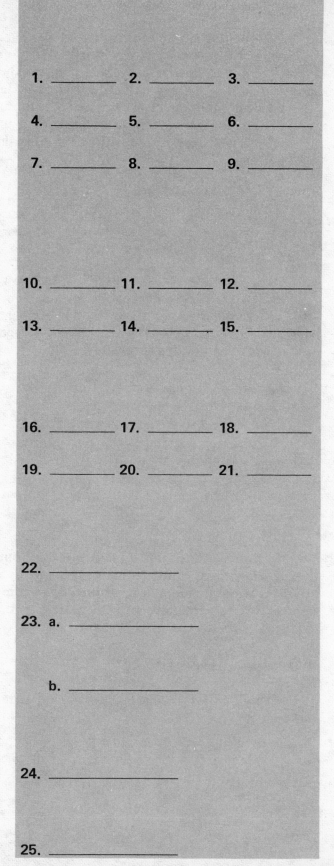

1. _____ 2. _____ 3. _____

4. _____ 5. _____ 6. _____

7. _____ 8. _____ 9. _____

10. _____ 11. _____ 12. _____

13. _____ 14. _____ 15. _____

16. _____ 17. _____ 18. _____

19. _____ 20. _____ 21. _____

22. _____

23. a. _____

b. _____

24. _____

25. _____

26. On a day in January, 11 inches of snow fell in 7 hours. What was the average snowfall per hour in hundredths of an inch?

26. _____

10. Dividing by a decimal

Consider $2.44 \div .4$. This may be written as the fraction $\frac{2.44}{.4}$. If the divisor (.4) were a whole number, we could divide as in Section 9. We can make .4 a whole number if we remember that we may multiply the numerator and denominator of a fraction by the same number without changing its value.

In this case, we must multiply .4 by 10 to make it a whole number. Thus,

$$\frac{2.44}{.4} = \frac{2.44 \times 10}{.4 \times 10} = \frac{24.4}{4}$$

Now we can divide as we have learned:

$$4\overline{)24.4}^{\;6.1}$$

Hence, $2.44 \div .4 = 6.1$.
We can check this by multiplication.

$$\begin{array}{r} 6.1 \\ \times .4 \\ \hline 2.44 \end{array}$$

If we wish to divide .144 by .12, we would have to multiply both dividend and divisor by 100 to make the divisor .12 a whole number. Thus,

$$\frac{.144}{.12} = \frac{.144 \times 100}{.12 \times 100} = \frac{14.4}{12} \qquad 12\overline{)14.4}^{\;1.2}$$

These two examples indicate the following procedure:

Rule: To divide by a decimal:

1. **Change the divisor to a whole number by multiplying it by a power of ten.**
2. **Multiply the dividend by the same number.**
3. **Perform the division with the new dividend and divisor.**

ILLUSTRATIVE PROBLEM

Divide 1.645 by .35.

$$\begin{array}{r} 4.7 \\ .35\overline{)1.64.5} \\ \underline{1\ 40} \\ 245 \\ \underline{245} \end{array}$$

Check:

$$\begin{array}{r} .35 \\ \times 4.7 \\ \hline 245 \\ 140 \\ \hline 1.645 \end{array}$$

Exercises

In 1 to 6, divide.

1. $.7\overline{).056}$ **2.** $.08\overline{)\$7.20}$ **3.** $1.6\overline{)2.352}$

4. $.012\overline{).156}$ **5.** $1.52\overline{)6.536}$ **6.** $2.24\overline{).3584}$

In 7 to 12, find the quotient to the nearest tenth.

7. $.6\overline{).10}$ **8.** $1.2\overline{)8.8}$ **9.** $.15\overline{)1.28}$

10. $7.7\overline{)27.43}$ **11.** $.18\overline{).040}$ **12.** $.25\overline{).163}$

13. Mr. Jones drove 248 miles and used 14.5 gallons. How many miles per gallon did he average, to the nearest tenth?

14. How many shirts costing $4.75 each can be bought for $95.00?

15. If a man earns $3.25 per hour, how many hours must he work in a week when he earns $110.50?

16. An auto travels 243 miles in 4.5 hours. What is its average rate in miles per hour?

17. How many rods .6 feet long can be cut from a wooden rod 9 feet long?

18. A package of paper is 2.8 inches thick. If each sheet is .008 inch thick, how many sheets are there in the package?

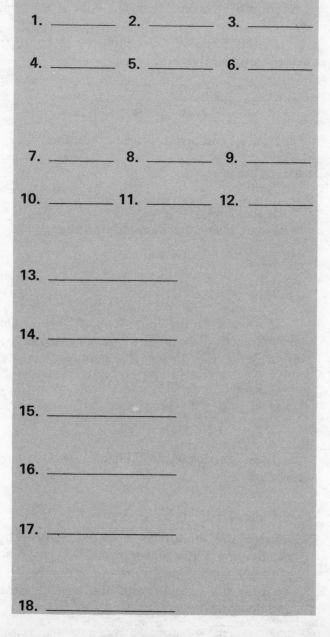

1. _____ 2. _____ 3. _____

4. _____ 5. _____ 6. _____

7. _____ 8. _____ 9. _____

10. _____ 11. _____ 12. _____

13. _____

14. _____

15. _____

16. _____

17. _____

18. _____

19. A boy saves $7.50 per week. How many weeks will it take him to save $135?

19. _____

20. If books cost $4.25 each, how many can be purchased for $119?

20. _____

11. Dividing by 10, 100, 1000, etc.

In a previous section, we saw that, when we *multiply* a number by 10, 100, 1000, etc., we move the decimal point in the number as many places to the *right* as there are zeros in the multiplier. Consequently, when we *divide* a number by 10, 100, 1000, etc., we move the decimal in the number as many places to the *left* as there are zeros in the divisor.

ILLUSTRATIVE PROBLEM

Divide 256.8 by 100.

Solution: Move the decimal point in 256.8 two places to the left.

$$\frac{256.8}{100} = 2.568$$

Exercises

In 1 to 12, divide by 10.

1. 45.12   **2.** 370   **3.** 52

4. 7.25   **5.** .03   **6.** 800

7. $8.60   **8.** 945.7   **9.** .23

10. 2.63   **11.** 78600   **12.** 32.2

13. In 1 to 12, divide by 100.

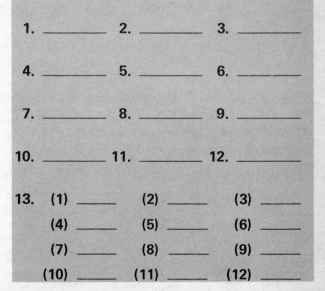

1. _____ 2. _____ 3. _____

4. _____ 5. _____ 6. _____

7. _____ 8. _____ 9. _____

10. _____ 11. _____ 12. _____

13. (1) _____ (2) _____ (3) _____

(4) _____ (5) _____ (6) _____

(7) _____ (8) _____ (9) _____

(10) _____ (11) _____ (12) _____

14. In 1 to 12, divide by 1000.

15. A car travels 2237 miles in 10 days. How many miles does it average per day?

15. _____

16. If 100 shirts cost a retailer $472, how much does each shirt cost him?

16. _____

17. A roll of 1000 ft. of wire cost $380. How much does it cost per foot?

17. _____

18. If a 100-pound bag of potatoes costs $18.00, how much do the potatoes cost per pound?

18. _____

19. A 100-gallon tank of oil is filled for $41.20. What is the cost per gallon?

19. _____

20. If 100 flower bulbs cost $14, how much does each bulb cost?

20. _____

12. Solving Simple Decimal Equations

If we wish to solve an equation with decimals, such as

$$.3x = 2.1$$

we may proceed by methods used in Chapter 2.

$$\frac{.3x}{.3} = \frac{2.1}{.3}$$

$$x = \frac{21}{3} = 7$$

Or, we may start by clearing the equation of decimals by multiplying both sides by 10, 100, 1000, or a greater power of 10. In this case, we multiply both sides by 10.

$$10 \times .3x = 10 \times 2.1$$

$$3x = 21$$

$$\frac{3x}{3} = \frac{21}{3}$$

$$x = 7$$

This technique of solving decimal equations by clearing of decimals usually makes the work easier.

ILLUSTRATIVE PROBLEM

Solve: $.05y = .725$

Solution: Multiply both sides by 1000.

$$1000 \times .05y = 1000 \times .725$$
$$50y = 725$$
$$y = \frac{725}{50} = \frac{145}{10} = 14.5 \quad (answer)$$

Exercises

In 1 to 10, solve the equations.

1. $.75t = 40$

2. $1.50m = 72$

3. $.5p = 30$

4. $.18k = 2.7$

5. $.06y = 7.2$

6. $2.3r + .9r = 64$

7. $3.14d = 9.42$

8. $.03z = 48$

9. $1.5r - r = .9$

10. $2.5x = 1.25$

In 11 to 15, write an equation and then solve it.

11. .4 of what number is 76?

12. .35 of a certain number is 70. What is the number?

13. Bill bought a football for $12. This was .8 of the regular price. What was the regular price?

14. The selling price of a suit is 1.2 of its cost. If the selling price is $84, what is the cost of the suit?

1. _____

2. _____

3. _____

4. _____

5. _____

6. _____

7. _____

8. _____

9. _____

10. _____

11. _____

12. _____

13. _____

14. _____

15. The freshman class of a school is made up of 180 pupils. If this is .36 of the total number of pupils in the school, how many students are there in the school?

15. _____

Chapter review exercises

1. Write each of the following as a decimal:

   a. $\dfrac{3}{10}$ b. $\dfrac{7}{20}$

   c. $\dfrac{8}{25}$ d. $\dfrac{17}{50}$

1. a. _____ b. _____

   c. _____ d. _____

2. Write each of the following as a common fraction or a mixed number:

   a. .65 b. 4

   c. 2.75 d. 1.375

2. a. _____ b. _____

   c. _____ d. _____

3. A cubic foot of water weighs 62.5 pounds. What is the weight, in pounds, of 10 cubic feet of water?

3. _____

4. John buys $3.87 worth of groceries. What change does he get from a $5.00 bill?

4. _____

5. Arrange according to size, starting with the smallest:

   .3   .03   .33   3.3   .003

5. _____

6. The noon temperatures for five successive days were: 63.2°, 65.5°, 61.3°, 59.8°, and 59.7°. What was the average noon temperature?

6. _____

7. Divide 23.24 by 2.8 and check.

7. _____

8. Change $\dfrac{5}{7}$ to a decimal. Round off to the nearest hundredth.

8. _____

9. Mr. Jones spends $188.50 per year for subway fares. What is his average monthly expense for subway fares (to the nearest cent)?

9. _____

10. How many sheets of tin each .12 inch thick are needed to make a pile 15 inches high?

10. _____

11. Jane earns $2.35 an hour working after school. How much does she earn in a week if she works $24\frac{1}{2}$ hours (to the nearest cent)?

11. _____

12. .7 of a certain number is .035. Write an equation for this statement and solve it to find the number.

12. _____

RATIO AND PROPORTION

1. Meaning of ratio

If Jim is 9 years old and his mother is 27 years old, we may compare their ages by saying that Jim's mother is 18 years older than he is. This is a comparison by subtraction.

Another way of comparing their ages is to say that Jim's mother is 3 times as old as he is. This is a comparison by division; that is, $27 \div 9 = 3$.

When we compare two numbers by division, we say that we are finding their *ratio;* thus we say that the mother's age to Jim's age is in the ratio of 3 to 1. We are considering the fraction $\frac{27}{9}$ and reducing it to $\frac{3}{1}$.

Thus, a ratio is a comparison of two quantities by division. We may write the ratio 3 to 1 as $3 \div 1$ or $\frac{3}{1}$ or $3:1$. What we are, in effect, saying here is that, for every 3 years in the mother's age, there is one year in Jim's age. Note that the order here is important. We may reverse the order by saying that the ratio of Jim's age to his mother's age is $1:3$. This means that Jim's age is $\frac{1}{3}$ of his mother's age. The numbers 1 and 3 are called the *terms* of the ratio.

Since a ratio is really a fraction, we may use the rules for reducing fractions to find equivalent ratios. Thus, in the example above, we can say that

$$\frac{27}{9} = \frac{9}{3} = \frac{3}{1} \quad \text{or} \quad 27:9 = 9:3 \quad \text{and} \quad 9:3 = 3:1.$$

We see that the ratio $27:9$ is the same as the ratio $9:3$ or the ratio $3:1$.

Likewise, if we start with a ratio, say $\frac{3}{5}$, we may multiply the terms by any number—for example 4—and get an equivalent ratio, $\frac{12}{20}$.

We may now state the following:

Principle: If both terms of a ratio are divided or multiplied by the same number (not zero), an equivalent ratio is obtained.

If we wish to compare 1 yard to 1 foot by means of a ratio, we have to change both lengths to the same units. Thus, since 1 yard = 3 feet, the ratio would be $3:1$.

The ratio of 2 pounds to 12 ounces is $\dfrac{32}{12} = \dfrac{8}{3}$ or $8:3$.

Rule: To find the ratio of two quantities in different units of measure, convert both quantities to the same unit. Then reduce the resulting ratio to lowest terms.

When we say that a car travels 90 miles in 2 hours, we can compare the number of miles with the number of hours by saying that the ratio of these two quantities is $90:2$ or $45:1$. We usually state the latter by saying that the rate of the car is 45 miles per hour.

Thus, a rate usually indicates a ratio where the unit following the word "per" is understood to be 1. If we say that milk is selling for 50¢ per quart, we mean that the ratio of the price to the number of quarts is $50:1$.

If we buy 9 bars of chocolate for 3 children, we say that the ratio is $9:3$ or $3:1$, meaning 3 bars per child.

ILLUSTRATIVE PROBLEM 1

Mary has 3 quarters and Anne has 5 dimes.

a. What is the ratio of Mary's amount to Anne's?

b. What is the ratio of Anne's amount to Mary's?

c. What is the ratio of Anne's amount to the total that they both have?

Solution:

a. $\dfrac{3 \text{ quarters}}{5 \text{ dimes}} = \dfrac{3 \times 25}{5 \times 10} = \dfrac{75}{50} = \dfrac{3}{2}$ *(answer)*

b. $\dfrac{50}{75} = \dfrac{2}{3}$ *(answer)*

c. $\dfrac{50¢}{75¢ + 50¢} = \dfrac{50}{125} = \dfrac{2}{5}$ *(answer)*

ILLUSTRATIVE PROBLEM 2

A rectangular room has dimensions of 9 feet by 12 feet.

a. What is the ratio of its width to its length?

b. What is the ratio of its length to its width?

c. What is the ratio of its length to its perimeter?

Solution:

a. $\dfrac{9}{12} = \dfrac{3}{4}$ *(answer)*

b. $\dfrac{12}{9} = \dfrac{4}{3}$ (*answer*)

c. perimeter $= 2(9 + 12) = 2 \cdot 21 = 42$

$\dfrac{\text{length}}{\text{perimeter}} = \dfrac{12}{42} = \dfrac{2}{7}$ (*answer*)

Exercises

1. Write the following ratios as fractions and reduce to lowest terms:

   a. 5 pounds to 15 pounds

   b. $16 to $12   **c.** 3:9

   d. a quart to a gallon   **e.** 15:21

2. In the ratios in exercise **1**, write the ratio of the second quantity to the first (inverse ratio) as a fraction and reduce to lowest terms.

3. What is the ratio of the lengths of two lines, one 12 inches long and the other 15 inches long?

4. A baseball team won 10 games and lost 12. What is the ratio of the games won to the games played?

5. In each of the following, give the ratio of the first quantity to the second:

   a. 1 pound to 2 ounces

   b. 1 dollar to 1 quarter

   c. 1 kilogram to 100 grams

   d. 1 hour to 20 minutes

   e. 1 pint to 1 gallon

   f. 1 dime to 1 quarter

6. A living room is 15 feet wide and 20 feet long. Give the ratio of the:

   a. length to the width.

   b. width to the length.

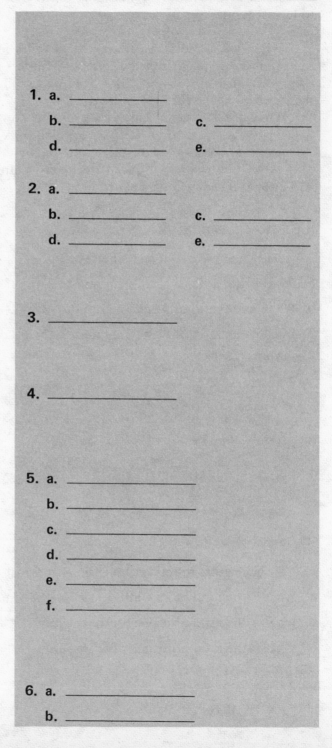

1. a. _____

  b. _____   c. _____

  d. _____   e. _____

2. a. _____

  b. _____   c. _____

  d. _____   e. _____

3. _____

4. _____

5. a. _____

  b. _____

  c. _____

  d. _____

  e. _____

  f. _____

6. a. _____

  b. _____

c. length to the perimeter.

d. perimeter to the width.

7. A class consists of 20 boys and 12 girls. Give the ratio of:

a. the number of boys to the number of girls.

b. the number of girls to the number of boys.

c. the number of boys to the total number of pupils.

d. the number of girls to the total number of pupils.

8. Express the following ratios in reduced form:

a. $15:18$ **b.** $\dfrac{2}{3}:\dfrac{5}{3}$ **c.** $125:175$

d. $.4:1.0$ **e.** $\dfrac{1}{5}:2$ **f.** $\dfrac{3}{4}:\dfrac{5}{8}$

g. $1\dfrac{1}{2}:2\dfrac{3}{4}$ **h.** $4.0:.75$ **i.** $.23:.023$

9. A student did 16 problems correctly on a 20-problem test.

a. What is the ratio of the number right to the total number of problems?

b. What is the ratio of the number wrong to the total number of problems?

c. What is the ratio of the number right to the number wrong?

10. Express the following ratios in reduced form:

a. 40 minutes to 2 hours

b. 1 meter to 20 centimeters

c. 2 miles to 440 yards

d. 3 days to 1 week

e. 3 lb. to 8 oz.

f. 1 yd. to 8 in.

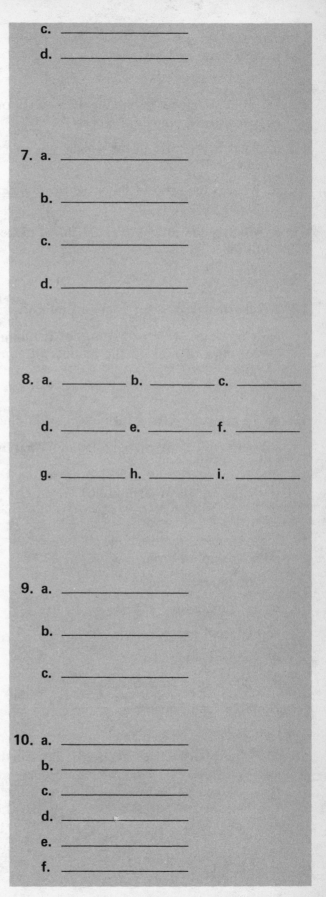

c. _____

d. _____

7. a. _____

b. _____

c. _____

d. _____

8. a. _____ **b.** _____ **c.** _____

d. _____ **e.** _____ **f.** _____

g. _____ **h.** _____ **i.** _____

9. a. _____

b. _____

c. _____

10. a. _____

b. _____

c. _____

d. _____

e. _____

f. _____

g. 2 yd. to 15 ft.

h. 250 grams to 1 kilogram

g. _____

h. _____

11. An alloy is made by mixing 12 pounds of copper with 20 pounds of nickel.

    a. What is the ratio of the weight of copper to nickel?

    b. What is the ratio of the weight of copper to the total alloy?

    c. What is the ratio of the weight of nickel to the total alloy?

11. a. _____

    b. _____

    c. _____

12. A cake recipe calls for $\frac{2}{3}$ cup of milk to $1\frac{1}{2}$ cups of flour. What is the ratio of the number of cups of milk to the number of cups of flour?

12. _____

13. A 12-ounce bottle of tincture of iodine contains $\frac{2}{3}$ ounce of pure iodine. What is the ratio of the weight of pure iodine to the weight of the total mixture?

13. _____

14. Express each of the following rates as a ratio in simplest form:

    a. 200 miles in 4 hours

    b. 12 cookies for 3 girls

    c. 80¢ for 4 bars of candy

    d. 1 mile in 4 minutes

    e. 100 yards in 10 seconds

    f. $1.25 for 5 pounds

14. a. _____

    b. _____

    c. _____

    d. _____

    e. _____

    f. _____

15. The "most attractive" rectangle has length and width in the ratio of $3:2$. Which of the following choices are "most attractive" rectangles? Length : width is *a.* $18:15$ *b.* $20:14$ *c.* $27:18$ *d.* $4\frac{1}{4}:2\frac{1}{2}$ *e.* $3\frac{3}{4}:2\frac{1}{2}$ *f.* $8.1:5.4$

15. _____

2. Solving ratio problems using equations

Consider the following problem:

In a certain class, the ratio of the number of boys to the number of girls is $5:3$. If there are 32 students in the class, how many boys and how many girls are there?

Although the problem can be done by an arithmetic approach, the use of equations can give us a very direct way of solving many different types of such problems.

Since the ratio of boys to girls is $5:3$, we may represent the number of boys as $5x$ and the number of girls by $3x$, where x, in this case, is any positive integer. Remember that our aim is not merely to find x, but to find $5x$ and $3x$. The form of the solution follows:

Solution:

Let $5x =$ the number of boys

and $3x =$ the number of girls. Then

$$5x + 3x = 32$$
$$8x = 32$$
$$x = 4$$
$$5x = 20 \quad \text{(number of boys)}$$
$$3x = 12 \quad \text{(number of girls)}$$

Check:

Is $\dfrac{20}{12} = \dfrac{5}{3}$? $\quad \dfrac{20}{12} = \dfrac{5 \cdot 4}{3 \cdot 4} = \dfrac{5}{3}$

Is $20 + 12 = 32$? $\quad 32 = 32$ ✓

Note that finding x is not the final answer. It is merely the common multiplier and, once x is found, we must determine $5x$ and $3x$ as our desired answers.

Exercises

1. Find two numbers in the ratio of $3:5$ whose sum is 96.

2. Divide a 35-inch line segment into two segments whose lengths are in the ratio $2:3$. How many inches are there in the length of each segment?

1. _____

2. _____

3. Jim and his younger brother divide a profit of $78 in the ratio of 8:5. How much does each get?

3. _____

4. Two numbers are in the ratio of 7:4 and their difference is 42. Find the numbers.

4. _____

5. Two numbers are in the ratio of 7:5 and their difference is 16. Find the numbers.

5. _____

6. The three angles of a triangle are in the ratio 3:4:5. The sum of the angles is 180°. Find the number of degrees in each angle. (*Hint:* Let the angles be 3x, 4x, 5x.)

6. _____

7. The sides of a triangle are in the ratio 5:6:7. If the perimeter of the triangle is 126 inches, find the length of each side.

7. _____

8. In a certain high school, the ratio of freshmen to sophomores is 6:5. If there are 880 students in both classes combined, how many students are there in each class?

8. _____

9. Two business partners divide a profit in the ratio of 11:10. If the profit one year is $10,500, how much does each receive?

9. _____

10. Two numbers are in the ratio of 7:10. If 8 is added to their sum, the result is 93. Find the numbers.

10. _____

11. The ratio of the length to the width of a rectangle is 8:7. If the perimeter of the rectangle is 480 feet, find the length and width in feet.

11. _____

12. In a basketball game, Tom and Jim scored points in the ratio of 9:5. If Tom made 12 more points than Jim, how many points did each make?

12. _____

3. Proportion

The ratio $\frac{4}{6}$ is equal to the ratio $\frac{2}{3}$. We may thus write the equation $\frac{4}{6} = \frac{2}{3}$. Such an equation is called a **proportion**. A proportion is an equation stating that two ratios are equal.

The proportion above may also be written as $4:6 = 2:3$. We read it as "4 is to 6 as 2 is to 3."

In general, we may write any proportion in the form

$$\frac{p}{q} = \frac{r}{s} \quad \text{or} \quad p:q = r:s$$

where $q \neq 0$ and $s \neq 0$

There are four terms in this proportion, namely, p, q, r, and s. The first and fourth terms are called the **extremes** and the second and third are called the **means**:

```
    ┌─extremes─┐
    │          │
  p:q    =    r:s
    │          │
    └─means────┘
```

Note that, in the proportion $15:20 = 3:4$, the product of the means, 20×3, is equal to 60 and the product of the extremes, 15×4, also equals 60.

Likewise, in the proportion, $3:8 = 9:24$, the product of the means, 8×9, and the product of the extremes, 3×24, both equal 72.

These examples illustrate a most important principle of proportions, namely:

Principle: In a proportion, the product of the means is equal to the product of the extremes.

By treating the general proportion $\frac{p}{q} = \frac{r}{s}$ as a fractional equation, we can show that the principle above is always true. That is, $ps = qr$.

One way of testing to see if two ratios are equal is to take the products of the means and the extremes (cross-multiply). If these products are not equal, the two ratios do not form a proportion.

ILLUSTRATIVE PROBLEM 1

Solve for p: $\dfrac{3}{16} = \dfrac{p}{80}$

Solution: $16p = 3 \cdot 80$

$16p = 240$

$p = 15$ (*answer*)

Check: $\dfrac{3}{16} \overset{?}{=} \dfrac{15}{80}$

$\dfrac{3}{16} = \dfrac{3}{16}$ ✓

ILLUSTRATIVE PROBLEM 2

Is $\dfrac{4}{5} = \dfrac{8}{9}$ a proportion?

Solution: product of extremes $= 4 \cdot 9 = 36$

product of means $= 5 \cdot 8 = 40$

Since these products are not equal, this equation is not a true proportion and $\dfrac{4}{5} \neq \dfrac{8}{9}$.

ILLUSTRATIVE PROBLEM 3

If an automobile runs 35 miles on 3 gallons of gas, how many miles will it run on 7 gallons of gas?

Solution: Let $x =$ number of miles run on 7 gallons of gas. Then

$\dfrac{35}{3} = \dfrac{x}{7}$

$3x = 245$ (cross-multiply)

$x = 81\dfrac{2}{3}$ miles   (*answer*)

ILLUSTRATIVE PROBLEM 4

Solve for t: $\dfrac{40}{36} = \dfrac{10}{3t}$

Solution: $40 \cdot 3t = 36 \cdot 10$ (cross-multiply)

$$120t = 360$$

$$t = 3 \quad (\textit{answer})$$

Check: $\dfrac{40}{36} \overset{?}{=} \dfrac{10}{3 \cdot 3}$

$$\dfrac{40}{36} \overset{?}{=} \dfrac{10}{9}$$

$$\dfrac{10}{9} = \dfrac{10}{9} \; \checkmark$$

Exercises

In 1 to 9, solve the proportions.

1. $\dfrac{6}{3} = \dfrac{12}{x}$ 　　 **2.** $\dfrac{4}{5} = \dfrac{9}{b}$ 　　 **3.** $\dfrac{7}{5} = \dfrac{q}{6}$

4. $\dfrac{p}{4} = \dfrac{15}{12}$ 　　 **5.** $\dfrac{24}{66} = \dfrac{3}{r}$ 　　 **6.** $\dfrac{25}{t} = \dfrac{5}{2}$

7. $6:5 = m:45$ 　　 **8.** $15:2k = 5:12$

9. $16:4y = 3:12$

In 10 to 15, state whether or not the given ratios form a true proportion. (Answer *yes* or *no*.)

10. $\dfrac{2}{7}, \dfrac{4}{49}$ 　　 **11.** $\dfrac{6}{10}, \dfrac{9}{15}$ 　　 **12.** $\dfrac{p}{4p}, \dfrac{2}{8}$

13. $\dfrac{5}{9}, \dfrac{9}{5}$ 　　 **14.** $\dfrac{5}{4}, \dfrac{10}{8}$ 　　 **15.** $\dfrac{21}{27}, \dfrac{28}{36}$

16. The speed of two cars is in the ratio of 3 to 5. If the slower car goes 36 mph, what is the speed of the faster car?

17. If 12 typewriters cost $1,020, how much will 9 cost at the same rate?

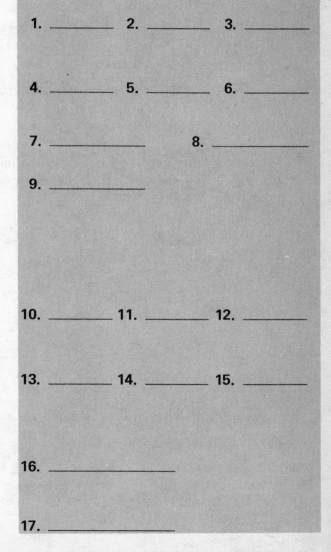

1. _____ 　 2. _____ 　 3. _____

4. _____ 　 5. _____ 　 6. _____

7. _____ 　　　 8. _____

9. _____

10. _____ 11. _____ 12. _____

13. _____ 14. _____ 15. _____

16. _____

17. _____

18. If 1 inch on a map represents 50 miles, how many inches on a map represent 540 miles?

18. _____

19. If 6 bananas cost 40 cents, find the cost of 15 bananas at the same rate.

19. _____

20. If eggs cost 80¢ a dozen, how much should 5 eggs cost at the same rate?

20. _____

21. The weight of 80 feet of telephone wire is 5 pounds. Find the weight of 360 feet of this wire in pounds.

21. _____

22. An auto mechanic received $90 for working 14 hours. At the same rate of pay, how many hours must he work to earn $150?

22. _____

23. A boy travels 80 miles on his motorcycle in 3 hours. At the same rate, how many miles will he go in 5 hours?

23. _____

24. Two numbers are in the ratio of $8:5$. If the smaller number is 75, what is the larger number?

24. _____

25. The ratio of the length of a rectangle to its width is $7:4$. If the width is 68 inches, how many inches are in the length?

25. _____

26. A house worth $24,000 pays $1800 in taxes. At this rate, how much tax should a house pay if it is worth $30,000?

26. _____

27. A car travels 240 miles in $4\frac{3}{4}$ hours. At this rate, how far will it travel in 6 hours?

27. _____

28. A picture $3'' \times 5''$ is to be enlarged so that its width is $6\frac{1}{2}''$. What will be the length in inches of the enlarged picture?

28. _____

29. A board is cut into two pieces having the ratio $3:5$. If the longer piece is 12 feet, how many feet in the shorter piece?

29. _____

30. If 3 cans of peas are selling for 78 cents, how much would 8 such cans cost?

30. _____

31. It took a typist 32 minutes to type 6 pages of a report. At this rate, how many minutes will it take her to type the remaining 27 pages of the report?

31. _____

4. Scale drawings

In making floor plans for an apartment or a house, it is common practice for architects to draw the rooms to *scale*. For example, in the figure, a $16' \times 20'$ living room is drawn to a scale of $\frac{1}{8}$ inch to 1 foot. To find the size of the drawing, we can determine the width of the rectangle by solving the proportion:

$$\frac{1''}{8} : x'' = 1' : 16'$$

This gives $x = \frac{1}{8} \cdot 16 = 2''$ (width of rectangle).

To determine the actual length of the drawing, we must solve the proportion:

$$\frac{1''}{8} : y'' = 1' : 20'$$

This gives $y = \frac{1}{8} \cdot 20 = 2\frac{1''}{2}$ (length of rectangle).

Thus, a rectangle $2'' \times 2\frac{1''}{2}$ will represent the living room on the floor plan.

Remember that the first number on the scale indicates the drawing dimension and the second number represents the actual dimension of the figure or object. In the figure above, the drawing was a reduction of the actual living room. In some cases, the drawing may be an enlargement of the actual object or figure. For example, a drawing of an ant in a biology book may require an enlargement of 8 times its actual size for details to be seen. In this case, the scale would read $8:1$ or $1'' = \frac{1''}{8}$. Remember again that the first number is the drawing size and the second number is the actual size. Drawings showing enlargements are

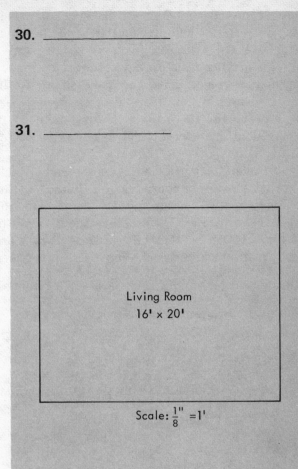

Living Room
16' × 20'

Scale: $\frac{1''}{8} = 1'$

very common in making diagrams of small machine tools. When drawings are made to actual size, the scale in this case is simply $1:1$.

In making scale drawings, we are constructing figures which have the same shape as the actual figures but are reduced or enlarged in size in a proportionate manner. Figures reduced or enlarged in this way are said to be *similar* to the actual figures.

A map of a particular region is merely a scale drawing showing a considerable reduction of the region. Usually, in one corner of the map, the scale is shown. In the figure, the scale is shown to be 1 in. = 100 mi. If this is the scale of a New York State map and the straight-line distance between Albany and New York City measures $1\frac{1}{4}$ inches, what is the actual distance in miles?

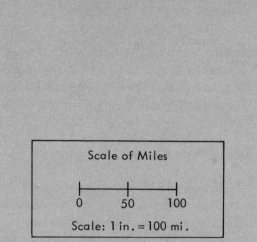

We form the proportion: $\dfrac{1 \text{ in.}}{100 \text{ mi.}} = \dfrac{1\frac{1}{4} \text{ in.}}{x \text{ mi.}}$

Cross-multiplying, we obtain

$1 \cdot x = 100 \cdot 1\frac{1}{4}$, or $x = 125$ miles.

ILLUSTRATIVE PROBLEM 1

In a photograph, the height of a boy is $1\frac{1}{2}$ inches. If the boy's height is actually 4 feet 6 inches, what is the scale of the photograph?

Solution: The scale is $1\frac{1}{2}$ in. to $4\frac{1}{2}$ ft. Thus,

$$\frac{1\frac{1}{2}''}{4\frac{1}{2}'} = \frac{1''}{x}$$

Cross-multiply: $\qquad 1\frac{1}{2}x = 4\frac{1}{2}$

Multiply both sides by 2: $\qquad 3x = 9$

$$x = 3$$

The scale is 1 in. = 3 ft. (*answer*)

ILLUSTRATIVE PROBLEM 2

If $\frac{3}{4}$ inch represents 20 yards, how many inches long must a scale length be to represent a football field 100 yards long?

Solution:

$$\frac{\frac{3}{4}}{20} = \frac{x}{100}$$

Cross-multiply:

$$20x = \frac{3}{4} \cdot 100$$

$$20x = 75$$

Divide both sides by 20:

$$x = 3\frac{3}{4} \text{ in.}$$

(*answer*)

ILLUSTRATIVE PROBLEM 3

The measured distance on a map between Pittsburgh and New York City is $3\frac{1}{2}$ inches. If the scale of the map is 1 inch to 70 miles, what is the actual distance in miles between these two cities?

Solution:

$$\frac{1 \text{ in.}}{70 \text{ mi.}} = \frac{3\frac{1}{2} \text{ in.}}{x \text{ mi.}}$$

Cross-multiply:

$$x = 70 \cdot 3\frac{1}{2}$$

$$x = 245 \text{ mi.} \quad (\textit{answer})$$

Exercises

1. Using a scale of $\frac{1}{8}$ in. = 1 ft., give the length of the lines in inches you would use to represent each of the following:

   a. 40 feet   **b.** 30 feet   **c.** 26 feet

   d. 120 feet   **e.** 33 feet   **f.** 58 feet

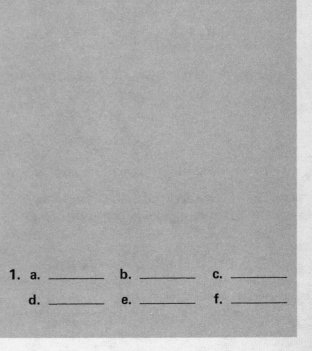

1. a. _____   **b.** _____   **c.** _____

   d. _____   **e.** _____   **f.** _____

2. The scale used in making a scale drawing of a house is $\frac{1}{2}$ in. = 1 ft. What are the actual dimensions in feet of the rooms whose dimensions on the drawing are as follows:

a. 4 in. by 6 in.   **b.** $8\frac{1}{2}$ in. by 12 in.

c. $5\frac{1}{4}$ in. by $7\frac{1}{2}$ in.   **d.** $6\frac{3}{4}$ in. by 10 in.

3. a. Two towns are $4\frac{3}{4}$ inches apart on a map drawn to a scale of 1 in. = 50 mi. What is the distance in miles between the towns?

    b. On this map, how long a line in inches will have to be drawn to represent a distance of 425 miles?

4. A U.S. dollar bill is $6\frac{1}{8}$ inches long and $2\frac{5}{8}$ inches wide. If we draw it to a scale of $1'':3''$, how many inches are there in the length and width of the drawing?

5. In the following, tell whether the scale drawing will be a *reduction*, an *enlargement*, or the *same size* as the object if the scale is:

a. $\frac{1}{2}$ in. = 10 ft.   **b.** $\frac{1}{8}$ in. = 100 mi.

c. 1 in. = $\frac{1}{8}$ in.   **d.** 10:10

e. 8:5   **f.** 1000:1

6. Two towns are $8\frac{3}{4}$ inches apart on a map drawn to a scale of 1 inch = 60 miles. Find the distance in miles between the towns.

7. In the scale at the right, how many miles does 1 inch represent?

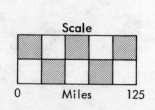

Scale

0   Miles   125

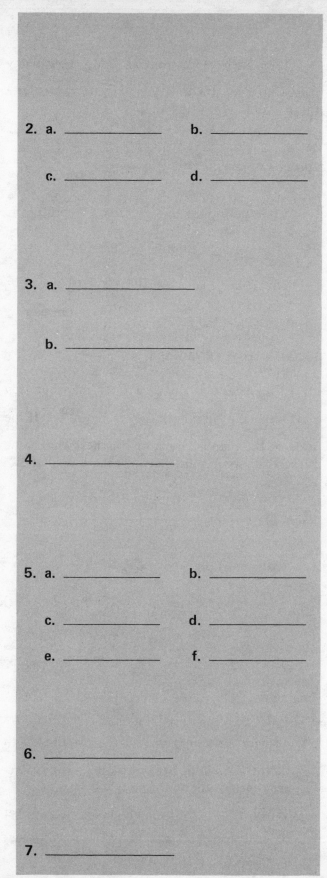

2. a. _____   **b.** _____

c. _____   **d.** _____

3. a. _____

    b. _____

4. _____

5. a. _____   **b.** _____

c. _____   **d.** _____

e. _____   **f.** _____

6. _____

7. _____

8. A map of Europe is drawn to the scale of 1 inch = 400 miles. Find the airline distance in miles represented on the map by each of the following lengths:

a. 3 inches   b. $4\frac{1}{2}$ inches   c. $2\frac{3}{4}$ inches

d. $4\frac{7}{8}$ inches   e. $3\frac{5}{16}$ inches   f. $\frac{5}{8}$ inches

9. On the map in exercise **8,** find the number of inches on the map that would represent a distance of:

a. 250 miles   b. 840 miles   c. 1000 miles

d. 325 miles   e. 420 miles   f. 1400 miles

10. Find the scale of a drawing if:

a. a man 6′ tall is represented by a line 4″ long;

b. a bee $\frac{1}{2}″$ long is represented by a line 2″ long;

c. two towns 150 miles apart are separated on a map by a distance of 6 inches;

d. an auto 10 ft. long is represented by a figure $2\frac{1}{2}$ in. long.

11. Using the scale 1 inch = 8 feet, how many inches would you use to represent:

a. a horse 6 feet high?

b. a piano 5 ft. 4 in. long?

c. a room 30 feet by 44 feet?

12. In making a model airplane, a boy used a scale of 1:80. If the length of the plane is actually 100 feet, how long should the model plane be?

13. A pole is 20 ft. high. A wire is stretched from the top of the pole to a point on the ground 15 ft. from the base of the pole. Using a scale of 1 in. = 5 ft., make a scale drawing of the

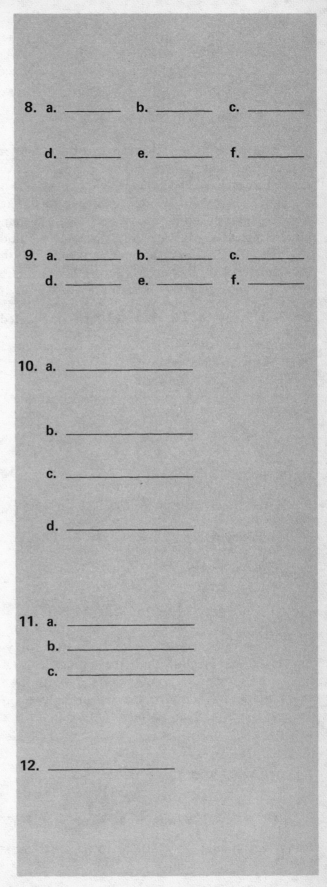

8. a. _____ b. _____ c. _____

d. _____ e. _____ f. _____

9. a. _____ b. _____ c. _____

d. _____ e. _____ f. _____

10. a. _____

b. _____

c. _____

d. _____

11. a. _____

b. _____

c. _____

12. _____

pole and wire. Measure the number of inches in the line in the drawing that represents the wire. What is the length of the wire in feet?

13. _____

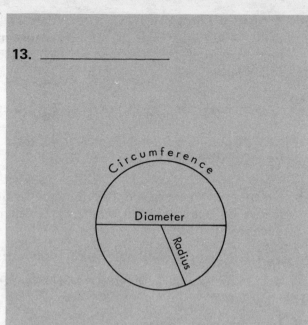

5. Some other uses of ratio and proportion

In a circle, it is quite clear that the diameter is twice the radius, or the ratio of the diameter to the radius is 2:1. The *circumference* of a circle is the distance around the circle. It is very much like the perimeter of a polygon. If we measure the circumference of any circle and its diameter, we find that the ratio of the circumference of the circle to its diameter is always slightly more than 3. More precise measurement indicates that this ratio is about $3\frac{1}{7}$ or 3.14. The ancient Greeks designated this ratio by the Greek letter π, pronounced "pie." Thus, we may write

$$\frac{C}{D} = \pi = \frac{22}{7} = 3\frac{1}{7} = 3.14 \quad (approximately)$$

We may also write $C = \pi D$.

ILLUSTRATIVE PROBLEM 1

Find the length of the circumference of a circle of diameter 14 inches. Use $\pi = \frac{22}{7}$.

Solution: $C = \pi D$

$$C = \frac{22}{7} \cdot 14 = 44 \text{ inches} \quad (answer)$$

The ancient Greeks also decided, after studying many rectangles, that the rectangle that "looks best" is one whose length and width have the ratio 3:2. Many of the rectangles used in ancient Greek art and architecture maintain this ratio.

ILLUSTRATIVE PROBLEM 2

An enlarged picture is $4\frac{1}{2}$ feet long. How many feet should its width be to make it "look best"?

Solution: Let $x =$ the number of feet in the width. Then

$$\frac{4\frac{1}{2}}{x} = \frac{3}{2}$$

$$3x = 9$$

$$x = 3 \text{ feet} \quad (answer)$$

Ratios are also used to determine the standing of teams in various sports. For example, if a baseball team wins 50 games out of 75 games played, we say its record is $\frac{50}{75} = \frac{2}{3} = .667$. The ratio is converted to its decimal form carried out to the nearest thousandth.

Exercises

1. Find in inches the circumference of a circle whose diameter is 21 inches.

1. _____

2. The width of a rectangle is 24 inches. What must be its length in inches if it is to look best?

2. _____

3. What is the radius in inches of a circle whose circumference is 176 inches?

3. _____

4. A baseball team won 80 games and lost 60 games one season. What was its record?

4. _____

5. What is the ratio of the circumference of a circle to its radius? Write a formula for the circumference of a circle in terms of its radius.

5. _____

6. A team plays 120 games one season. How many games must it win to achieve a record of .875?

6. _____

7. A rectangle has a perimeter of 75 feet. What must be its dimensions in feet in order to look best?

7. _____

8. A circle has a diameter of 3 ft. 6 in. What is its circumference in feet?

8. _____

9. After winning 45 games, a team's record is .625. How many games did it play?

9. _____

Chapter review exercises

1. The length of a rectangle is 14 inches and its width is 8 inches.

    a. What is the ratio of the length to the width?

    b. What is the ratio of the width to the length?

    c. What is the ratio of the length to the perimeter of the rectangle?

1. a. _____

   b. _____

   c. _____

2. The distance from New York to Buffalo is 400 miles. How many inches would represent this distance on a map whose scale is 1 inch = 60 miles?

2. _____

3. Find the value of y in each of the following proportions:

    a. $2:3 = 16:y$ **b.** $3:4 = 5:y$

    c. $12:18 = y:\dfrac{1}{2}$ **d.** $y:\dfrac{2}{3} = 1\dfrac{1}{4}:2\dfrac{1}{2}$

3. a. _____ b. _____

   c. _____ d. _____

4. If a recipe for 3 dozen cookies calls for 2 cups of sugar, how much sugar is needed for 5 dozen cookies?

4. _____

5. Two circles have diameters of 8″ and 10″. What is the ratio of their

    a. diameters? **b.** radii? **c.** circumferences?

5. a. _____ b. _____ c. _____

6. In the following two rectangles:

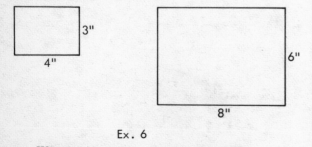

Ex. 6

    a. What is the ratio of their lengths?

6. a. _____

b. What is the ratio of their widths?

c. What is the ratio of their perimeters?

7. If $1\frac{1}{2}$ inches on a map represents 120 miles, what distance in miles does $2\frac{7}{8}$ inches represent?

8. Two boys divide a profit of $36 in the ratio of $5:3$. How much does each get?

9. A 1-pound object on the earth weighs .16 pounds on the moon.

    a. At this rate, what would a 180-pound man (on earth) weigh on the moon?

    b. If a rock on the moon weighs 8 pounds, how much would it weigh on earth?

10. If 5 pounds of potatoes cost 67¢, what will 12 pounds of potatoes cost at the same rate?

11. A man uses 24 gallons of gasoline for a trip of 340 miles. At this rate, how many gallons will he use on a 500-mile trip?

12. A team wins 80 games and loses 40 games in one season. What was its record?

13. If 45 feet of copper wire weighs 9 pounds, what will 60 feet of the same wire weigh?

14. A typist found that it took her 18 minutes to type 4 pages of a report. At this rate, how long will it take her to type the entire 30-page report?

15. The sides of a triangle are in the ratio $8:9:10$. The perimeter of the triangle is 135 inches. Find the length in inches of the shortest side.

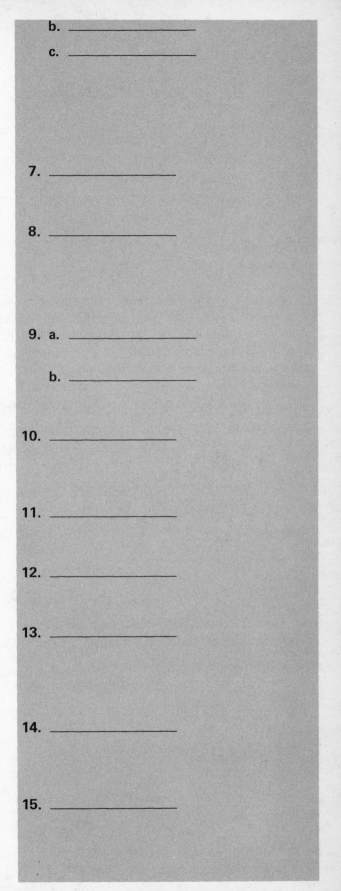

b. _____

c. _____

7. _____

8. _____

9. a. _____

b. _____

10. _____

11. _____

12. _____

13. _____

14. _____

15. _____

PERCENTAGE

7

1. Meaning of Percent

As early as the 15th century, businessmen made use of certain decimal fractions so much that they gave them the special name *percent*. Percent means "per hundred" or "by the hundred." The symbol for percent is %. Thus, if 20 students are absent in a freshman class of 100, we may say that 20% are absent. Since 80 students would then be present, we may say that 80% of the class is present.

Thus, we say that *percent* simply means *hundredths*. For example, 73% is $\frac{73}{100}$, or .73. Also, 1% is 1 out of 100 which is $\frac{1}{100}$, or .01. If a pupil answers 87 questions correctly in a test of 100 questions, we say his score is 87%, which is equal to $\frac{87}{100}$ written as a fraction, or .87 written as a decimal. A score of 100% would mean he answered 100 correctly out of 100 questions.

$$\text{Definition: } n\% = \frac{n}{100}$$

Here are some questions about the meaning of percent. Try to answer them before looking at the answers to the right.

1. Write seven hundredths as a percent. 7% (*answer*)

2. Write $\frac{19}{100}$ as a percent. 19% (*answer*)

3. Write 83% as a common fraction. $\frac{83}{100}$ (*answer*)

4. Write $6\frac{1}{2}\%$ as a fraction. $\frac{6\frac{1}{2}}{100}$ (*answer*)

5. In a class of 25 students, 100% are present. How many students are present? 25 (*answer*)

ILLUSTRATIVE PROBLEM

If 17% of a class is absent, what percent is present?

Solution: Since the entire class is represented by 100%, subtract 17% from 100%. Thus, 100% − 17% = 83%   (*answer*).

Exercises

1. Write as a fraction with denominator 100:

   a. 17%   **b.** 8%   **c.** 35%

   d. 42%   **e.** 88%   **f.** 63%

   g. $12\frac{1}{2}\%$ **h.** $9\frac{1}{4}\%$

1. a. _____	b. _____	c. _____
d. _____	e. _____	f. _____
g. _____	h. _____	

2. Write as a percent:

   a. 9 hundredths   **b.** 27 hundredths

   c. 49 hundredths   **d.** 73 hundredths

   e. $\dfrac{18}{100}$ **f.** $\dfrac{37}{100}$

   g. $\dfrac{54}{100}$ **h.** $\dfrac{68}{100}$

2. a. _____	b. _____
c. _____	d. _____
e. _____	f. _____
g. _____	h. _____

3. Anne earned $100 one month. She spent $28 for lunches, $12 for transportation, $33 for clothes, $15 for books, and put the rest in the bank.

   a. What percent of her earnings did she spend for lunches?

   b. What percent did she spend for transportation?

   c. What percent did she spend for clothes?

   d. For books?

   e. What percent did she put in the bank?

   3. a. _____

   b. _____

   c. _____

   d. _____

   e. _____

4. In a spelling test of 27 words, Jack got 100% right. How many did he get right?

   4. _____

5. In a class of 100 sophomores, 42 were boys. What percent of the class was made up of girls?

   5. _____

6. The cost of butter in 1970 was 36¢ per pound. By 1974, the price had increased 100%. What was the cost per pound in 1974?

6. _____

7. A tie made of polyester and silk is 60% polyester. What percent is silk?

7. _____

8. A baseball player one season got hits 45% of the times he was at bat. What percent of the times at bat did he not get hits?

8. _____

9. In his will, Mr. Scott left 55% of his estate to his wife, 12% to his son, 12% to his daughter, and the rest to charity. What percent went to charity?

9. _____

10. In a crate of 100 oranges, 8% are spoiled. What percent of the oranges are not spoiled?

10. _____

11. A man buys a $100 armchair and has to pay an additional 7% of the cost as sales tax. How many dollars does he pay as sales tax?

11. _____

2. Changing percents to decimals and decimals to percents

Using our definition of percent, we may change percents to decimals as shown at the right.

Examples

1. $37\% = \dfrac{37}{100} = .37$

2. $8\% = \dfrac{8}{100} = .08$

3. $7.4\% = \dfrac{7.4}{100} = \dfrac{7.4 \times 10}{100 \times 10} = \dfrac{74}{1000} = .074$

4. $.5\% = \dfrac{.5}{100} = \dfrac{.5 \times 10}{100 \times 10} = \dfrac{5}{1000} = .005$

5. $6\frac{1}{2}\% = \dfrac{6\frac{1}{2}}{100} = .06\frac{1}{2}$ $\left.\begin{array}{c} \\ \\ \end{array}\right\}$ (same value)
   $6.5\% = \dfrac{6.5}{100} = .065$

From these examples, we form the following general rule:

Rule: To change a percent to a decimal, drop the percent sign and move the decimal point two places to the *left*.

It then follows that, if we want to write a decimal as a percent, we simply reverse the procedure:

Rule: To change a decimal to a percent, move the decimal point two places to the *right* and write the % sign.

Using this rule, we may change decimals and fractions to percents as shown at the right.

Note that a mixed number or a mixed decimal, as in examples **11, 12,** and **13,** changes to a percent that is greater than 100%.

Examples

6. $.41 = 41\%$ **7.** $.03 = 3\%$

8. $.045 = 4.5\%$ **9.** $.007 = .7\%$

10. $.37\frac{1}{2} = 37\frac{1}{2}\%$ **11.** $1.20 = 120\%$

12. $1\frac{1}{2} = 1.50 = 150\%$

13. $2\frac{1}{4} = 2.25 = 225\%$

Exercises

In 1 to 16, change each percent to a decimal.

1. 32%   **2.** 25%   **3.** 9%

4. 1%   **5.** 73%   **6.** 2.5%

7. $9\frac{1}{2}\%$ **8.** 100%   **9.** $5\frac{3}{4}\%$

10. .63%   **11.** 125%   **12.** .2%

13. $\frac{1}{2}\%$ **14.** 7.25%   **15.** $66\frac{2}{3}\%$

16. 5.3%

In 17 to 32, change each decimal to a percent.

17. .75   **18.** .47   **19.** .06

1. _____   **2.** _____   **3.** _____

4. _____   **5.** _____   **6.** _____

7. _____   **8.** _____   **9.** _____

10. _____   **11.** _____   **12.** _____

13. _____   **14.** _____   **15.** _____

16. _____

17. _____   **18.** _____   **19.** _____

20. .32   **21.** .8   **22.** .035

23. $.07\frac{1}{2}$ **24.** .009   **25.** .363

26. .897   **27.** 1.00   **28.** 1.25

29. 2.1   **30.** $.63\frac{1}{3}$ **31.** .0065

32. .6

33. a. If there is an 8% sales tax, how many cents tax do you pay on a purchase of a dollar?

     b. How much do you pay on a 10-dollar purchase?

34. The "cost of living" in one year increased 11%. At this rate, how many cents more would you pay for an item that cost $1.00 last year? $8.00 last year?

35. A team won .7 of the games it played last year. What percent of games played did it win?

36. A bank pays $6\frac{1}{2}\%$ interest on all money deposited for a year. Write this rate of interest as a decimal fraction.

37. A salesman receives $12\frac{1}{2}\cancel{c}$ for every dollar of merchandise he sells. Write this rate of commission as a percent.

38. A family spends .275 of its income for rent.

     a. What percent of its income does it spend for rent?

     b. What percent of its income is left?

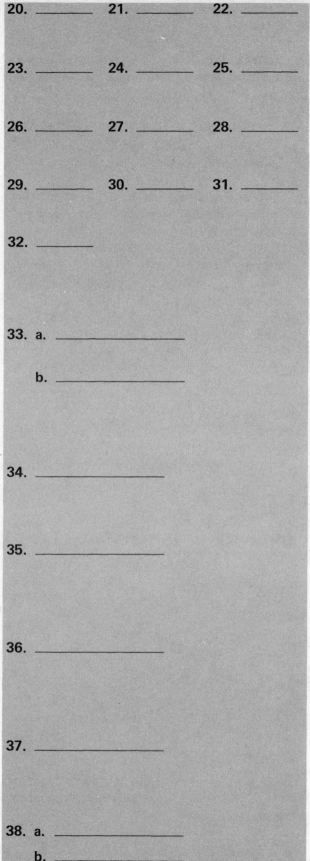

20. _____ **21.** _____ **22.** _____

23. _____ **24.** _____ **25.** _____

26. _____ **27.** _____ **28.** _____

29. _____ **30.** _____ **31.** _____

32. _____

33. a. _____

     b. _____

34. _____

35. _____

36. _____

37. _____

38. a. _____

     b. _____

3. Changing percents to fractions and fractions to percents

ILLUSTRATIVE PROBLEM 1

A student receives a mark of 80% on a short-answer test. What fractional part of the questions did he answer correctly?

Solution: $80\% = \dfrac{80}{100} = \dfrac{4}{5}$

Answer: He answered $\dfrac{4}{5}$ of the questions correctly.

Rule: To change n% to a fraction, write the fraction $\dfrac{n}{100}$ and reduce it to lowest terms.

In a class of 25 students, 20 are present. What percent of the class is present?

Solution: $\dfrac{20}{25} = \dfrac{20 \times 4}{25 \times 4} = \dfrac{80}{100} = 80\%$

Answer: 80 percent of the class is present.

Rule: To change a fraction to a percent, change the fraction to an equivalent fraction with a denominator of 100. This fraction is then easily changed to a percent.

Another way of changing a fraction to a percent is to change the fraction to a two-place decimal by dividing the numerator by the denominator. This hundredth-place decimal can then be written as a percent. For example, let us change $\dfrac{1}{8}$ to a percent:

$$\frac{1}{8} = 1 \div 8 = 8\overline{\smash{\big)}1.00} = 12\frac{1}{2}\%$$

$$
\begin{array}{r}
.12\frac{1}{2} \\
8\overline{\smash{\big)}1.00} \\
\underline{8} \\
20 \\
\underline{16} \\
\frac{4}{8} = \frac{1}{2}
\end{array}
$$

This latter method is particularly useful when the denominator of the given fraction is not a divisor of 100.

Examples

1. $75\% = \dfrac{75}{100} = \dfrac{3}{4}$

2. $7\dfrac{1}{2}\% = \dfrac{7\frac{1}{2}}{100} = 7\frac{1}{2} \div \dfrac{100}{1} = \dfrac{\overset{3}{15}}{2} \times \dfrac{1}{\underset{20}{100}} = \dfrac{3}{40}$

ILLUSTRATIVE PROBLEM 2

Change $\frac{3}{4}$ to a percent.

Solution:

$$\frac{3}{4} = \frac{3 \times 25}{4 \times 25} = \frac{75}{100} = 75\% \quad (answer)$$

ILLUSTRATIVE PROBLEM 3

Change $\frac{5}{8}$ to a percent.

Solution: $\quad 8\overline{)5.00}^{.62\frac{1}{2}} = 62\frac{1}{2}\% \quad (answer)$

Exercises

In 1 to 16, change each percent to a fraction in *lowest terms* or to a mixed number.

1. 15%	**2.** 65%	**3.** 70%	**4.** 85%	1. ___	2. ___	3. ___	4. ___
5. 18%	**6.** 6%	**7.** 132%	**8.** 125%	5. ___	6. ___	7. ___	8. ___
9. $66\frac{2}{3}\%$	**10.** $37\frac{1}{2}\%$	**11.** 12.5%	**12.** $83\frac{1}{3}\%$	9. ___	10. ___	11. ___	12. ___
13. $6\frac{1}{4}\%$	**14.** $87\frac{1}{2}\%$	**15.** $33\frac{1}{3}\%$	**16.** $8\frac{1}{3}\%$	13. ___	14. ___	15. ___	16. ___

In 17 to 28, change each fraction to a percent.

17. $\frac{1}{3}$	**18.** $\frac{3}{4}$	**19.** $\frac{1}{2}$	**20.** $\frac{3}{8}$	17. ___	18. ___	19. ___	20. ___
21. $\frac{1}{6}$	**22.** $\frac{5}{6}$	**23.** $\frac{1}{4}$	**24.** $\frac{7}{8}$	21. ___	22. ___	23. ___	24. ___
25. $\frac{21}{25}$	**26.** $\frac{12}{18}$	**27.** $\frac{15}{24}$	**28.** $\frac{5}{12}$	25. ___	26. ___	27. ___	28. ___

29. If 90% of a class passes a test, what fractional part of the class passes? What fractional part fails?

29. _____

30. A radio is being sold for "20% off" the marked price.

   a. What fractional part of the marked price is the radio being reduced by?

30. a. _____

   b. What fractional part of the marked price must you pay for the radio?

     b. _____

31. In running for mayor of a town, a man receives $\frac{3}{5}$ of the votes cast.

   a. What percent of the total vote does he get?

31. a. _____

   b. What percent does his opponent receive?

     b. _____

32. Bill saved $33\frac{1}{3}\%$ of his earnings. What fractional part of his earnings did he spend?

32. _____

33. Pick the largest number: $\frac{3}{5}$; 58%; .61

33. _____

34. A team has won $\frac{5}{8}$ of the games played.

   a. What percent of its games has it won?

34. a. _____

   b. What percent of its games has it lost?

     b. _____

35. One or more of the following is (are) equal to $\frac{3}{8}$: $.37\frac{1}{2}$, $37\frac{1}{2}$, $37\frac{1}{2}\%$, $.37\frac{1}{2}\%$, $\frac{3}{8}\%$, 37.5 Which one(s)?

35. _____

36. a. What percent of the circle is shaded?

   b. What percent is unshaded?

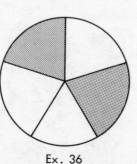

Ex. 36

36. a. _____

     b. _____

37. Mr. Jones used $\frac{7}{8}$ of the oil in his tank.

a. What percent of his oil did he use?

b. What percent of oil remains in the tank?

37. a. _____

b. _____

Following are some commonly used percents and their fractional equivalents. Learn them.

Percent	Fractional equivalent
10% =	$\frac{1}{10}$
20% =	$\frac{1}{5}$
30% =	$\frac{3}{10}$
40% =	$\frac{2}{5}$
50% =	$\frac{1}{2}$
60% =	$\frac{3}{5}$
70% =	$\frac{7}{10}$
80% =	$\frac{4}{5}$
90% =	$\frac{9}{10}$
100% =	1
$12\frac{1}{2}\%$ =	$\frac{1}{8}$
25% =	$\frac{1}{4}$
$37\frac{1}{2}\%$ =	$\frac{3}{8}$
$62\frac{1}{2}\%$ =	$\frac{5}{8}$
75% =	$\frac{3}{4}$

$$87\frac{1}{2}\% = \frac{7}{8}$$

$$16\frac{2}{3}\% = \frac{1}{6}$$

$$33\frac{1}{3}\% = \frac{1}{3}$$

$$66\frac{2}{3}\% = \frac{2}{3}$$

$$83\frac{1}{3}\% = \frac{5}{6}$$

4. Finding a percent of a number

Jim buys a radio marked $48 and gets 25% off the marked price. In order to find out how much he saves, we can change 25% to .25 and multiply this decimal by $48. We see that he gets $12 off the marked price:

$$\begin{array}{r} \$48 \\ \times\,.25 \\ \hline 2\ 40 \\ 9\ 6 \\ \hline \$12\,.00 \end{array}$$

It is also possible to do this problem by changing 25% to the fraction $\frac{1}{4}$ and then multiplying $\frac{1}{4}$ by $48. Thus:

$$\frac{1}{\underset{1}{\cancel{4}}} \times \overset{12}{\cancel{48}} = \$12$$

Rule: To find a percent of a number, change the percent to an equivalent decimal or fraction and multiply this decimal or fraction by the number.

Note that, in example **2,** it is simpler to multiply 32 by $\frac{3}{8}$ than to multiply 32 by .375. Use this method when you can find a common fraction equivalent to the given percent.

Examples

1. Find 28% of 45.

$$28\% = .28$$

$$\begin{array}{r} 45 \\ \times\,.28 \\ \hline 3\ 60 \\ 9\ 0 \\ \hline 12.60 = 12.6 \end{array}$$

2. Find $37\frac{1}{2}\%$ of $32.

$$37\frac{1}{2}\% = \frac{3}{8}$$

$$\frac{3}{\underset{1}{\cancel{8}}} \times \overset{4}{\cancel{32}} = \$12$$

3. Find $\frac{1}{4}\%$ of $1200.

$$\frac{1}{4}\% = .00\frac{1}{4}$$

$$\begin{array}{r} 1200 \\ \times\,.00\frac{1}{4} \\ \hline \$3.00 \end{array}$$

4. Find 7% of $12.40 to the nearest cent.

$$7\% = .07$$

$$\begin{array}{r} 12.40 \\ \times\,.07 \\ \hline .8680 = \$.87 \end{array}$$

Exercises

In 1 to 30, find:

1. 25% of 740

2. 6% of 50

3. $12\frac{1}{2}$% of 88

4. 16% of 85

5. 2.7% of 30

6. 82% of 94

7. $5\frac{1}{2}$% of $780

8. $33\frac{1}{3}$% of 63

9. $8\frac{1}{4}$% of $2400

10. 30% of 110

11. $62\frac{1}{2}$% of 96

12. 60% of 75

13. $66\frac{2}{3}$% of $360

14. 75% of 84

15. 80% of $65

16. $87\frac{1}{2}$% of 400

17. 12% of 320

18. 9% of 1400

19. $\frac{1}{2}$% of 1600

20. $3\frac{1}{2}$% of 600

21. 120% of 85

22. 1% of $820

23. $83\frac{1}{3}$% of 720

24. 90% of 380

25. $37\frac{1}{2}$% of 640

26. 8.4% of $300

27. 4.5% of 40

28. $\frac{1}{3}$% of 630

1. _____ 2. _____

3. _____ 4. _____

5. _____ 6. _____

7. _____ 8. _____

9. _____ 10. _____

11. _____ 12. _____

13. _____ 14. _____

15. _____ 16. _____

17. _____ 18. _____

19. _____ 20. _____

21. _____ 22. _____

23. _____ 24. _____

25. _____ 26. _____

27. _____ 28. _____

29. 150% of 78   **30.** $112\frac{1}{2}$% of 16

29. _____ **30.** _____

31. A man earning $185 per week saves 20% of his salary. How much does he save each week?

31. _____

32. There are 2400 students in a school. On a certain day 94% are present. How many students are present that day?

32. _____

33. 70% of the body weight is water. If Anne weighs 110 pounds, how much of her weight (in pounds) is water?

33. _____

34. A boy pays an 8% sales tax on a $60 radio. How much tax does he pay?

34. _____

35. A roast beef loses 25% of its weight in cooking. How much will a 6-pound roast weigh after it is cooked?

35. _____

36. When shipping oranges, about 4% spoil in the process. In a shipment of 1100 boxes of oranges, how many boxes of oranges will remain unspoiled?

36. _____

37. A team lost 18% of its games one season. If it played 50 games, how many did it win?

37. _____

38. A family spends 30% of its income for rent. If it earns $680 per month, how much does it spend for rent?

38. _____

39. A salesman receives a $12\frac{1}{2}$% commission on whatever he sells. If his sales are $1680 one week, how much is his commission?

39. _____

40. In buying a house for $24,600, a man makes a down payment of $16\frac{2}{3}$%. How much is his down payment?

40. _____

5. Finding what percent one number is of another

In a class of 30 students, 6 are absent. What percent of the class is absent?

We already know how to find what fractional part 6 is of 30: it is $\frac{6}{30} = \frac{1}{5}$. We then know from our table that $\frac{1}{5} = 20\%$. Or, we can convert $\frac{1}{5}$ to a percent by division.

To avoid difficulty, remember that the number with the word "of" is in the denominator of the fraction formed and the number with "is" is in the numerator.

ILLUSTRATIVE PROBLEM

3 is what percent of 7?

Solution: $\dfrac{\text{is}}{\text{of}} = \dfrac{3}{7}$

$$7\overline{)3.000}^{.428} = .43 = 43\% \text{ (to nearest whole percent)}$$

Exercises

1. 12 is what percent of 60?

2. 32 is what percent of 40?

3. 50 is what percent of 150?

4. What percent of 20 is 18?

5. What percent of 40 is 28?

6. What percent of 40 is 15?

7. 18 is what percent of 18?

8. What percent of $30 is $1.50?

9. What percent of $17 is $.34?

1. _____

2. _____

3. _____

4. _____

5. _____

6. _____

7. _____

8. _____

9. _____

10. 1.5 is what percent of 9?

11. What percent of 12 is 15?

12. 100 is what percent of 250?

13. Answer, correct to the *nearest percent*:

    a. What percent of 28 is 4?

    b. 35 is what percent of 120?

    c. 6 is what percent of 90?

    d. $14 is what percent of $78?

    e. What percent of 9 is 4?

    f. 15 is what percent of 48?

14. Nancy got 4 questions wrong on a test of 25 questions. What percent of the questions did she get wrong?

15. A class is made up of 12 girls and 18 boys. What percent of the class consists of girls?

16. A $35 jacket is reduced to $28. What percent of the original cost is the reduction?

17. 9 inches is what percent of a foot?

18. A pint is what percent of a gallon?

19. A 150-pound man on earth weighs 24 pounds on the moon. His weight on the moon is what percent of his weight on earth?

20. A man earning $180 per week in salary is given an increase to $200 per week. The increase is what percent of his original salary?

21. In a class of 32 students, 4 are absent. What percent of the class is absent?

22. A team won 24 games out of a total of 33 played in one season. What percent of its games played did it win (correct to nearest percent)?

10. _____

11. _____

12. _____

13. a. _____

    b. _____

    c. _____

    d. _____

    e. _____

    f. _____

14. _____

15. _____

16. _____

17. _____

18. _____

19. _____

20. _____

21. _____

22. _____

23. In 15 quarts of milk, there is 1 quart of butter-fat. What is the percent of butterfat?

23. _____

24. A man buys an $18.00 tire and pays a total of $19.44, including tax.

   a. How much is the sales tax?

24. a. _____

   b. The sales tax is what percent of the price before the tax?

b. _____

25. The population of a town was 2000 in 1970 and 5000 in 1976.

   a. How much is the increase in population?

25. a. _____

   b. What percent is the increase of the original population in 1970?

b. _____

26. A clothing dealer buys a suit for $40 and sells it for $90.

   a. How much is his profit on the sale?

26. a. _____

   b. His profit is what percent of his cost?

b. _____

6. Finding a number when a percent of it is known

Twenty-five percent of a number is 21. Find the number.

For this type of problem, it is frequently convenient to use equations. Let x represent the number. Then:

Method 1

$$25\%x = 21$$
$$.25x = 21 \quad (25\% = .25)$$
$$25x = 2100 \quad \text{(multiply both sides by 100)}$$
$$\frac{25x}{25} = \frac{2100}{25} \quad \text{(divide both sides by 25)}$$
$$x = 84$$

Method 2

$$25\%x = 21$$
$$\frac{1}{4}x = 21 \quad \left(25\% = \frac{1}{4}\right)$$

$$\frac{1}{4}x \cdot 4 = 21 \cdot 4 \quad \text{(multiply both sides by 4)}$$

$$x = 84$$

ILLUSTRATIVE PROBLEM

Carl spent $76.50 for a suit, which was 85% of the original price. What was the original price?

Solution: Let x = the original price. Then

$$.85x = \$76.50$$

$$85x = 7650 \quad \text{(multiply both sides by 100)}$$

$$\frac{85x}{85} = \frac{7650}{85}$$

$$x = \$90 \quad (\textit{answer})$$

Exercises

1. 40% of what number is 32?

1. _____

2. 50% of a certain number is 13. What is the number?

2. _____

3. 30 is 20% of what number?

3. _____

4. If $32 is 15% of a certain amount, what is the amount? (Answer to the nearest cent.)

4. _____

5. If 18 is $33\frac{1}{3}$% of a number, find the number.

5. _____

6. 7% of what number is 28?

6. _____

7. 24 is $37\frac{1}{2}$% of what number?

7. _____

8. 35 is $62\frac{1}{2}$% of what number?

8. _____

9. 75% of what number is 120?

9. _____

10. $83\frac{1}{3}$% of what number is 65?

10. _____

11. 120% of some number is 35. Find the number.

11. _____

12. David bought a camera for $45, which was 75% of the original price. What was the original price?

12. _____

13. How much must a salesman sell per week to earn $160, if he is paid 8% commission on sales?

13. _____

14. The selling price of a radio is 130% of its cost. If the selling price is $65, what is the cost of the radio?

14. _____

15. The graduating class of a school consists of 180 pupils. If this is 16% of the school's enrollment, what is the total enrollment of the school?

15. _____

16. A family spends $180 per month for rent, which is 24% of their monthly income. What is their monthly income?

16. _____

17. A team won 48 games, which was $66\frac{2}{3}$% of the games it played that season. How many games did it play?

17. _____

18. Nancy saved $3.25, which was $62\frac{1}{2}$% of her allowance for the week. What was her weekly allowance?

18. _____

7. Discount problems

A suit marked $80 is sold at a 25% discount. How much does the buyer pay for the suit?

The buyer figures that the amount of the discount (or reduction) is 25% of $80, which is .25 × $80 = $20. He then subtracts $20 from $80 and arrives at $60, which he pays for the suit.

The original price, $80, is called the *list*

price or *marked price*. The percent of reduction, 25%, is called the *rate of discount*. The amount of reduction, $20, is called the *discount*. The reduced price paid by the buyer, $60, is called the *net price* or *sale price*. To summarize:

Discount = List price × Rate of discount

Net price = List price − Discount
(Sale price)   (Marked   (Amount of
                  price)   reduction)

Another way of solving the problem above is to think of the original price as 100% and the net price as 100% − 25% = 75% of the original price. Thus, the net price is 75% of $80 = .75 × 80 = $60.

ILLUSTRATIVE PROBLEM 1

A $360 TV set is offered at a discount of 40%. What is the sale price of the set?
Solution:

Method 1

$360 × .40 = $144.00   (discount)

$360 − $144 = $216   (sale price)

Method 2

100% − 40% = 60%

$360 × .60 = $216   (sale price)

ILLUSTRATIVE PROBLEM 2

Tom paid $45 for a suit marked at $60. What was the rate of discount?

Solution: $60   (marked price)
              −$45   (sale price)
              $15   (discount)

We must now find what percent the discount, $15, is of the marked price, $60.

$$\frac{\text{Amount of discount}}{\text{Marked price}} = \frac{\$15}{\$60} = \frac{1}{4}$$

$$= 25\%   \textit{(answer)}$$

Rule: Rate of discount $= \dfrac{\text{Amount of discount}}{\text{Marked price}}$.
Express the fraction as a percent.

ILLUSTRATIVE PROBLEM 3

A dealer buys a sofa, listed at $350, at a discount of 20%. He decides to pay cash for it and gets a further discount of 2%. What was the net price?

Solution: Such discounts are called **successive discounts** and are common in the business world. We figure successive discounts step by step:

Step 1. $350   (list price)
         X.20   (first rate of discount)
         $70.00 (first discount)

Step 2. $350   (list price)
         —70   (first discount)
         $280   (price after first discount)

Step 3. $280   (price after first discount)
         X.02   (rate of second discount)
         $5.60   (second discount)

Step 4. $280.00 (price after first discount)
         —5.60   (second discount)
         $274.40 (net price)

Note that the second discount is applied to the price after the first discount.

ILLUSTRATIVE PROBLEM 4

Tom buys a bicycle for $35 after receiving a 30% discount. What was the original (marked) price of the bicycle?

Solution: We may use equations to solve such problems. If the rate of discount was 30%, then Tom paid $100\% - 30\% = 70\%$ of the original price.

Let x = the original price in dollars. Then

$.70x$ = the amount Tom paid. Thus:

$$.70x = 35$$

$$70x = 3500$$

$$\frac{70x}{70} = \frac{3500}{70}$$

$$x = \$50 \quad \text{(original or marked price)}$$

Exercises

1. Mrs. Gomez bought a $40 dress at a discount of 15%. How much did she pay for the dress?

   1. _____

2. A shirt listed at $12 is sold for a 20% discount.

   a. How much is the discount?

   b. How much is the sale price?

   2. a. _____

      b. _____

3. Mr. Gold buys a $2800 car at a discount of 12%.

   a. How much is his discount?

   b. How much does he pay?

   3. a. _____

      b. _____

4. A man buys a $40 jacket for $30.

   a. How much was his discount?

   b. What was the rate of discount?

   4. a. _____

      b. _____

5. A $30 toaster is sold for $25.

   a. How much was the discount?

   b. What was the rate of discount?

   5. a. _____

      b. _____

6. A steam iron marked $40 is sold at a discount of 18%.

   a. How much is the discount?

   b. How much is the sale price?

   6. a. _____

      b. _____

7. Two stores were selling the same model camera. In shop A, the sign said "$80 less 20%". In shop B, the sign said "$88 less 25%".

   a. Which store made the better offer?

   b. How much better is it?

   7. a. _____

      b. _____

8. A $20 tennis racket is sold for $17. What is the rate of discount?

   8. _____

9. A school buys textbooks listed at $5.40 each at a 10% discount. How much does it pay for each book?

   9. _____

10. A dealer receives a bill for $480. He pays within 10 days and receives a 3% discount. How much does he pay?

10. _____

11. An auto dealer offers a discount of 15% on a $3000 car. He offers a further 3% discount for each payment. For how much can the car be purchased?

11. _____

12. If you received a $3 discount on a $25 bill, what rate of discount did you receive?

12. _____

In 13 to 18, find the *rate of discount*.

	List price	Net price
13.	$80	$50
14.	$125	$110
15.	$42.50	$30.00
16.	$120	$110
17.	$245	$195
18.	$58.40	$52.56

13. _____
14. _____
15. _____
16. _____
17. _____
18. _____

19. A refrigerator listed at $240 is sold with discounts of 30% and 5%. What was the sale price?

19. _____

In 20 to 22, find the *net price*.

	List price	Rates of successive discount
20.	$400	20% and 10%
21.	$80	10% and 4%
22.	$480	$12\frac{1}{2}$% and 5%

20. _____
21. _____
22. _____

23. A man can buy a $200 motor from dealer A at a 15% discount. He can get the same $200 motor from dealer B with discounts of 10% and 5%.

a. Which is cheaper?

23. a. _____

b. How much cheaper is it?

24. Mrs. White buys a desk chair for $54 after a 10% discount. What was the list price of the chair?

25. Mr. Roberts pays $68 for a lawn mower after a 15% discount. What was the list price of the mower?

In 26 to 28, find the *list price*.

	Net price	Rate of discount
26.	$51.80	30%
27.	$11.50	8%
28.	$150.00	$37\frac{1}{2}\%$

29. Mr. Finney bought a $160 power saw at a sale and got a 15% discount.

a. What was the net price of the saw?

b. If he paid a 7% sales tax, what was the total amount of the bill?

30. Bill paid $36.00 for a baseball uniform after receiving a 20% discount. What was the marked price of the uniform?

8. Interest formula

When a businessman borrows money for a period of time, he must pay for the use of this money. If Mr. A borrows $1000 from Mr. B for a period of a year, and then pays him back $1060, he pays $60 for the use of the $1000 for a year. This $60 is called the *interest* on the loan.

Likewise, when you put money in the bank, you receive interest for "lending" it to the bank. (The bank, in turn, lends it out to others.) If you put $100 in the bank at an annual rate of interest of 6%, you get back $106 at the end of the year.

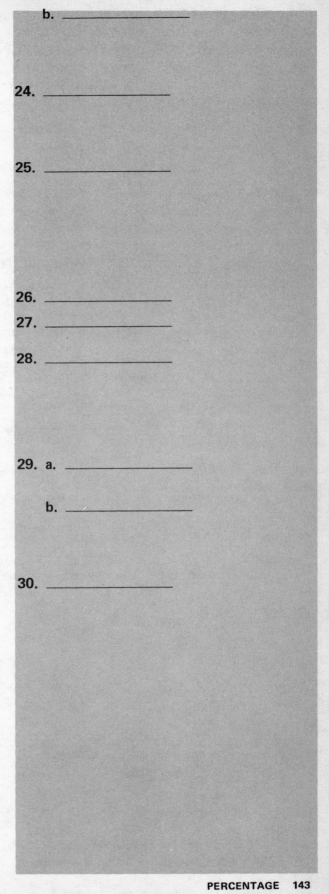

b. _____

24. _____

25. _____

26. _____

27. _____

28. _____

29. a. _____

b. _____

30. _____

This is the original $100 plus 6% of $100, which is $6. The $100 is called the **principal**; the 6% is the **rate of interest**; the $6 is the **interest**; the $106 is the **amount** (meaning the amount returned).

The rate of interest is usually stated **annually**, that is, for a one-year period. If the loan described above were for $\frac{1}{2}$ year, the interest would be $\frac{1}{2}$ of $6, or $3. If the loan were for 2 years, the interest would be 2 × $6, or $12. Thus, we see that we must multiply the annual interest by the time in years to obtain the interest for any loan.

We may summarize the relationship as follows:

Interest =

   Principal × Rate of interest × Time in years

As a formula, we may write

$$I = PRT$$

where I is the interest, P is the principal, R is the rate of interest, and T is the time in years.

ILLUSTRATIVE PROBLEM 1

Find the interest on $650 at 4% for 9 months.

Solution: $I = PRT$

Since 9 months $= \frac{9}{12} = \frac{3}{4}$ year, we substitute $P = 650$, $R = \frac{4}{100}$, and $T = \frac{3}{4}$:

$$I = 650 \times \frac{\overset{1}{\cancel{4}}}{100} \times \frac{3}{\underset{1}{\cancel{4}}} = \frac{1950}{100}$$

$I = \$19.50$ (*answer*)

Note that to find the *amount* we must add the principal to the interest. As a formula, $A = P + I$, where A is the amount.

ILLUSTRATIVE PROBLEM 2

What principal will yield an interest of $22.50 if invested at 5% annually for 6 months?

Solution: $I = PRT$

Since 6 months $= \frac{1}{2}$ year, we substitute

$I = 22.50, R = \frac{5}{100}$, and $T = \frac{1}{2}$:

$$22.50 = P \times \frac{5}{100} \times \frac{1}{2}$$

$$22.50 = \frac{5}{200}P$$

$$22.50 = \frac{1}{40}P \quad \text{or} \quad \frac{1}{40}P = 22.50$$

Multiplying both sides by 40, we have

$$P = 40 \times 22.50$$

$$P = \$900 \quad (answer)$$

ILLUSTRATIVE PROBLEM 3

At what annual rate of interest will a loan of \$450 yield an interest payment of \$67.50 in $2\frac{1}{2}$ years?

Solution: $\qquad I = PRT$

Substitute: $\$67.50 = \overset{225}{\cancel{450}} \times R \times \frac{5}{\underset{1}{\cancel{2}}}$

$$\frac{67.50}{1125} = \frac{1125R}{1125}$$

$$R = \frac{67.50}{1125} = .06$$

$$R = 6\% \quad (answer)$$

Exercises

In 1 to 5, find the interest on the loans.

1. \$600 at 5% for $2\frac{1}{2}$ years

2. \$350 at 4% for 2 years

3. \$1200 at $4\frac{1}{2}\%$ for 9 months

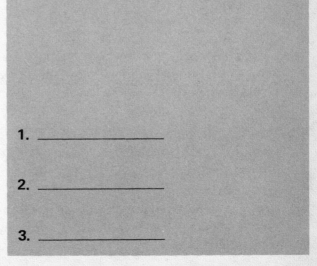

1. _____

2. _____

3. _____

4. $1500 at 6% for 6 months

5. $2400 at 5% for 1 yr. 6 months

6. Mr. Jones borrowed $1200 at 6% interest. How much interest did he pay at the end of 2 years?

7. What principal yields an interest of $80 after 2 years at an annual rate of interest of 4%?

8. Sue's father borrowed some money at 7% annual interest for 9 months. When he repaid the principal, he paid $24.15 in interest. How much did he borrow?

In 9 to 15, find the missing item.

	Principal	Rate	Time	Interest
9.	?	7%	2 yr.	$14
10.	$325	?	1 yr. 6 mo.	$39
11.	$375	6%	?	$56.25
12.	$1200	?	$2\frac{1}{2}$ yr.	$165
13.	$1560	$5\frac{1}{2}$%	2 yr.	?
14.	?	$7\frac{1}{2}$%	$1\frac{1}{2}$ yr.	$87.75
15.	$4000	?	2 yr. 6 mo.	$750

16. Mr. Perkus paid $96 interest for a 2-year loan at 6% annual interest. How much did he borrow?

17. Bill's father paid $21 interest for a $175 loan for 1 yr. 6 mo. What was the rate of interest?

18. If you borrow $450 at 7% interest, for what period of time would you have the money if the interest is $63?

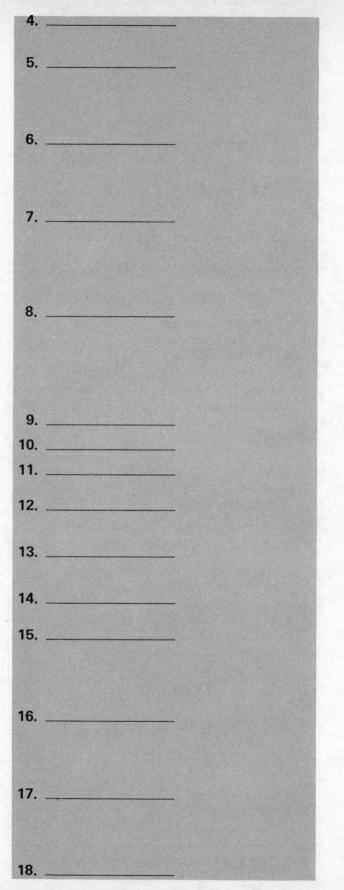

4. _____

5. _____

6. _____

7. _____

8. _____

9. _____

10. _____

11. _____

12. _____

13. _____

14. _____

15. _____

16. _____

17. _____

18. _____

19. How much must you deposit in a bank at $4\frac{1}{2}\%$ annual interest in order to earn an interest payment of $54 in $1\frac{1}{2}$ years?

19. _____

20. The interest on a $680 loan for $2\frac{1}{2}$ years is $110.50. What rate of interest is charged?

20. _____

Chapter review exercises

1. A baseball park with 20,000 seats had 30% of its seats vacant on a particular day. How many spectators were present?

1. _____

2. The principal of a school with 2400 students expects a 12% decrease in the number of students next year. How many students does he expect to have in the school next year?

2. _____

3. Find 32% of 1800.

3. _____

4. 16 is what percent of 40?

4. _____

5. Find 125% of 220.

5. _____

6. 26 is what percent of 20?

6. _____

7. Find 8.2% of $970.

7. _____

8. Thirty percent of what number is equal to 72?

8. _____

9. A turkey loses 15% of its weight in roasting. If a turkey weighs 12 pounds after roasting, how much did it weigh before? (Answer to the nearest pound.)

9. _____

10. 14 is what percent of 30? (Answer to the nearest percent.)

10. _____

11. What percent of 80 is 15?

11. _____

12. A $180 set of books is sold at a discount of $9\frac{1}{2}$%. What is the sale price?

12. _____

13. Find the interest on $850 at $7\frac{1}{2}$% for 2 years.

13. _____

14. A $200 washing machine was purchased for $170. What was the rate of discount?

14. _____

15. A boy paid $48 for a radio after a $33\frac{1}{3}$% discount. What was the list price of the radio?

15. _____

16. A salesman earns 12% of his total sales as commission. If he sells $2500 worth of merchandise one week, how much does he earn?

16. _____

17. A man deposits some money in a bank at 6% interest and receives $22.50 in interest after $2\frac{1}{2}$ years. How much did he deposit?

17. _____

18. A woman buys a $42 dress at a 30% discount.

   a. What is the reduced price?

18. a. _____

   b. How much does she pay if there is an 8% sales tax on the dress?

     b. _____

19. A girl gets 25 questions right on a 30-question short-answer quiz. What percent does she have right?

19. _____

20. What principal will yield an interest of $45 at a rate of 6% for $1\frac{1}{2}$ years?

20. _____

LINEAR MEASURE, AREA, AND VOLUME

1. Measurement of length

Measurements are always made by comparing the object being measured with a standard unit of measure. In the U.S.A., the most common units for measuring lengths are the inch, the foot, the yard, and the mile.

The relationships between these units are indicated in the following table:

Units of Linear Measure
12 inches = 1 foot
36 inches = 1 yard
3 feet = 1 yard
5280 feet = 1 mile
1760 yards = 1 mile

As you know, we often abbreviate feet by ft. or by a single stroke ′; likewise, we abbreviate inches by in. or by a double stroke ″. Thus, 5 feet 3 inches may be written as 5 ft. 3 in. or as 5′3″.

We measure length with a ruler which is usually marked off in inches; each inch is subdivided into quarters, eighths, and sixteenths. For larger lengths, we use a yardstick or a tape, and indicate the measurements in feet, yards, or miles.

It frequently becomes necessary to change from one unit of measure to another, and the table of units of linear measure will help us to do this.

ILLUSTRATIVE PROBLEM 1

Change 66 inches to feet.

Solution: Since there are 12 inches in 1 foot, we must see how many times 12 is contained in 66. Thus,

$$\frac{66}{12} = 5\frac{6}{12} = 5\frac{1}{2}$$

Answer: 66 in. = $5\frac{1}{2}$ ft.

ILLUSTRATIVE PROBLEM 2

A race track is 440 yards in length. How many laps must a boy run in a 1-mile race?

Solution: Since there are 1760 yards in 1 mile, we must see how many times 440 is contained in 1760. Thus,

$$440\overline{)1760}^{4}$$
$$\underline{1760}$$

Answer: The boy must run 4 laps.

ILLUSTRATIVE PROBLEM 3

How many feet are in: **a.** 5 yards? **b.** x yards?

Solution:

a. Since each yard contains 3 feet, 5 yards contain $5 \times 3 = 15$ feet.

b. x yards contain $x \cdot 3 = 3x$ feet.

Exercises

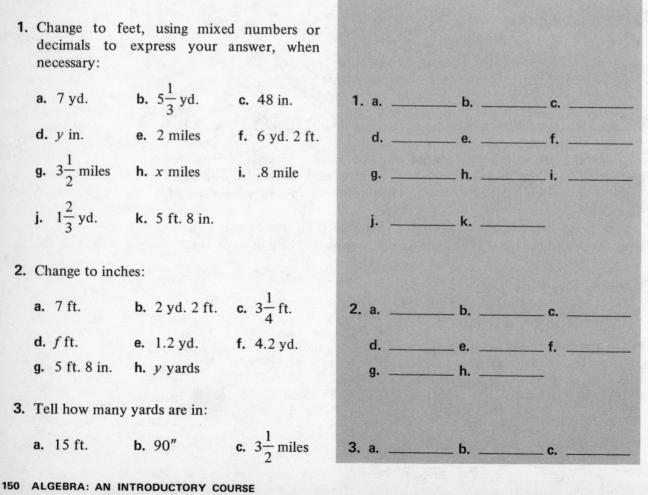

1. Change to feet, using mixed numbers or decimals to express your answer, when necessary:

   a. 7 yd. **b.** $5\frac{1}{3}$ yd. **c.** 48 in.

   d. y in. **e.** 2 miles **f.** 6 yd. 2 ft.

   g. $3\frac{1}{2}$ miles **h.** x miles **i.** .8 mile

   j. $1\frac{2}{3}$ yd. **k.** 5 ft. 8 in.

   1. a. _____ b. _____ c. _____
   d. _____ e. _____ f. _____
   g. _____ h. _____ i. _____
   j. _____ k. _____

2. Change to inches:

   a. 7 ft. **b.** 2 yd. 2 ft. **c.** $3\frac{1}{4}$ ft.

   d. f ft. **e.** 1.2 yd. **f.** 4.2 yd.

   g. 5 ft. 8 in. **h.** y yards

   2. a. _____ b. _____ c. _____
   d. _____ e. _____ f. _____
   g. _____ h. _____

3. Tell how many yards are in:

   a. 15 ft. **b.** 90" **c.** $3\frac{1}{2}$ miles

   3. a. _____ b. _____ c. _____

d. 2.2 miles   **e.** k ft.   **f.** x miles

g. i inches   **h.** 127 ft.   **i.** 8′6″

d. _____ **e.** _____ **f.** _____

g. _____ **h.** _____ **i.** _____

4. A furlong, used in horseracing, is a distance of $\frac{1}{8}$ mile.

   a. How many miles are in 12 furlongs?

   b. How many yards are in a furlong?

4. a. _____

   b. _____

5. Bill is 5 feet 4 inches in height. How tall is he in inches?

5. _____

6. A jet plane can fly at an altitude of 35,000 feet. How many miles high is this (to the nearest tenth of a mile)?

6. _____

7. Depth of water is often expressed in fathoms. A fathom is 6 feet. If the depth of a bay at a certain point is 68 feet, what is its depth in fathoms?

7. _____

8. A board 6 feet long is cut into pieces, each 8 inches long. How many pieces are obtained?

8. _____

9. What part of a yard is 20 inches?

9. _____

10. A woman buys $\frac{3}{4}$ yard of ribbon and cuts off 4 pieces, each 5 inches long. How many inches of ribbon are left?

10. _____

11. A truck 90 inches high enters a tunnel which is 8 feet high. By how many inches does the truck clear the tunnel?

11. _____

12. Represent the total number of inches in x ft. y in.

12. _____

13. A rod is $5\frac{1}{2}$ yards. How many rods are in a mile?

13. _____

14. A nautical mile is 1.15 land miles. How many feet (to the nearest foot) are in a nautical mile?

14. _____

2. Metric system—linear measure

The system of linear measure that we have been using is known as the *English system* and is used mainly in the United States. Most other countries now use the *metric system,* which is gradually being introduced here as well.

The great advantage of the metric system is that it is a decimal system, since each unit is $\frac{1}{10}$ of the next larger unit. We shall deal here only with the most commonly used metric units of length, as listed in the following table:

Metric-English Approximations

$$1 \text{ kilometer (km)} = 1000 \text{ meters} = \frac{5}{8} \text{ mile}$$

$$1 \text{ meter (m) (basic unit)} = 39 \text{ inches}$$

$$1 \text{ centimeter (cm)} = \frac{1}{100} \text{ of a meter} = \frac{2}{5} \text{ inch}$$

$$1 \text{ millimeter (mm)} = \frac{1}{1000} \text{ of a meter} = \frac{1}{25} \text{ inch}$$

In the figure, we see that each of the numbered markings on the lower edge of the ruler indicates 1 centimeter. The small markings within each centimeter indicate millimeters. Since each centimeter is divided into 10 equal parts, 1 millimeter $= \frac{1}{10}$ centimeter. Ten centimeters would be a decimeter, which is $\frac{1}{10}$ of a meter, but this unit is not commonly used. A 1-meter long ruler (meterstick) is slightly longer than a yardstick and is equal to 100 centimeters.

ILLUSTRATIVE PROBLEM 1

An artillery shell is 120 mm in diameter.
a. What is its diameter in centimeters?
b. What is its diameter in inches?

Solution:

a. Since 10 mm = 1 cm, we must see how many times 10 mm is contained in 120 mm:

$$120 \div 10 = 12 \text{ cm} \quad (answer)$$

b. Since 1 cm = $\frac{2}{5}$ in., 12 cm is equal to:

$$12 \times \frac{2}{5} = \frac{24}{5} = 4\frac{4}{5} \text{ in.} \quad (answer)$$

ILLUSTRATIVE PROBLEM 2

The distance between two towns in France is 40 km.

a. How many meters is this?
b. How many miles is this?

Solution:

a. Since 1 kilometer = 1000 meters, then

$$40 \text{ km} = 40 \times 1000 = 40,000 \text{ m} \quad (answer)$$

b. Since 1 km = $\frac{5}{8}$ mi., then

$$40 \text{ km} = 40 \times \frac{5}{8} = 25 \text{ mi.} \quad (answer)$$

Exercises

In the following exercises, use the values given in the table on page 152.

1. What is the difference in inches between a yardstick and a meterstick?

1. _____

2. What is the difference in yards between a 100-yard dash and a 100-meter dash?

2. _____

3. Film comes in widths of 8 mm, 16 mm, and 35 mm. How many inches are in each of these?

3. _____

4. A one-mile race equals:

  a. ? kilometers   **b.** ? meters

5. a. 7 cm = ? mm   **b.** 2.4 cm = ? mm

  c. x cm = ? mm   **d.** 73 mm = ? cm

  e. 87 mm = ? cm   **f.** y mm = ? cm

6. a. 6 m = ? cm   **b.** 8.3 m = ? cm

  c. 700 cm = ? m   **d.** 340 cm = ? m

  e. k meters = ? cm   **f.** t cm = ? m

7. a. 6 km = ? m   **b.** 4.2 km = ? m

  c. 3000 m = ? km   **d.** 4700 m = ? km

  e. x meters = ? km   **f.** y km = ? m

8. The distance between two cities in Europe is 740 kilometers. How many miles is this?

9. The high jump record a few years ago was 2.1 meters. How high is this in feet and inches? (Answer to the nearest inch.)

10. Which is shorter, a millimeter or $\frac{1}{16}$ of an inch? How much shorter in inches? (Answer to the nearest hundredth.)

11. Tell how many miles are in:

  a. 80 km **b.** 400 km **c.** 60 km **d.** n km

12. Tell how many km are in:

  a. 20 mi. **b.** 100 mi. **c.** 72 mi. **d.** r mi.

13. A plane flies at 450 miles per hour. How many kilometers per hour is this?

14. The circumference of the earth is about 25,000 miles. About how many kilometers is this?

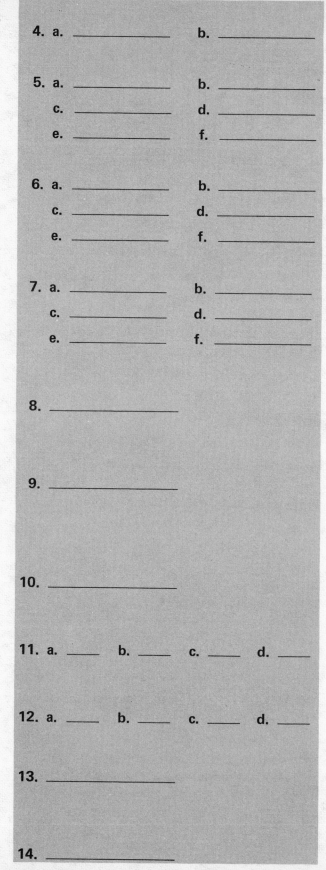

4. a. _____   **b.** _____

5. a. _____   **b.** _____

  c. _____   **d.** _____

  e. _____   **f.** _____

6. a. _____   **b.** _____

  c. _____   **d.** _____

  e. _____   **f.** _____

7. a. _____   **b.** _____

  c. _____   **d.** _____

  e. _____   **f.** _____

8. _____

9. _____

10. _____

11. a. ___ **b.** ___ **c.** ___ **d.** ___

12. a. ___ **b.** ___ **c.** ___ **d.** ___

13. _____

14. _____

15. A barometer reading one day in Rome is 750 mm. How many inches is this?

15. _____

16. On a road near Brussels the speed limit is 80 kilometers per hour. About how many miles per hour is this?

16. _____

17. About how many centimeters in:

a. an inch?   **b.** a foot?

17. a. _____   **b.** _____

3. Area measure—square and rectangle

The smaller figure at the right represents a square one inch on each side. Such a square is called a *square inch*. The larger figure represents a rectangle whose base is 4 inches and whose altitude is 3 inches. We count the number of squares in the rectangle and we see that there are 12.

The number of square units that are contained within a figure is called the *area* of the figure. The area of the large rectangle is 12 square inches. We may use other units of area such as square foot, square yard, square mile, square centimeter, or square meter.

Looking at the figure of the rectangle, we see that we could have obtained the area more quickly by multiplying the base (4 in.) by the height (3 in.), which gives us 12 sq. in. This example indicates to us that, in general, if the base and height are in the same units, we may obtain the area, A, by the formula

$$A = bh$$

where b is the base of the rectangle and h is its height.

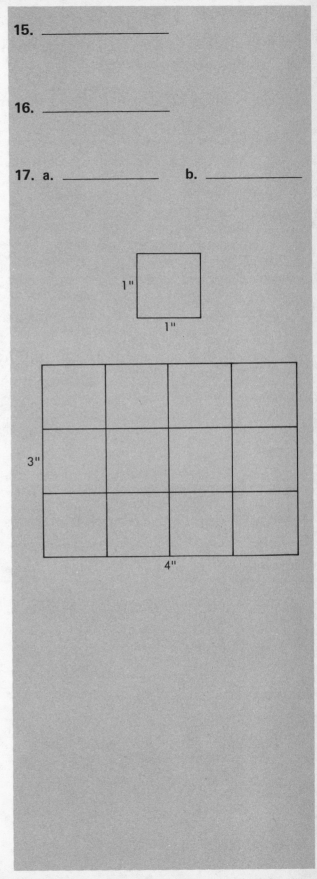

ILLUSTRATIVE PROBLEM 1

A classroom is 30′ × 28′. How many square feet are in its area?

Solution: $A = bh$

$A = 30 \times 28$

$A = 840$

Answer: The area is 840 sq. ft.

ILLUSTRATIVE PROBLEM 2

Find the area of a rectangular table that is 5 ft. 6 in. long and 4 ft. wide.

Solution: Convert 5 ft. 6 in. to $5\frac{6}{12} = 5\frac{1}{2}$ ft.

$A = bh$

$A = 5\frac{1}{2} \times 4$

$A = \frac{11}{2} \times 4$

$A = 22$

Answer: The area is 22 sq. ft.

ILLUSTRATIVE PROBLEM 3

The area of a rectangle is 350 sq. ft. If its base is 35 ft., what is its height?

Solution: $A = bh$

$350 = 35h$

$\frac{350}{35} = \frac{35h}{35}$

$h = 10$

Answer: The height of the rectangle is 10 ft.

Exercises

In 1 to 13, find the area of the rectangle.

1. 15 ft. by 12 ft.

2. 18″ × 11″

3. 30′ × $10\frac{2}{3}'$

4. 7.2 yd. by 5.4 yd.

5. $3\frac{1}{2}$ mi. by $2\frac{1}{4}$ mi.

1. _____

2. _____

3. _____

4. _____

5. _____

6. 20 cm by 15 cm

7. 85 cm by 1 m

8. 18 ft. by 10 ft. 6 in.

9. 5 ft. 6 in. by 6 ft. 3 in.

10. x ft. by y ft.

11. k ft. by 8 ft. 6 in.

12. 7 ft. by 3 yd.

13. l ft. long by w ft. wide

14. A rectangular mirror 32″ × 20″ is to be re-silvered at a cost of 5¢ per square inch. What will be the total cost?

15. What is the cost of a 9′ × 12′ rug at a cost of $3 per square foot?

16. How many square yards of carpeting are needed to cover a living room 9 yards long and 5 yards 2 feet long?

17. How many tiles each 1 sq. ft. in area are needed to cover the floor of a bathhouse 40 ft. long and 35 ft. wide?

18. A rectangular plot of ground has an area of 3760 sq. ft. If its base is 80 ft., find its height in feet.

19. A tennis court is to have an area of 880 sq. yd. If it is 40 yd. long, how many yards are in its width?

20. How many ceiling tiles each 1 sq. ft. in area are needed to cover the ceiling of a room which is 14 ft. by 18 ft.?

6. _____

7. _____

8. _____

9. _____

10. _____

11. _____

12. _____

13. _____

14. _____

15. _____

16. _____

17. _____

18. _____

19. _____

20. _____

21. A quart of a certain paint will cover 100 sq. ft. of wall space. How many quarts are needed to cover a wall of a house that is 45 ft. long and 20 ft. high?

22. How many sq. ft. of carpeting are needed for the following living room and dining room?

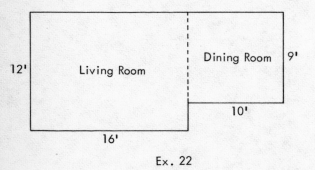

Ex. 22

(*Hint:* Divide the figure into two rectangles by drawing the dotted line as shown.)

23. Find the area of the following figure:

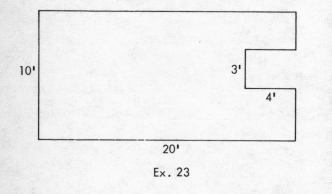

Ex. 23

21. _____

22. _____

23. _____

4. Changing units of area

How many square yards of carpeting are needed to cover a floor that is 72 square feet in area?

To answer this question, we must know how many square feet are in a square yard. A square yard is a square whose base and height are both 1 yard or 3 feet long. Hence,

$$A = bh$$

$$A = 3 \times 3 = 9 \text{ sq. ft.}$$

We see that 1 sq. yd. = 9 sq. ft.

In the problem above we see that, since 1 sq. yd. = 9 sq. ft., then 72 sq. ft. is equivalent to $\frac{72}{9}$ = 8 sq. yd.

A square foot is a square whose base and height are both 1 foot or 12 inches long. Hence,

$A = bh$

$A = 12 \times 12 = 144$ sq. in.

We see that 1 sq. ft. = 144 sq. in.

ILLUSTRATIVE PROBLEM

How much linoleum is needed to cover a rectangular tabletop 72 inches by 46 inches? Answer in **(a)** square inches, **(b)** square feet, and **(c)** square yards.

Solution:

a. $A = bh$

$A = 72 \times 46 = 3312$ sq. in.   (*answer*)

b. $A = \frac{3312}{144} = 23$ sq. ft.   (*answer*)

c. $A = \frac{23}{9} = 2\frac{5}{9}$ sq. yd.   (*answer*)

Exercises

1. 7 sq. yd. = _____ sq. ft.

2. 3 sq. ft. = _____ sq. in.

3. 63 sq. ft. = _____ sq. yd.

4. $7\frac{2}{3}$ sq. yd. = _____ sq. ft.

5. 72 sq. in. = _____ sq. ft.

6. 1 sq. yd. = _____ sq. in.

1. _____

2. _____

3. _____

4. _____

5. _____

6. _____

7. What is the cost of carpeting a floor 15 ft. by 21 ft. if the carpeting costs $8 per sq. yd.?

7. _____

8. What is the total charge for resurfacing a tennis court 78 ft. by 36 ft. if the surfacing costs $2.50 per sq. yd.?

8. _____

9. A man completely panels a closet 9 feet long, 6 feet wide, and 15 feet high. If he must panel the ceiling, the floor, and all four walls, how many square yards of paneling are needed?

9. _____

10. A room is 18 ft. long, 14 ft. wide, and 8 ft. 6 in. high. How much will it cost to paper the walls and ceiling at $4.50 per sq. yd.? (Disregard waste due to doors and windows.)

10. _____

11. Find the number of square yards of linoleum needed to cover a kitchen floor 12 ft. wide and 15 ft. long.

11. _____

12. At $7.50 per square yard, find the cost of paving a concrete walk 120 feet long and 6 feet wide.

12. _____

13. How many tiles one square inch in size are needed to cover a bathroom floor 4 ft. by 5 ft.?

13. _____

5. Area of a triangle

In right triangle PQS, base b and height h are also the legs of the triangle.

In the figure, we see rectangle $PQRS$ with diagonal QS drawn. If we fold the rectangle along diagonal QS, we find that the figure is divided into two triangles that are equal in area. Thus, triangle PQS is equal in area to one-half the area of the rectangle. Since the area of a rectangle is equal to bh, we may write the formula for the area of the triangle as

$$A = \frac{1}{2} bh$$

where b = base and h = height.

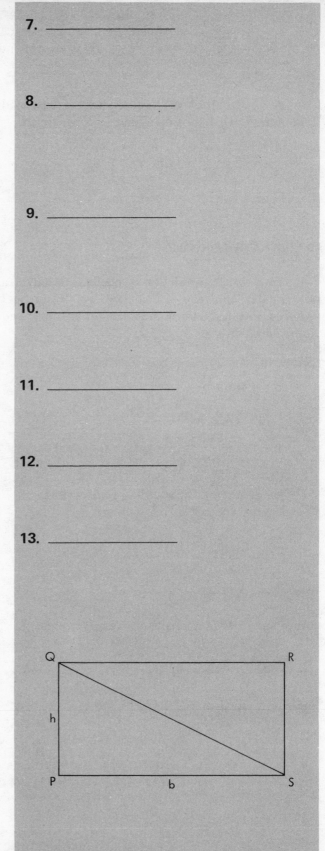

Note that the triangle and the rectangle have the same base and height. Although the figure on page 160 shows how we get the area of a right triangle (a triangle with a 90-degree angle), we can show that the formula holds for any triangle. In the figures at the right, the area of each triangle is found by using the formula $A = \frac{1}{2} bh$.

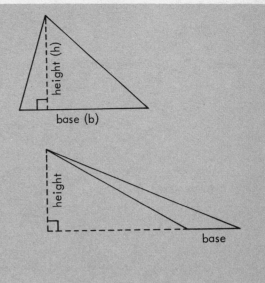

ILLUSTRATIVE PROBLEM 1

Find the area of a triangle whose base is 18″ and height is 7″.

Solution: $A = \frac{1}{2} bh$

$$A = \frac{1}{\cancel{2}} \cdot \overset{9}{\cancel{18}} \cdot 7$$

$$A = 9 \cdot 7 = 63$$

Answer: The area is 63 sq. in.

ILLUSTRATIVE PROBLEM 2

The area of a triangle is 192 sq. in. If the height is 16 in., find the base.

Solution: $A = \frac{1}{2} bh$

$$192 = \frac{1}{2} \cdot b \cdot 16$$

$$192 = 8b$$

$$\frac{192}{8} = \frac{8b}{8}$$

$$b = 24$$

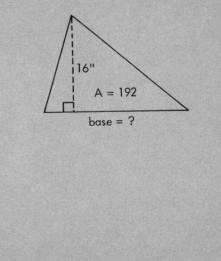

Answer: The base is 24 inches.

Exercises

1. Find the area of each of the following triangles:

   a. $b = 18″, h = 5″$

   b. $b = 12$ ft., $h = 8$ ft.

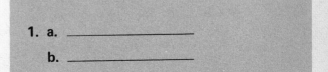

1. a. _____

b. _____

c. $b = 15$ yd., $h = 7$ yd.

d. $b = 14$ ft., $h = 7$ ft. 6 in.

e. $b = 18$ ft., $h = 6\frac{1}{2}$ ft.

f. $b = 10$ in., $h = 2\frac{1}{2}$ ft.

2. A triangular sail has a base of 8 ft. and a height of 6 ft. 3 in. How many square feet are in its area?

3. A triangular piece of plywood weighing $1\frac{1}{2}$ lb. per sq. ft. has a base 2 ft. 8 in. and a height of 1 ft. 6 in. How many pounds does it weigh?

4. A triangle has an area of 46 sq. ft. If its base is 16 ft., find its height.

5. Fill in the missing dimensions of the following triangles:

	Base	Height	Area
a.	28 in.	?	140 sq. in.
b.	?	26 yd.	390 sq. yd.
c.	60 cm	?	720 sq. cm
d.	?	9 in.	3 sq. ft.

6. A triangular plate has a base of 9″ and a height of 6″. A square slot 2″ on a side is cut out of the plate. Find the area of the remaining metal surface of the plate.

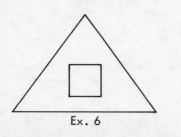

Ex. 6

c. _____

d. _____

e. _____

f. _____

2. _____

3. _____

4. _____

5. a. _____

   b. _____

   c. _____

   d. _____

6. _____

7. A triangular plot of ground has a base of 121 ft. and a height of 60 ft. How many acres of land are in this plot? (1 acre = 43,560 sq. ft.)

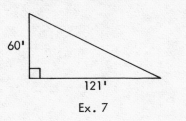

Ex. 7

7. _____

8. The figure shows a triangle mounted on a rectangle. Using the dimensions given, find the area of the entire figure.

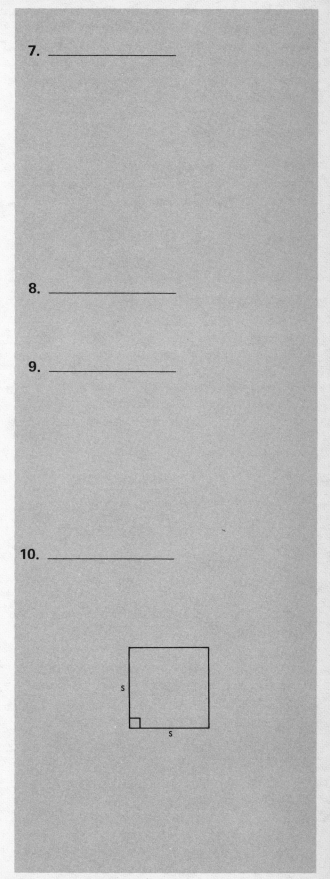

12" 18" 15"

Ex. 8

8. _____

9. Find the area of the figure by breaking it up into triangles and rectangles.

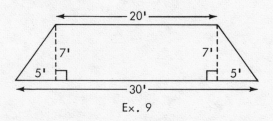

20' 7' 7' 5' 5' 30'

Ex. 9

9. _____

10. A triangular gas station has an area of 2400 sq. ft. If the base of the triangle is 80 ft., how many feet are in the height?

10. _____

6. Use of exponents

Earlier in the chapter, we saw that the area of a rectangle is given by the formula $A = bh$. In a square, the base and altitude are equal, so that, if we designate the side of the square by s, the formula for the area of a square becomes $A = s \times s$.

We usually write this $A = s^2$ (read "s squared") where the small 2 indicates that s appears twice in the product $s \times s$. This small 2 is called an *exponent* and we say that s is raised to the second power. The number s used as a factor is called the *base*.

Exponents are very commonly used in algebra. Thus y^3 (read "y cubed") would mean $y \times y \times y$ and *aaaa* would be written a^4 and read "a to the fourth power." An expression such as *ppqqq* would be written $p^2 q^3$ and is read "p squared q cubed." An expression with numerical base such as $2 \cdot 2 \cdot 2 \cdot 2$ is written 2^4, and is read "2 to the fourth power" or simply "2 to the fourth"; its value is 16.

If we write $2x^3$, it is only the x which appears 3 times in the product. If we wish to indicate that the 2 is also to be cubed, we write $(2x)^3$, which would mean $(2x)(2x)(2x)$.

ILLUSTRATIVE PROBLEM 1

Write, using exponents, $3bbbcc$.

Solution: $3b^3 c^2$

ILLUSTRATIVE PROBLEM 2

Find the value of $2a^3 + 6b^2$ if $a = 4$ and $b = 5$.

Solution:

$$2a^3 + 6b^2 = 2(4)^3 + 6(5)^2$$
$$= 2 \cdot 4 \cdot 4 \cdot 4 + 6 \cdot 5 \cdot 5$$
$$= 128 + 150 = 278 \quad (\textit{answer})$$

Exercises

1. Name the base and exponent in each of the following:

   a. t^2

   b. d^3

   c. z^7

   d. 3^4

   e. 10^5

2. Find the value of:

   a. 7^2 b. 2^3 c. 1^7

   d. 3^4 e. 4^3

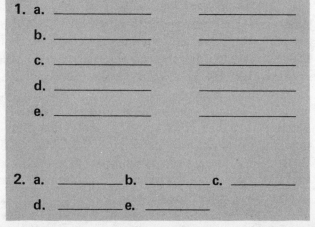

1. a. _____   _____
   b. _____   _____
   c. _____   _____
   d. _____   _____
   e. _____   _____

2. a. _____ b. _____ c. _____
   d. _____ e. _____

3. Write each of the following using exponents:

    a. *rrr*   **b.** *ccccc*

    c. $tt + pppp$ **d.** $3xxx + 2yy$

    e. *7bbmmm*   **f.** $5aab - 7dddxx$

4. Find the area of a square whose side is:

    a. $8''$ **b.** 10 ft.   **c.** $\frac{1}{2}$ in.

    d. 2.5 cm   **e.** $2\frac{1}{3}$ yd.

5. If $x = 2$, $y = 3$, and $z = 4$, find the value of each of the following:

    a. $3y^2$ **b.** $4x^3$ **c.** z^2

    d. $x^2 y$ **e.** $y^2 - x^2$ **f.** $3x^2 + y^2$

    g. $z^3 - xy^2$ **h.** $(5x)^3$ **i.** $5x^3$

    j. $x^3 y^2 z$ **k.** $(x + y)^2$ **l.** $(z - y)^5$

    m. $xy^3 - z^2$

6. Find the area of a square whose side is 4 ft. 6 in.

7. A baseball diamond is a square 30 yd. on a side. What is the area enclosed by the base lines in sq. yd.?

8. The formula $s = 16t^2$ gives the distance, s, in feet, that an object above ground falls in t seconds. How many feet does an object fall in:

    a. 10 seconds?   **b.** 20 seconds?

9. A cube has 6 equal faces, each of which is a square. If each edge of the cube is e, then the total surface area of the cube, S, is given by the formula $S = 6e^2$. Find the total surface area of a cube whose edge is:

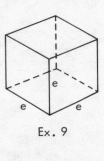

Ex. 9

    a. 4 inches

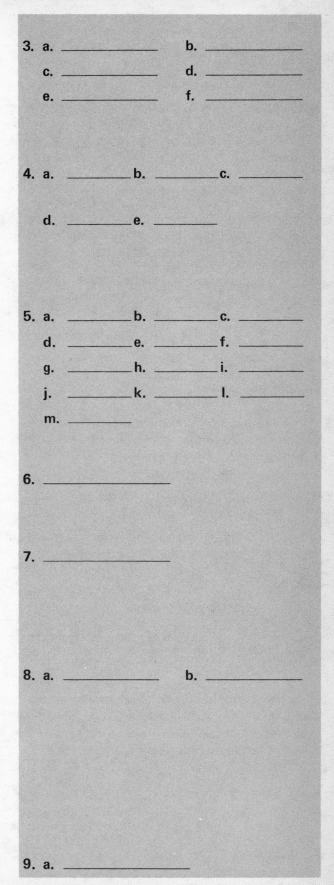

3. a. _____   **b.** _____

    c. _____   **d.** _____

    e. _____   **f.** _____

4. a. _____ **b.** _____ **c.** _____

    d. _____ **e.** _____

5. a. _____ **b.** _____ **c.** _____

    d. _____ **e.** _____ **f.** _____

    g. _____ **h.** _____ **i.** _____

    j. _____ **k.** _____ **l.** _____

    m. _____

6. _____

7. _____

8. a. _____   **b.** _____

9. a. _____

b. $2\frac{1}{3}$ yd.

c. 3 ft. 6 in.

10. A square metal plate 8″ on a side has a smaller square hole punched out of it 3″ on a side. How many square inches of metal remain?

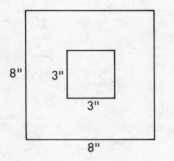

b. _____

c. _____

10. _____

7. Area of a circle

In Chapter 4, we discussed the problem of finding the circumference of a circle when its radius or diameter is given.

We used the formula

$$C = \pi d$$

where d is the diameter and π is $\frac{22}{7}$ or $3\frac{1}{7}$ or 3.14, approximately. Since $d = 2r$, the formula may be written

$$C = 2\pi r$$

We can find the area of a circle, when its radius is given, by means of the formula

$$A = \pi r^2$$

This formula has been discovered by mathematicians and is in common use. Remember that r is in linear units (inches, feet, etc.) and that A is in square units (sq. in., sq. ft., etc.).

ILLUSTRATIVE PROBLEM 1

Find the area of a circle whose radius is $3\frac{1}{2}$ inches.

Solution:

$$A = \pi r^2$$

$$A = \frac{22}{7}\left(3\frac{1}{2}\right)^2$$

$$A = \frac{22}{7}\left(\frac{7}{2}\right)^2$$

$$A = \frac{\overset{11}{\cancel{22}}}{\underset{1}{\cancel{7}}} \cdot \frac{\overset{7}{\cancel{49}}}{\underset{2}{\cancel{4}}}$$

$$A = \frac{77}{2} = 38\frac{1}{2}$$

Answer: The area is $38\frac{1}{2}$ sq. in.

ILLUSTRATIVE PROBLEM 2

Find, to the nearest square inch, the area of a phonograph record with a 9-inch diameter. (Use $\pi = 3.14$.)

Solution:

$$A = \pi r^2$$

Since $d = 9''$, $r = 4\frac{1}{2}'' = 4.5''$.

$$A = 3.14 \, (4.5)^2$$

$$A = 3.14 \, (20.25)$$

$$A = 63.5850$$

$$A = 64 \text{ sq. in.}$$

Answer: The area is 64 sq. in., to the nearest sq. in.

Exercises

1. Using $\pi = \frac{22}{7}$, find the area of a circle whose radius is:

   a. 7 cm   **b.** 21 ft.

   c. 14 yd.   **d.** 35 in.

2. Find the area of the top of a circular piston of diameter 14 inches. $\left(\text{Use } \pi = \frac{22}{7}.\right)$

1. a. _____ b. _____

   c. _____ d. _____

2. _____

3. An artillery shell is 40 mm in diameter. Find the area of the circular base of the shell to the nearest sq. mm. (Use $\pi = 3.14$.)

3. _____

4. A circular lawn is 12 yd. in diameter.

   a. Find its area to the nearest sq. yd. (Use $\pi = 3.14$.)

4. a. _____

   b. About how many square feet of sod are needed to cover this lawn?

b. _____

5. How many square feet of linoleum are needed to cover a circular table top that is 4.2 feet in diameter? $\left(\text{Use } \pi = \dfrac{22}{7}.\right)$

5. _____

6. A circular flower bed has a diameter of 40 feet. What is its area? (Use $\pi = 3.14$.)

6. _____

7. A boy measures the circumference of a half-dollar and finds it to be about 3.96 inches.

   a. Find its diameter to the nearest hundredth of an inch. (Use $\pi = 3.14$.)

7. a. _____

   b. Find its area to the nearest hundredth of a square inch.

b. _____

8. A circular plate 14″ in diameter is cut out of a square piece of tin 14″ on a side, as shown in the figure.

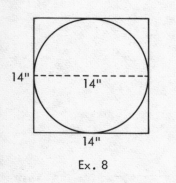

Ex. 8

   a. What is the area of the square tin plate?

8. a. _____

b. What is the area of the circular piece cut out, to the nearest sq. in.? $\left(\text{Use } \pi = \dfrac{22}{7}.\right)$

c. What is the area of tin that remains?

9. a. What is the diameter of the largest circle that can be cut from a square 20 cm on a side?

b. What is the area of the circular cutout? (Use $\pi = 3.14$.)

c. What is the area of the part of the square that remains?

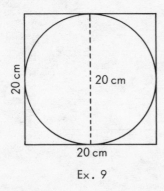

Ex. 9

10. A cow is tied with a 10-yard rope to a post where two fences meet at right angles. She may graze freely over an area allowed by the stretched rope, as shown in the figure.

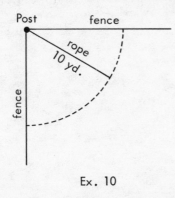

Ex. 10

a. Over what fractional part of a circle may she graze?

b. Over how many square yards may she graze, to the nearest yard? (Use $\pi = 3.14$.)

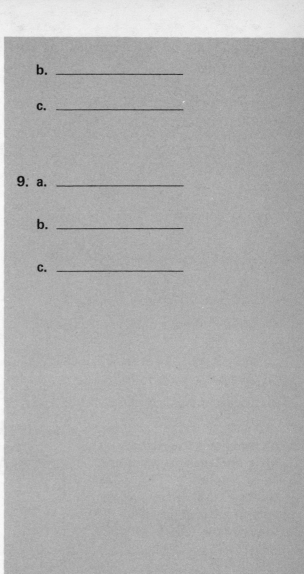

b. _____

c. _____

9. a. _____

b. _____

c. _____

10. a. _____

b. _____

11. A circular pool 35 ft. in radius has a walk 7 ft. wide around it.

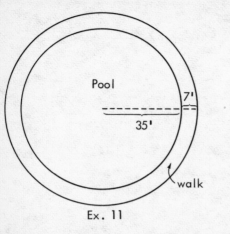

Ex. 11

a. What is the area of the pool? $\left(\text{Use } \pi = \dfrac{22}{7}.\right)$

11. a. _____

b. What is the area of the circle that includes the pool and the walk?

b. _____

c. What is the area of the walk?

c. _____

12. A church window is made up of a rectangle surmounted by a semicircle on top as shown. How many square feet of stained glass are in this window? (Use $\pi = 3.14$.)

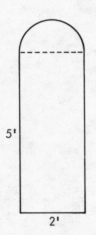

5'

2'

12. _____

13. A football field consists of a rectangle with semicircles at each end, as shown. Using the dimensions given, find, to the nearest square yard, the number of square yards of sod needed to cover the field. (Use $\pi = 3.14$.)

13. _____

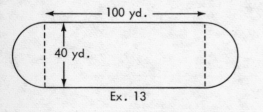

100 yd.

40 yd.

Ex. 13

8. Volume of a rectangular solid

The *volume* of a solid figure is the amount of space it contains. Volume is measured in cubic units. A cubic inch is the space contained in a cube one inch on each edge, as shown in the figure. We may also use units of volume such as the cubic foot, cubic yard, cubic centimeter, and cubic meter.

A common solid figure is the *rectangular solid*. Such objects as a box, a board, a book, a room, etc., are in the shape of a rectangular solid, as shown in the figure. In a rectangular solid, the top, bottom, front, back, and both sides are all rectangles or squares meeting at right angles to each other. These rectangles are called the *faces* of the solid. There are always six faces. The lines in which the faces meet are called the *edges* of the solid, of which there are twelve.

The lengths of these edges are the dimensions of the solid, called *length*, *width*, and *height*, as shown in the above figure.

The rectangular solid in the figure has a length of 4″, a width of 3″, and a height of 5″.

In the figure, we see that there are 3 × 4 or 12 cubic inches in the bottom layer. Since the solid is 5″ high, we see that it could contain 5 such layers. Thus its volume is 3 × 4 × 5 = 60 cubic inches.

This illustrates the general formula for finding the volume of a rectangular solid. If the length (l), width (w), and height (h) are all in the same linear unit, then the volume (V) is given by the formula

$$V = lwh$$

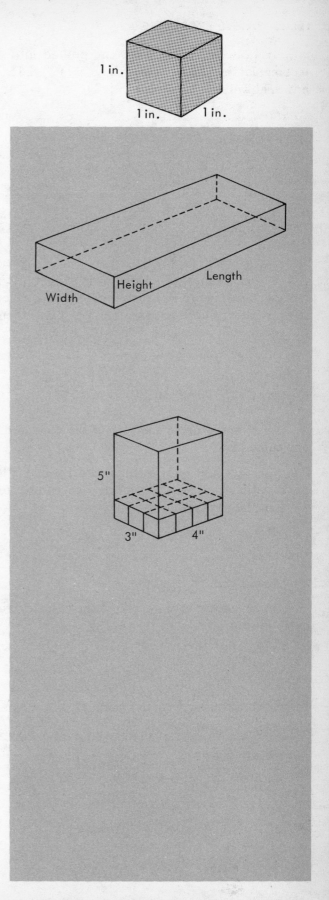

ILLUSTRATIVE PROBLEM 1

How many cubic feet are there in a coal bin 12 feet long, 6 feet high, and 5 feet wide?

Solution: $V = lwh$

$V = 12 \times 6 \times 5$

$V = 360$ cu. ft.   (*answer*)

ILLUSTRATIVE PROBLEM 2

If 1260 cu. in. of water are poured into a rectangular aquarium whose base is 12″ × 15″, how high will the water rise?

Solution:

$$V = lwh$$

$$1260 = 15 \times 12 \times h$$

$$1260 = 180h$$

$$\frac{1260}{180} = \frac{180h}{180}$$

$$h = 7'' \quad (answer)$$

When the length, width, and height of a rectangular solid are all equal, the figure is a cube. If we represent each edge of the cube by e, then the volume, V, becomes $V = e \times e \times e$ or

$$V = e^3$$

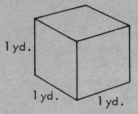

ILLUSTRATIVE PROBLEM 3

How many cubic feet are in the volume of one cubic yard?

Solution: Each edge of a cubic yard has a length of 1 yard, or 3 feet. Therefore, we substitute $e = 3$ in the formula:

$$V = e^3$$

$$V = 3^3$$

$$V = 27 \text{ cu. ft.} \quad (answer)$$

In like manner, we can find the volume of a cubic foot in inches:

$$1 \text{ cu. ft.} = 12^3 = 1728 \text{ cu. in.}$$

Exercises

1. Find the volume of a rectangular solid whose dimensions are:

a. $l = 8''$, $w = 5''$, $h = 4''$

b. $l = 7'$, $w = 6'$, $h = 5'$

c. $l = 10$ yd., $w = 6$ yd., $h = 8$ yd.

d. $l = 8\frac{1}{2}$ ft., $w = 6$ ft., $h = 7$ ft.

1. a. _____

b. _____

c. _____

d. _____

e. $l = 12$ ft., $w = 8$ ft. 9 in., $h = 3$ ft. 4 in.

f. $l = 8$ cm, $w = 7$ cm, $h = 5$ cm

2. How many cu. ft. of air space are there in a room 30′ long, 20′ wide, and 12′ high?

3. A cu. ft. of ice weighs 57 lb. What is the weight of a block of ice in the shape of a cube 4 ft. on each edge?

4. Find the missing dimension for each of the following rectangular solids:

	Length	Width	Height	Volume
a.	10″	10″	?	250 cu. in.
b.	3′9″	?	2 ft.	30 cu. ft.
c.	?	8 cm	5 cm	420 cu. cm
d.	2.5 ft.	1.5 ft.	?	15 cu. ft.

5. A walk 40 ft. long and 5 ft. wide is to be paved. It is dug to a depth of 6 in. and filled with crushed rock.

    a. How many cu. ft. of crushed rock are needed?

    b. Find the cost of the crushed rock at $1.25 per cu. ft.

6. An aquarium is 44 in. long, 28 in. wide, and 15 in. high. How many gallons of water will the tank hold? (1 gallon = 231 cu. in.)

7. What is the weight, in pounds, of a plate of glass 2 ft. long, $1\frac{1}{2}$ ft. wide, and $\frac{1}{2}$ in. thick? (1 cu. in. of glass weighs 2 oz.)

8. A swimming pool is 30 ft. long, 15 ft. wide, and has an average depth of $4\frac{1}{2}$ ft. How many gallons of water does it hold if there are $7\frac{1}{2}$ gallons to 1 cu. ft.?

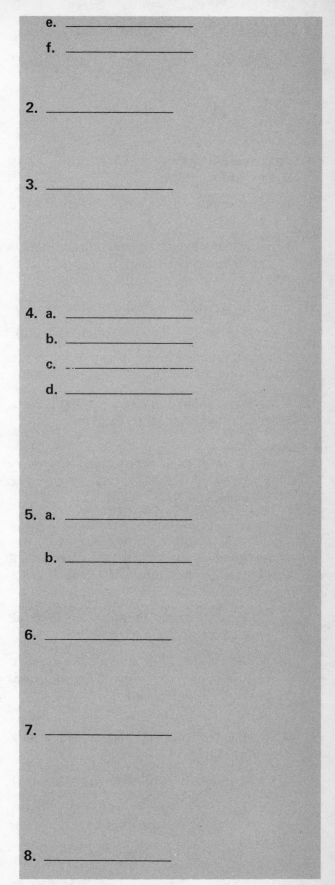

e. _____

f. _____

2. _____

3. _____

4. a. _____

   b. _____

   c. _____

   d. _____

5. a. _____

   b. _____

6. _____

7. _____

8. _____

9. Find how many cu. ft. there are in:

   a. 5 cu. yd.   **b.** $\frac{1}{3}$ cu. yd.   **c.** $\frac{1}{6}$ cu. yd.

   d. $1\frac{2}{3}$ cu. yd.   **e.** 864 cu. in.

10. A concrete driveway is 60 ft. long, 12 ft. wide, and 6 in. thick.

   a. How many cu. ft. of concrete does it contain?

   b. How many cu. yd. of concrete are there in the driveway?

11. Find the weight of a steel plate that is 20 in. long, 8 in. wide, and $\frac{3}{4}$ in. thick. (A cu. in. of steel weighs .28 lb.)

12. What is the volume of a box car that is 30 ft. long, 10 ft. wide, and 8 ft. high?

13. A liter is 1000 cubic centimeters. How many liters of water will fill a tank 60 cm long, 30 cm wide, and 20 cm deep?

14. The unit of weight in the metric system is the gram, which is the weight of 1 cc of water. (cc is the abbreviation for "cubic centimeter.")

   a. How many grams of water are in a full tank 25 cm × 40 cm × 10 cm?

   b. A kilogram is 1000 grams or the weight of a liter of water. How many kilograms of water are in this tank?

15. A rectangular tank has dimensions 80 cm × 50 cm × 20 cm.

   a. How many liters of water does this tank hold?

   b. How many kilograms (kg) does this water weigh?

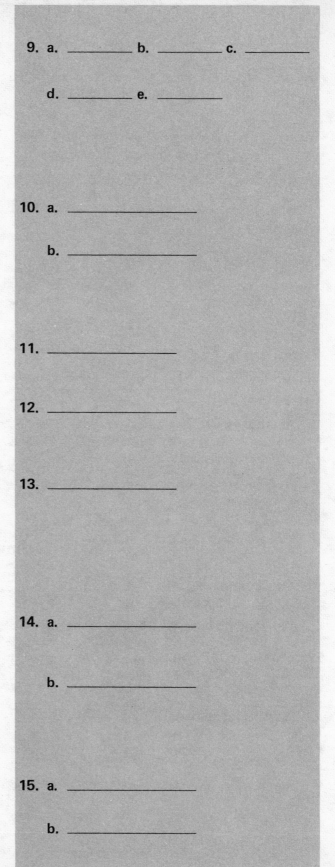

9. a. _____ b. _____ c. _____

   d. _____ e. _____

10. a. _____

   b. _____

11. _____

12. _____

13. _____

14. a. _____

   b. _____

15. a. _____

   b. _____

16. How many cubes, 6 in. on each edge, can be stored in a rectangular box 3 ft. wide, 4 ft. long, and 2 ft. high?

16. _____

17. How many liters are in the volume of a cube 20 cm on each edge?

17. _____

18. A coal bin contains 360 cu. yd. Find its height if its length is 12 yd. and its width is 6 yd.

18. _____

Chapter review exercises

1. A rectangular garden plot is 24 feet long. If its area is 288 square feet, how many feet are in its width?

1. _____

2. Explain the meaning of each of the following formulas:

  a. $A = S^2$ **b.** $A = bh$ **c.** $V = lwh$

  d. $A = \frac{1}{2}bh$ **e.** $V = S^3$ **f.** $A = \pi r^2$

2. a. _____ b. _____ c. _____

   d. _____ e. _____ f. _____

3. A living room is 18 ft. by 14 ft. Find the cost of carpeting the floor of the room if the carpet used costs $11.50 per square yard.

3. _____

4. A man owns $\frac{1}{2}$ acre of land in the shape of a rectangle. If the length of the plot is 180 ft., how many feet are in its width? (1 acre = 43,560 sq. ft.)

4. _____

5. a. Find the value of $5t^3$ if $t = 2$.

  b. Find the value of $8s^3 - 3t^4$ if $s = 3$ and $t = 2$.

5. a. _____

   b. _____

6. A circular tablecloth has a diameter of 70 in. Find its area:

  a. to the nearest sq. in.

  b. to the nearest sq. ft. $\left(\text{Use } \pi = \frac{22}{7}.\right)$

6. a. _____

   b. _____

7. A triangular plate is cut out of a rectangular plate 18″ by 12″, as shown in the figure. What is the area of the triangular plate?

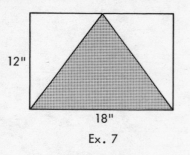

12″

18″

Ex. 7

7. _____

8. A mason is making a sidewalk 4 feet wide and 12 feet long. After digging out the area, he must fill it with concrete to a depth of 4 inches. How many cubic feet of concrete does he need?

8. _____

9. A cube measures 4 in. on each edge.

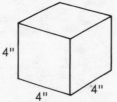

4″

4″   4″

a. What is the area of each square face of the cube?

b. What is the total surface area of the cube? (Surface area is the sum of all 6 faces.)

c. What is the volume of the cube?

d. If each edge of the cube is doubled, what is its volume then?

e. If we double the edge of a cube, by what number do we multiply its volume?

9. a. _____

b. _____

c. _____

d. _____

e. _____

10. a. How many cc (cubic centimeters) are in the volume of a rectangular solid 30 cm × 40 cm × 50 cm?

b. How many liters would it hold? (1 liter = 1000 cc)

10. a. _____

b. _____

11. A coal bin has a capacity of 650 cu. ft. Find its height if its length is 13 ft. and its width is 10 ft.

11. _____

12. In the figure, a triangle is drawn in a circle, as shown.

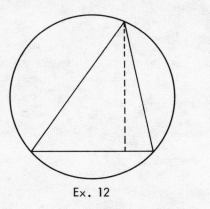

Ex. 12

The radius of the circle is 10″, the base of the triangle is 15″, and its altitude is 16″.

a. What is the area of the circle?

b. What is the area of the triangle?

c. What is the area of the region between the circle and the triangle?

12. a. _____

b. _____

c. _____

SIGNED NUMBERS

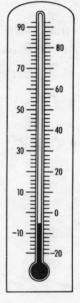

1. Meaning of signed numbers

If we look at a thermometer, such as the one in the figure, we see that there is a zero reading (0°), readings above zero, and readings below zero. Those above zero are called *positive* readings and those below are called *negative* readings. These readings, which are numbers with plus and minus signs, are called *signed numbers*.

For example, the thermometer in the figure shows a reading of 5° below zero. We indicate this temperature as −5°, using the signed number −5.

In reading a thermometer, we used signed numbers (also called *directed numbers*) to represent temperatures above and below zero. We may use signed numbers to represent any quantities that are *opposite* in direction from a starting point, a *zero point*, or an *origin*.

One use of signed numbers is in representing profit and loss. If we talk about a *profit* as a *positive* number (+), we would treat a *loss* as a *negative* number (−). If we treat a $10 deposit in the bank as +$10, we would treat a $10 withdrawal as −$10.

If no sign appears before a number, it is understood to be positive. Thus the number 4 means +4.

We find it convenient to represent signed numbers on a number line as shown below:

```
◄——┼——┼——┼——┼——┼——┼——┼——┼——┼——┼——┼——┼——┼——┼——┼——┼——┼——┼——┼——┼——►
  -10 -9 -8 -7 -6 -5 -4 -3 -2 -1  0  +1 +2 +3 +4 +5 +6 +7 +8 +9 +10
```

We represent the positive numbers to the right of the zero point, or origin, and the negative numbers to the left of the origin.

Suppose that a football team gains 10 yards (+10) and then loses 7 yards (−7). We can show the result of both events on the number line by first moving 10 units to the right of zero, and then moving seven units to the left from +10. We thus arrive at +3, which indicates a 3-yard gain as the combined effect of both plays.

```
                                        +10
                              ┌─────────────────────→
◄——┼——┼——┼——┼——┼——┼——┼——┼——┼——┼——┼——┼——┼——┼——┼——┼——┼——┼——┼——┼——┼——►
  -10 -9 -8 -7 -6 -5 -4 -3 -2 -1  0  +1 +2 +3 +4 +5 +6 +7 +8 +9 +10
                                        ←───────────────┘
                                             -7
```

ILLUSTRATIVE PROBLEM

If the temperature rises from $-7°$ to $+5°$, what is the increase in temperature?

Solution: In going from $-7°$ to zero, the temperature rises $7°$. In going from zero to $+5°$, the temperature rises $5°$. Thus the increase is

$7° + 5° = 12°$.   (*answer*)

Exercises

In 1 to 14: **a.** Represent the expression by a signed number. **b.** State the opposite number. **c.** Indicate what the opposite number represents.

1. 200 ft. above sea level

2. a profit of $30

3. 150 miles north of the equator

4. an 8-yard loss in football

5. a $20 deposit in the bank

6. a $3 drop in price

7. 9 lb. overweight

8. 18 miles east

9. 30° Celsius (above zero)

10. 250 B.C. (a date)

11. 50 kilometers south of Paris

12. 8 points below average

13. a saving of $14

14. a loss of $\frac{1}{2}$ of a point

Example

a saving of $14

Answer: **a.** $+14$ **b.** -14 **c.** spending $14

1. _____

2. _____

3. _____

4. _____

5. _____

6. _____

7. _____

8. _____

9. _____

10. _____

11. _____

12. _____

13. _____

14. _____

15. a. If the temperature goes from −8° to +12°, what is the change in temperature?

    b. Represent the change as a signed number.

16. RCA stock went from $19\frac{3}{4}$ on Thursday to $20\frac{3}{8}$ on Friday.

    a. What was the change in value of the stock?

    b. Represent the change as a signed number.

17. An auto driving in the Dead Sea area went from an altitude of 150 feet above sea level to one of 200 feet below sea level.

    a. What was the change in altitude?

    b. Represent the change as a signed number.

18. The average of a class on a math test was 78. For each mark, indicate by a signed number how much each student's mark was above (+) or below (−) the average. As an example, part **a** has been done.

Name	Mark
a. Tom	83
b. Terry	81
c. Beverly	72
d. Joan	90
e. Dale	69

19. Represent each change in temperature as a signed number.

    a. from +49° to +52°

    b. from +12° to −7°

    c. from −8° to +24°

    d. from −15° to −6°

    e. from −18° to zero

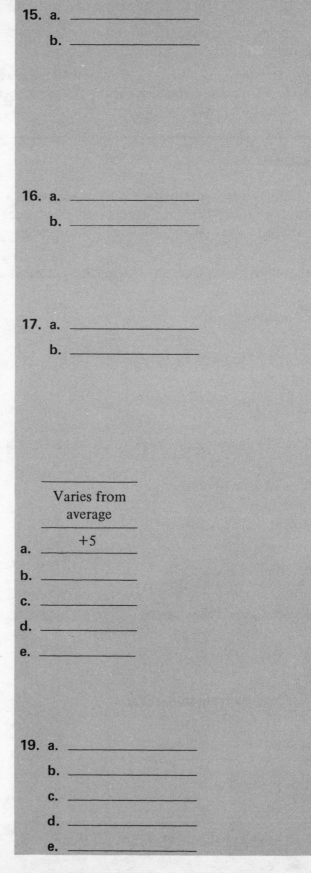

15. a. _____
    b. _____

16. a. _____
    b. _____

17. a. _____
    b. _____

Varies from average

a.   +5
b. _____
c. _____
d. _____
e. _____

19. a. _____
    b. _____
    c. _____
    d. _____
    e. _____

f. from −8° to −19°

g. from +17° to zero

h. from +13° to −12°

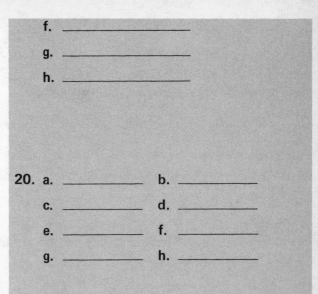

f. _____

g. _____

h. _____

20. By using the number line in each problem below, represent by a signed number the change in going from:

a. +3 to +12   **b.** −4 to +14

c. −6 to −15   **d.** −7 to −2

e. +20 to −12   **f.** 0 to −13

g. −32 to −20   **h.** −11 to 0

20. a. _____   **b.** _____

 c. _____   **d.** _____

 e. _____   **f.** _____

 g. _____   **h.** _____

2. Adding signed numbers

If the temperature rises 5° (+5) and then rises 4° (+4), the combined effect is a rise of 9° (+9). We have added +5 and +4 and obtained +9. This process of finding the combined effect is called the *combination* or *addition* of signed numbers.

We may apply this process to both positive and negative numbers. If a storekeeper loses $3 (−3) on one sale and then loses $5 (−5) on the next sale, the combined effect is a loss of $8 (−8). Thus, we see that the sum of −3 and −5 is −8. We refer to the sum of signed numbers as their *algebraic sum*.

In order to develop rules for adding signed numbers, we shall refer to the *absolute value* of a signed number, which is simply the numerical value of a number regardless of its sign. Thus the absolute value of −3 is 3, which is the same as the absolute value of +3.

In the above examples, we added two numbers with like signs. In the first case, (+5) + (+4), both numbers were positive. In the second case, (−3) + (−5), both were negative. Note that, in both of these cases, the absolute value of the sum was the sum of the absolute values of the two signed numbers being added. We may state this idea in the following rule:

Rule: To add two numbers having the same sign, add their absolute values and place the common sign before the sum.

Let us examine the case where the signs of the two numbers are unlike. If a football team gains 7 yards (+7) in its first play and then loses 9 yards (−9) in its second play, its total loss is 2 yards (−2). We may write the sum vertically:

Add: +7
       −9
       −2

Or we may write the sum horizontally:

$$(+7) + (−9) = −2$$

If a team gains 9 yards (+9) and then loses 4 yards (−4), the result would be a gain of 5 yards (+5). This may be written as

Add: +9   or $(+9) + (−4) = +5$
       −4
       +5

Note that, in both of these examples, the absolute value of the sum is the difference of the absolute values of the two signed numbers being added. In the first case, (+7) + (−9), the sum has the same sign as −9, which is the number with the larger absolute value. In the second case, (+9) + (−4), the sum has the same sign as +9, which is the number with the larger absolute value.

We may summarize this idea in the following rule:

Rule: To add two signed numbers having unlike signs, find the difference of their absolute values and place before it the sign of the number having the larger absolute value.

ILLUSTRATIVE PROBLEM 1

Add: −15
       +7

Solution: Signs are unlike. Difference of absolute values is 8. Sign of larger absolute value (−15) is negative. Sum is (−8).

Answer: −8

ILLUSTRATIVE PROBLEM 2

Add: −14
       −8

Solution: Signs are alike. Sum of absolute values is 22. Common sign is negative. Sum is (−22).

Answer: −22

It is easy to show that, as with the counting numbers in arithmetic, the *order* of additions of signed numbers does not matter (the commutative principle). Thus,

$$(+10) + (-3) = (-3) + (+10) = +7$$

In adding three or more signed numbers, the way we *group* the numbers does not matter (the associative law). Thus,

$$[(+5) + (-2)] + (-4) = +5 + [(-2) + (-4)] = -1$$

ILLUSTRATIVE PROBLEM 3

Add: $(+12) + (-7) + (-2)$

Solution: Since the arrangement does not matter, we may take the numbers in any order. The sum of $(+12)$ and (-7) is $(+5)$, and the sum of $(+5)$ and (-2) is $(+3)$.

Answer: +3

Exercises

In 1 to 28, add.

1. $+4$ $\underline{-1}$	**2.** $+3$ $\underline{-7}$	**3.** -2 $\underline{-6}$

1. _____   **2.** _____   **3.** _____

4. $+12$ $\underline{-9}$	**5.** -18 $\underline{+12}$	**6.** $+12\frac{1}{8}$ $+7\frac{3}{8}$

4. _____   **5.** _____   **6.** _____

7. -4.7 $\underline{-8.2}$	**8.** $-9\frac{1}{2}$ $-3\frac{1}{4}$	**9.** $+7$ $\underline{-7}$

7. _____   **8.** _____   **9.** _____

10. $+14\frac{1}{3}$ $-8\frac{2}{3}$	**11.** $+11.4$ $\underline{-11.4}$	**12.** $+52$ $\underline{-75}$

10. _____   **11.** _____   **12.** _____

13. -8.7
$+3.9$

14. -93
$+47$

15. $-27\frac{1}{6}$
$+14\frac{1}{3}$

13. _____ **14.** _____ **15.** _____

16. a. $(+17) + (+11)$ **b.** $(-45) + (+20)$

c. $(-16) + (-15)$ **d.** $(-13) + (+13)$

e. $(-12) + (0)$ **f.** $(-10) + (-19)$

16. a. _____ **b.** _____

c. _____ **d.** _____

e. _____ **f.** _____

17. $-7\frac{1}{2}$
$+12$

18. -9.4
-11.7

19. -12
$+15\frac{3}{4}$

17. _____ **18.** _____ **19.** _____

20. $+9$
-4
-7

21. -23
$+11$
$+6$

22. -21
-17
$+24$

20. _____ **21.** _____ **22.** _____

23. $+11$
-17
-23
$+19$

24. $+12$
-27
-19
-8

25. $+4.2$
-5.8
-9.7
-12.3

23. _____ **24.** _____ **25.** _____

26. $-5\frac{3}{4}$
$+2\frac{1}{2}$
$-1\frac{7}{8}$

27. -18.4
-17.8
$+23.5$

28. $+5\frac{2}{3}$
$-3\frac{1}{6}$
$+11\frac{1}{3}$

26. _____ **27.** _____ **28.** _____

In 29 to 35, represent the quantities by signed numbers and find their algebraic sum:

29. A team gained 12 yards and then lost 9 yards.

29. _____

30. A dealer made a profit of $250 and then had a loss of $175.

30. _____

31. The temperature rose 14° and then dropped 20°.

31. _____

32. Nancy lost 7 pounds and then gained 12 pounds.

32. _____

33. In one month, Mr. Jones showed deposits of $18 and $42 and a withdrawal of $36.

33. _____

34. An auto went 180 miles south and then traveled 115 miles north.

34. _____

35. A plane rose 850 feet into the air and then dropped 260 feet.

35. _____

3. Subtracting signed numbers

If the temperature rises from 15° above zero (+15°) to 20° above zero (+20°), how many degrees is the rise? Here we simply *subtract* 15 from 20 and get 5 (20 − 15 = 5). In vertical form:

Subtract: +20   (minuend)
           +15   (subtrahend) —
            +5   (difference)

In general, when we are subtracting x from y, x is called the **subtrahend** and y the **minuend**. The result is called the **difference** of y and x.

x (minuend)
y (subtrahend)
$\overline{x-y}$ (difference)

We can show the subtraction of signed numbers very conveniently on the number line. If we wish to subtract +6 from +10, we first locate +6 (subtrahend) on the number line, then locate +10 (minuend), and then count the spaces from subtrahend to minuend (4). Since we moved to the *right*, the difference is positive and is equal to +4.

Let us subtract −3 from +6 in a similar manner. Locate −3 (subtrahend) and then +6 (minuend). We move 9 units to the *right*, so the result is +9. We are saying, in effect, that, to get from −3 to +6, we must add +9 to −3.

Now subtract −8 from −5. Locate −8 on the number line and then −5. To get from −8 to −5, we move 3 units to the *right* so that the difference is +3. If we subtract −5 from −8, we move 3 units to the *left* and the difference is −3.

We always move *from the subtrahend to the minuend*. If the movement is to the right, the difference is positive. If the movement is to the left, the difference is negative.

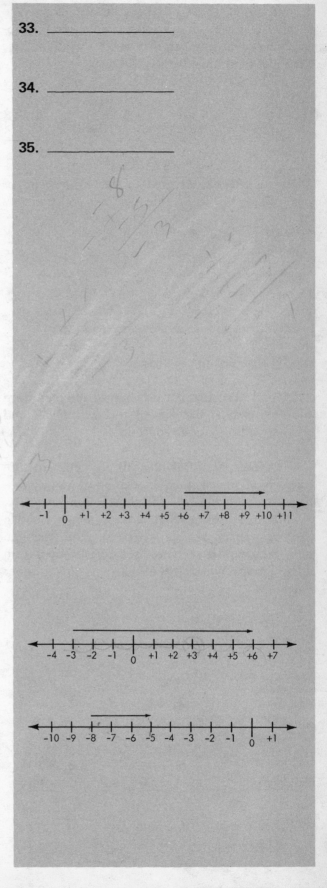

In order to avoid the constant use of the number line, we can develop a simple rule for subtracting signed numbers. We write the above four examples in vertical form:

Subtract:

1. $+10$	**2.** $+6$	**3.** -5	**4.** -8
$\underline{+6}$	$\underline{-3}$	$\underline{-8}$	$\underline{-5}$

Then we *change the sign of the subtrahend* in each case and proceed as in algebraic addition:

1. $+10$	**2.** $+6$	**3.** -5	**4.** -8
$\underline{\ominus 6}$	$\underline{\ominus 3}$	$\underline{\ominus 8}$	$\underline{\ominus 5}$
$+4$	$+9$	$+3$	-3

In each case, we have circled the sign, written the opposite sign above it, and then found the *algebraic sum*. Note that the correct difference is obtained in each case.

Rule: To subtract one signed number from another, change the sign of the *subtrahend* **and proceed as in algebraic addition.**

By means of this rule, all problems in subtraction of signed numbers can be done by addition. We may indicate the subtraction vertically, as above, or horizontally. Thus, example 1 above may be written as $(+10)-(+6)$. Note that the sign between parentheses is a sign of operation (subtraction) while the other signs are number signs.

Exercises

In 1 to 16, subtract.

1. $+5$	**2.** $+8$	**3.** -9
$\underline{+9}$	$\underline{-5}$	$\underline{+3}$
4. -11	**5.** $+17$	**6.** -12
$\underline{-6}$	$\underline{-10}$	$\underline{+8}$
7. -9	**8.** $+7$	**9.** -23
$\underline{-13}$	$\underline{+16}$	$\underline{-17}$

1. _____   2. _____   3. _____

4. _____   5. _____   6. _____

7. _____   8. _____   9. _____

10. $+7\dfrac{5}{8}$
$\underline{-3\phantom{\dfrac{5}{8}}}$

11. $-4\dfrac{5}{6}$
$\underline{-1\dfrac{2}{3}}$

12. -7.4
$\underline{+3.8}$

13. 0
$\underline{+9\dfrac{3}{4}}$

14. $+6\dfrac{1}{3}$
$\underline{-6\dfrac{1}{3}}$

15. -8.2
$\underline{+12.9}$

16. $-3\dfrac{3}{4}$
$\underline{+7\dfrac{1}{8}}$

In 17 to 28, perform the indicated operation.

17. $(+9)-(+7)$

18. $(+1)-(-5)$

19. $(-9)-(-2)$

20. $(-6)-(-8)$

21. $(+15)-(-4)$

22. $(-28)-(+23)$

23. From $+23$ subtract -11.

24. From -18 subtract -10.

25. From $+11\dfrac{3}{4}$ subtract $-4\dfrac{5}{8}$.

26. From -8.7 subtract -12.

27. From 0 subtract 15.

28. From -12 subtract 0.

29. How much is 24 decreased by -15?

30. What number is 11 less than -10?

10. _____ **11.** _____ **12.** _____

13. _____ **14.** _____ **15.** _____

16. _____

17. _____ **18.** _____

19. _____ **20.** _____

21. _____ **22.** _____

23. _____

24. _____

25. _____

26. _____

27. _____

28. _____

29. _____

30. _____

31. From the sum of $+32$ and -16, subtract -7.

31. _____

32. How much greater is $+12$ than -4?

32. _____

In 33 to 36, find the value of the expression in each case:

33. $(+8) + (-11) - (-3)$

33. _____

34. $(-19) + (+12) - (-20)$

34. _____

35. $(-7.4) - (-2.3) + (-8.5)$

35. _____

36. $(+7\frac{1}{2}) + (-5\frac{1}{4}) - (-3\frac{1}{8})$

36. _____

In 37 to 42, set up each exercise as a subtraction problem and solve.

37. The temperature went from $-8°$ to $+14°$. What was the change in temperature?

37. _____

38. A motorist drove from 200 feet above sea level to 100 feet below sea level. What was his change in altitude?

38. _____

39. A Roman emperor was born in the year 40 B.C. and died in the year 35 A.D. How old was he at the time of death?

39. _____

40. Bill had $15 on Friday and owed $8 on Monday. How much did he spend over the weekend?

40. _____

41. The temperature in Stockholm was $-20°$ when it was $-32°$ in Oslo? How much colder was it in Oslo?

41. _____

42. Tom weighed 6 pounds less than his sister in January and 7 pounds more than his sister in December of the same year. Assuming his sister's weight did not change, how many pounds did he gain over the year?

42. _____

4. Multiplying signed numbers

To illustrate the multiplication of two signed numbers, we will consider a man playing a game for money. We may think of *winning* a certain amount as a *positive* number and *losing* a certain amount as a *negative* number. We may also think of hours in the *future* as *positive* numbers and hours in the *past* as *negative* numbers.

CASE 1. The Product of Two Positive Numbers.

If the man wins $4 every hour, then in 3 hours he will be winning $12. This may be represented by:

$$(+4) \times (+3) = +12$$

Thus, the product of two positive numbers is a positive number.

CASE 2. The Product of a Negative Number and a Positive Number.

If the man loses $4 every hour, then in 3 hours he will be losing $12. This may be represented by:

$$(-4) \times (+3) = -12$$

Thus, the product of a negative number and a positive number is a negative number.

CASE 3. The Product of a Positive Number and a Negative Number.

If the man wins $4 every hour, then 3 hours ago he had $12 less than now. This may be represented by:

$$(+4) \times (-3) = -12$$

Thus, the product of a positive number and a negative number is a negative number.

CASE 4. The Product of Two Negative Numbers.

If the man is losing $4 every hour, then 3 hours ago he had $12 more than now. This may be represented by:

$$(-4) \times (-3) = +12$$

Thus, the product of two negative numbers is a positive number.

Note that, in each case, the absolute value of the product 12 is the product of the absolute values of the signed numbers 4 and 3.

The results above may be summarized in the following two rules:

Rule 1: The product of two numbers having the *same* sign is a positive number whose absolute value is the product of the absolute values of the two numbers.

Rule 2: The product of two numbers having *different* signs is a negative number whose absolute value is the product of the absolute values of the two numbers.

The *order* of multiplication does not matter (the commutative principle), so that

$$(+10)(-7) = (-7)(+10) = -70.$$

Also, in multiplying three or more signed numbers, the *grouping* does not matter (the associative principle). In multiplying three numbers, find the product of *any two*, and multiply this product by the third number.

ILLUSTRATIVE PROBLEM 1

Multiply: $(-5)(+2)(-7)$

Solution: $[(-5)(+2)](-7) =$

$\qquad (-10)(-7) = +70$ (*answer*)

We may also use exponents to show repeated multiplication of signed numbers.

ILLUSTRATIVE PROBLEM 2

Find the value of $(-2)^3$.

Solution: $(-2)^3 = (-2)(-2)(-2) =$

$\qquad (+4)(-2) = -8$ (*answer*)

Exercises

In 1 to 27, multiply.

1. $+7$	**2.** -8	**3.** $+12$
$\underline{+8}$	$\underline{+4}$	$\underline{-3}$

Examples

Multiply.

1. $\begin{array}{r} +8 \\ +5 \\ \hline +40 \end{array}$	**2.** $\begin{array}{r} -12 \\ +4 \\ \hline -48 \end{array}$
3. $\begin{array}{r} -15 \\ -6 \\ \hline +90 \end{array}$	**4.** $(+10)(-7) = -70$

1. _____ **2.** _____ **3.** _____

4. +4
    +6

5. −7
    −9

6. −12
    +5

7.   0
    −14

8. +32
    −7

9. +8
     0

10. −18
    $+\dfrac{2}{3}$

11. −3.4
    +2.7

12. −24
    $-3\dfrac{1}{2}$

13. $(+7)(-12)$

14. $(-38)(-10)$

15. $(+14)(-28)$

16. $(+9)\left(-4\dfrac{1}{3}\right)$

17. $(-24)\left(+\dfrac{5}{6}\right)$

18. $\left(-\dfrac{5}{7}\right)\left(-\dfrac{7}{5}\right)$

19. $\left(-3\dfrac{1}{2}\right)\left(+3\dfrac{1}{7}\right)$

20. $(-.45)(-60)$

21. $(-25)\left(4\dfrac{1}{5}\right)$

22. $(+7)(-5)(-2)$

23. $(+8)(-3)(-1)$

24. $(-6)(-4)(-3)$

25. $(+8)(-7)(0)$

26. $(-4)(-5)(-6)$

27. $(27)(0)(-15)$

In 28 to 43, find the value of each of the following:

28. $(-3)^2$

29. $(-4)^2$

30. $(-1)^4$

31. $\left(+\dfrac{1}{3}\right)^2$

32. $(-3)^3$

33. $(+5)^3$

34. $(-6)^2$

35. $\left(-\dfrac{1}{2}\right)^3$

36. $(-4)^3$

4. _____   5. _____   6. _____

7. _____   8. _____   9. _____

10. _____   11. _____   12. _____

13. _____   14. _____

15. _____   16. _____

17. _____   18. _____

19. _____   20. _____

21. _____   22. _____

23. _____   24. _____

25. _____   26. _____

27. _____

28. _____   29. _____   30. _____

31. _____   32. _____   33. _____

34. _____   35. _____   36. _____

37. $(+3)^4$ **38.** $(-12)^2$ **39.** $(-10)^3$

40. $(-.5)^2$ **41.** $\left(-\dfrac{2}{3}\right)^3$ **42.** $(-1)^{11}$

43. $(-10)^6$

37. _____ **38.** _____ **39.** _____

40. _____ **41.** _____ **42.** _____

43. _____

5. Dividing signed numbers

When we first learned to divide, we learned that $6 \div 2$ is defined as the number which, when multiplied by 2, gives a product of 6. Thus $\dfrac{6}{2} = 3$. The 6 is called the **dividend**, 2 is the **divisor**, and 3 is the **quotient**.

We may thus determine the quotient in all four cases of division of signed numbers.

CASE 1. $\dfrac{+12}{+4} = +3$ since $(+3)(+4) = +12$.

CASE 2. $\dfrac{-12}{-4} = +3$ since $(+3)(-4) = -12$.

CASE 3. $\dfrac{+12}{-4} = -3$ since $(-3)(-4) = +12$.

CASE 4. $\dfrac{-12}{+4} = -3$ since $(-3)(+4) = -12$.

Note that, in cases 1 and 2, the signs of the dividend and the divisor are *alike*, and the quotient in both cases is *positive*. In cases 3 and 4, the signs of the dividend and the divisor are *different* and the quotient in both cases is *negative*. In all cases, the absolute value of the quotient is the quotient of the absolute values of the dividend and the divisor.

From the four cases, we get the following rules for the division of signed numbers:

Rule 1: The quotient of two numbers having the *same* sign is a positive number which is the quotient of their absolute values.

Examples

Perform the indicated divisions.

1. $\dfrac{+18}{+6} = +3$ **2.** $\dfrac{-15}{+5} = -3$

3. $\dfrac{-36}{-9} = +4$ **4.** $\dfrac{+63}{-7} = -9$

Rule 2: The quotient of two numbers having *different* signs is a negative number whose absolute value is the quotient of the absolute values of the two numbers.

Exercises

In 1 to 20, perform the indicated divisions.

1. $\dfrac{+21}{+3}$　　2. $\dfrac{-22}{-2}$　　3. $\dfrac{-26}{+13}$　　4. $\dfrac{45}{-9}$

5. $\dfrac{-7}{7}$　　6. $\dfrac{+27}{-9}$　　7. $\dfrac{+81}{-9}$　　8. $\dfrac{-121}{-11}$

9. $\dfrac{0}{-11}$　　10. $\dfrac{20}{-5}$　　11. $\dfrac{+8.8}{-4}$　　12. $\dfrac{-75}{+15}$

13. $\dfrac{+36}{-7}$　　14. $\dfrac{-22}{-5}$　　15. $\dfrac{-100}{+12}$　　16. $\dfrac{-4.8}{1.2}$

17. $(+63) \div (-9)$　　18. $(-75) \div (-5)$

19. $(+15) \div \left(-\dfrac{5}{9}\right)$　　20. $(-7.2) \div (+.9)$

21. Divide each of the following numbers by -7:
   a. $+21$　　b. -14　　c. -56
   d. $+49$　　e. -50

In 22 to 27, divide as indicated.

22. $14 \div \dfrac{7}{9}$　　23. $\left(-\dfrac{5}{4}\right) \div (-20)$

24. $\left(-3\dfrac{3}{4}\right) \div \left(+6\dfrac{2}{3}\right)$　　25. $(-7250) \div (-10)$

26. $(-3.14) \div (100)$　　27. $(+25.25) \div (-5)$

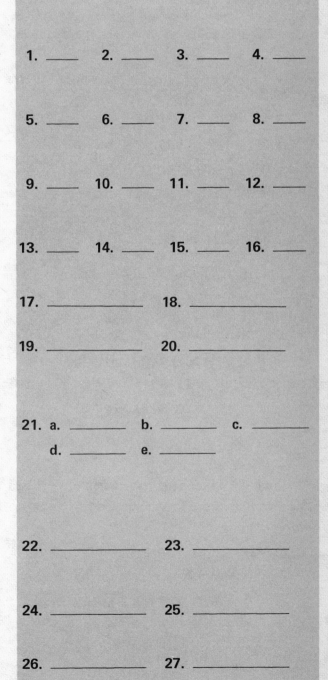

1. ____　　2. ____　　3. ____　　4. ____

5. ____　　6. ____　　7. ____　　8. ____

9. ____　　10. ____　　11. ____　　12. ____

13. ____　　14. ____　　15. ____　　16. ____

17. ____　　18. ____

19. ____　　20. ____

21. a. ____　　b. ____　　c. ____
    d. ____　　e. ____

22. ____　　23. ____

24. ____　　25. ____

26. ____　　27. ____

6. Evaluating expressions with signed numbers

In Chapter 1 we found the numerical value of algebraic expressions by substituting the numbers of arithmetic (the non-negative numbers) into the expressions. We follow the same procedure when we substitute any given signed numbers—positive or negative—into algebraic expressions.

ILLUSTRATIVE PROBLEM 1

Find the value of $3xy^2$ when $x = -2$ and $y = -5$.

Solution: Substitute the given values in the expression.

$$3xy^2 = 3(-2)(-5)^2$$
$$= 3(-2)(+25)$$
$$= (-6)(+25)$$
$$= -150 \quad (answer)$$

ILLUSTRATIVE PROBLEM 2

Find the value of $3p - 4q$ when $p = 5$ and $q = -6$.

Solution: Think of $3p - 4q$ as $3p + (-4q)$; then substitute the given values.

$$3p + (-4q) = (3)(5) + (-4)(-6)$$
$$= 15 + 24$$
$$= 39 \quad (answer)$$

ILLUSTRATIVE PROBLEM 3

Find the value of $r^2 - s^2$ when $r = -2$ and $s = -3$.

Solution:

$$r^2 - s^2 = (-2)^2 - (-3)^2$$
$$= 4 - 9$$
$$= (+4) + (-9) = -5 \quad (answer)$$

Exercises

In 1 to 36, find the value of the following expressions when $c = -2$, $d = +3$, $r = -4$, and $s = +5$.

1. $7c$

2. $-5d$

3. $6cr$

4. $-8rs$

5. $2r + 7s$

6. $c^2 - 2cd$

7. $cr - ds$

8. $c^3 - d^2$

9. $3c - 4d$

10. $5r - 4s$

11. $r^2 - s^2$

12. $4c^2 d^3$

13. $-r^2 s$

14. $\frac{1}{2}c^3$

15. $\frac{2}{3}dr^2$

16. $d^2 - c^2$

17. $cd - rs$

18. $(c + d)^2$

19. $3s^2 - r^2$

20. $r^2 + 2r$

21. $3c + 2d - r$

22. $s^2 - 2r$

23. $(r - s)^2$

24. $-2rs$

25. $c^2 - 2cd + d^3$

26. $c^2 dr$

27. $3(d - r)$

28. $2r^2 + c^2$

29. $s^2 + 2cs$

30. $2c + d + r$

31. $(r + s)(r - s)$

32. $c(s - r)$

33. $2(c - d) + 8$

34. $(r + 5)(s - 1)$

35. $r^2 - 2r + 1$

36. $(r - 1)^2$

In 37 to 46: using $x = -10$, $y = +6$, and $z = -1$, find the value of the expressions.

37. $\dfrac{x}{5}$

38. $\dfrac{y}{-3}$

39. $\dfrac{yz}{2}$

1. _____   2. _____   3. _____

4. _____   5. _____   6. _____

7. _____   8. _____   9. _____

10. _____   11. _____   12. _____

13. _____   14. _____   15. _____

16. _____   17. _____   18. _____

19. _____   20. _____   21. _____

22. _____   23. _____

24. _____   25. _____

26. _____   27. _____

28. _____   29. _____

30. _____   31. _____

32. _____   33. _____

34. _____   35. _____

36. _____

37. _____   38. _____   39. _____

40. $\dfrac{xy}{20}$ **41.** $\dfrac{xz}{y}$ **42.** $\dfrac{x^2z}{5y}$

40. _____ **41.** _____ **42.** _____

43. $\dfrac{3x + 10z}{5y}$ **44.** $\dfrac{x^2 + y^2}{8z}$

43. _____ **44.** _____

45. $\dfrac{x - y}{x + y}$ **46.** $\dfrac{x^2 + y^2}{x^2 - y^2}$

45. _____ **46.** _____

Chapter review exercises

1. Represent each quantity below with a signed number.

   a. 100 ft. below sea level

   b. a profit of $28

   c. 5 miles south

   d. 12° below zero

   e. the year 60 B.C.

   f. 10 lb. overweight

   g. $18 in debt

   h. 9 miles west

1. a. _____

   b. _____

   c. _____

   d. _____

   e. _____

   f. _____

   g. _____

   h. _____

2. What number added to $+9$ gives zero?

2. _____

3. What number added to $-\dfrac{2}{3}$ gives zero?

3. _____

4. Represent the change in each statement below by a signed number.

   a. a loss of 7 lb.

   b. a 3% rise in the cost of living

   c. a deposit of $20

   d. a withdrawal of $10

   e. a loss of $400

   f. a growth of 2 inches

4. a. _____

   b. _____

   c. _____

   d. _____

   e. _____

   f. _____

5. A football team makes a gain of 8 yards on one play and a loss of 3 yards on the next play. What was its total yardage for both plays?

6. On the number line, start at 0, move -8 units, $+5$ units, then -3 units. At what signed number do you stop?

In 7 to 20, perform the indicated operations.

7. $(+8) + (+11)$ **8.** $(-5) + (-7)$

9. $(-7.5) + (+.7)$

10. $(-2.8) + (+3.5) + (-7.4)$

11. $(-16) - (+9)$ **12.** $(-24) - (-30)$

13. $(-12)(+10)$ **14.** $\left(-3\frac{1}{2}\right)(-18)$

15. $(-5)(-7)(-1)$ **16.** $(+11)(-3)(-2)$

17. $(-27) \div (+3)$ **18.** $(-45) \div (-5)$

19. $\dfrac{+48}{-12}$ **20.** $\dfrac{-7.5}{+.5}$

In 21 and 22, subtract.

21. $\begin{array}{r} -23 \\ +15 \\ \hline \end{array}$ **22.** $\begin{array}{r} -12\frac{1}{2} \\ -2\frac{3}{4} \\ \hline \end{array}$

23. Find the value of:

     a. $(-4)^2$ **b.** $(-1)^7$ **c.** $(-3)^4$

In 24 to 42, find the value of the expressions when $p = 3$, $q = -1$, and $r = -4$.

24. $6pq$ **25.** pqr **26.** $5pr$

5. _____

6. _____

7. _____ 8. _____

9. _____

10. _____

11. _____ 12. _____

13. _____ 14. _____

15. _____ 16. _____

17. _____ 18. _____

19. _____ 20. _____

21. _____ 22. _____

23. a. _____ b. _____ c. _____

24. _____ 25. _____ 26. _____

27. $4p + 5q$ **28.** $3q - 2p$ **29.** $4q - 5r$

30. $p^2 q$ **31.** $q^2 + r^2$ **32.** $pq - qr$

33. $pq + r$ **34.** $(p + q)^2$ **35.** $p^3 q^2 r$

36. $2p^2 - 3r^2$ **37.** $2pq - 2pr$ **38.** $r^2 - r - 1$

39. $7(p - q)$ **40.** $\dfrac{pq}{r}$ **41.** $\dfrac{3qr}{p}$

42. $\dfrac{p - q}{r}$

27. _____   **28.** _____   **29.** _____

30. _____   **31.** _____   **32.** _____

33. _____   **34.** _____   **35.** _____

36. _____   **37.** _____   **38.** _____

39. _____   **40.** _____   **41.** _____

42. _____

OPERATIONS WITH ALGEBRAIC EXPRESSIONS

10

1. Adding monomials

In Chapter 1, we learned that we can add terms such as $5x$ and $3x$ and get the sum $8x$. We will now do this when the numerical coefficients are signed numbers.

First, let us define some of the words we will be using. A **term** is a number or letter or an expression written as a product or quotient of numbers and letters. Examples of terms are 7, x, $5x^2y$, $-3ab$, $\frac{2}{3}pq^3$, and $\frac{rst}{7}$. An algebraic expression which has only one term is called a **monomial**. Thus, all the expressions just mentioned as terms are monomials. **Like terms** are terms which have the same letters with the same exponents. For example, $3x^2y$ and $7x^2y$ are like terms. We call x^2y the **common literal factor**. Their sum would be $10x^2y$.

Rule: To add like terms (or monomials), add the numerical coefficients and multiply this sum by the common literal factor.

This same procedure applies to like terms when the coefficients are signed numbers. Thus the sum of $-3ab^2$ and $+8ab^2$ is $-5ab^2$.

We cannot add or combine unlike terms, such as $+7xy^2$ and $-2x^2y$.

The principle which we are using here is an application of what we call the **distributive property of multiplication over addition**.

Note that $3(4 + 5) = 3(9) = 27$; note also that $3(4) + 3(5) = 12 + 15 = 27$. It thus appears that

$$3(4 + 5) = 3(4) + 3(5)$$

In general, if x, a, and b are any three numbers, we may write the distributive property as follows:

$$x(a + b) = xa + xb$$

We may also write it in the form

$$(a + b)x = ax + bx$$

In adding two like terms or monomials, we are using the distributive property in reverse. Thus,

$$3x + 4x = (3 + 4)x = 7x$$

Here are some examples of adding monomials. Notice that the last two examples require two steps to do the addition.

1. $+11x$
    $\underline{+5x}$
    $+16x$

2. $+10b^2$
    $\underline{-3b^2}$
    $+7b^2$

3. $-9ab$
    $\underline{-4ab}$
    $-13ab$

4. $+12b^2c$
    $\underline{-12b^2c}$
    0

5. $(-7ab^2c) + (-3ab^2c) = -10ab^2c$

6. $(-17st) + (+9st) + (-8st) = (-8st) + (-8st) = -16st$

7. $-8rs - 4rs + 15rs = -12rs + 15rs = +3rs$

Exercises

In 1 to 12, add the monomials.

1. $-3x$
    $\underline{+5x}$

2. $-7b$
    $\underline{-4b}$

3. $+12ab$
    $\underline{-5ab}$

4. $+11b^2c$
    $\underline{+4b^2c}$

5. $+6pq$
    $\underline{-10pq}$

6. $-7t^2$
    $\underline{-5t^2}$

7. $+8m$
    $+5m$
    $\underline{+4m}$

8. $-12k$
    $+7k$
    $\underline{-6k}$

9. $-7rs^2$
    $-8rs^2$
    $\underline{+5rs^2}$

10. $-15dx^2y$
    $-dx^2y$
    $\underline{-8dx^2y}$

11. $+23rst$
    $-17rst$
    $\underline{-6rst}$

12. $+1.5ay^2$
    $+7.8ay^2$
    $\underline{-19.3ay^2}$

1. _____ 2. _____ 3. _____

4. _____ 5. _____ 6. _____

7. _____ 8. _____ 9. _____

10. _____ 11. _____ 12. _____

In 13 to 17, add like terms.

13. $(-7k) + (-2k) + (+4k)$

14. $(+13xy) + (-8xy) + (-7xy)$

15. $(-27rs^3) + (+18rs^3) + (+12rs^3)$

16. $(+12c^2d) + (-17c^2d) + (-30c^2d)$

17. $(+32p^2q^2) + (-40p^2q^2) + (-8p^2q^2)$

13. _____

14. _____

15. _____

16. _____

17. _____

In each of the following exercises, think of the signs as signs of the numerical coefficients of the terms. In 18 to 26, add like terms.

18. $+12x - 8x - 9x$

19. $-13ab - 15ab + 10ab - 7ab$

20. $s^2t - 5s^2t - 8s^2t + 3s^2t$

21. $\dfrac{3}{4}xy - \dfrac{1}{2}xy + \dfrac{3}{8}xy$

22. $9.4s^2 - 7.2s^2 - 8.7s^2 + s_i^2$

23. $-23b^2c^2 + 15b^2c^2 - 8b^2c^2 + 5b^2c^2$

24. $+18m^2n - 13m^2n - 15m^2n + 3m^2n$

25. $-32f^2g + 12f^2g + 20f^2g$

26. $-5r^2 + 8r^2 - 21r^2 - 7r^2$

18. _____

19. _____

20. _____

21. _____

22. _____

23. _____

24. _____

25. _____

26. _____

2. Subtracting monomials

Recall that, in subtracting signed numbers, we changed the sign of the subtrahend and then proceeded as in addition of signed numbers. We may do the same in subtracting one monomial from another. Thus,

$$(+8a) - (-5a) = (+8a) + (+5a) = +13a$$

In this case, the subtrahend $(-5a)$ is changed to $(+5a)$ and the subtraction operation is changed to addition.

Rule: To subtract one monomial from another, change the sign of the subtrahend and proceed as in addition.

Exercises

In 1 to 6, subtract like terms.

1. $(+8p) - (-2p)$

Examples

In 1 to 4, subtract.

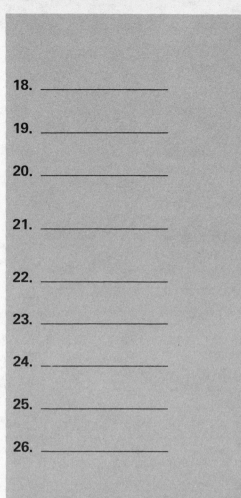

1. $+7k$	**2.** $-8r^2$	**3.** $+8p^2q$	**4.** 0
$\underline{+2k}$	$\underline{-3r^2}$	$\underline{-9p^2q}$	$\underline{-8xy^2}$
$+5k$	$-5r^2$	$+17p^2q$	$+8xy^2$

5. $(-12m^2n) - (-12m^2n) = 0$

6. $(-15z^2) - (0) = -15z^2$

1. _____

2. $(-17rs) - (-9rs)$

3. $(-11.4k) - (+4.7k)$

4. $(+43x^2) - (-22x^2)$

5. $(-17s^2 t) - (-17s^2 t)$

6. $0 - (-14mn^2)$

In 7 to 18, subtract.

7. $\begin{array}{r} +34x^2 y^3 \\ -12x^2 y^3 \\ \hline \end{array}$ **8.** $\begin{array}{r} -9pq^2 \\ -9pq^2 \\ \hline \end{array}$ **9.** $\begin{array}{r} -7rst \\ -7rst \\ \hline \end{array}$

10. $\begin{array}{r} 0 \\ 3y^2 z^2 \\ \hline \end{array}$ **11.** $\begin{array}{r} -17x \\ 0 \\ \hline \end{array}$ **12.** $\begin{array}{r} +.72a^2 b \\ -.35a^2 b \\ \hline \end{array}$

13. $\begin{array}{r} +2\frac{3}{4}\, m^2 n \\ -5\frac{1}{8}\, m^2 n \\ \hline \end{array}$ **14.** $\begin{array}{r} +\frac{3}{7}\, b^2 \\ +\frac{4}{7}\, b^2 \\ \hline \end{array}$ **15.** $\begin{array}{r} -7\frac{1}{2}\, ad^2 \\ +2\frac{3}{4}\, ad^2 \\ \hline \end{array}$

16. $\begin{array}{r} +9x^2 y^3 \\ -x^2 y^3 \\ \hline \end{array}$ **17.** $\begin{array}{r} -11(p + q) \\ -8(p + q) \\ \hline \end{array}$ **18.** $\begin{array}{r} -16s^2 t \\ +14s^2 t \\ \hline \end{array}$

19. Subtract $5r^2 h$ from $13r^2 h$.

20. Subtract $13r^2 h$ from $5r^2 h$.

21. How much greater is $18x$ than $12x$?

22. How much greater is $17x^2 y^3$ than $-3x^2 y^3$?

23. What is the difference of $19y^2$ and $10y^2$?

24. What is the difference of $-12ab$ and $-8ab$?

25. From the sum of $-7xy$ and $+13xy$, subtract $-3xy$.

2. _____

3. _____

4. _____

5. _____

6. _____

7. _____   **8.** _____   **9.** _____

10. _____   **11.** _____   **12.** _____

13. _____   **14.** _____   **15.** _____

16. _____   **17.** _____   **18.** _____

19. _____

20. _____

21. _____

22. _____

23. _____

24. _____

25. _____

26. From the sum of $-19p^2q$ and $-11p^2q$, subtract $-7p^2q$.

26. _____

27. What must be added to $7t$ to get $10t$?

27. _____

28. What must be added to $-11h$ to get $+5h$?

28. _____

29. By how much does $14rh$ exceed $9rh$?

29. _____

30. By how much does $-20z^2$ exceed $-5z^2$?

30. _____

3. Multiplying powers of the same base

We have already learned that $a^3 = a \cdot a \cdot a$ and $a^4 = a \cdot a \cdot a \cdot a$, so that

$$a^3 a^4 = \overbrace{(a \cdot a \cdot a)}^{3} \cdot \overbrace{(a \cdot a \cdot a \cdot a)}^{4}$$

$$= a \cdot a \cdot a \cdot a \cdot a \cdot a \cdot a = a^7$$

Likewise, $b^2 \cdot b^3 = \overbrace{(b \cdot b)}^{2} \cdot \overbrace{(b \cdot b \cdot b)}^{3}$

$$= b \cdot b \cdot b \cdot b \cdot b = b^5$$

Also, $p \cdot p^2 = \overbrace{(p)}^{1} \cdot \overbrace{(p \cdot p)}^{2}$

$$= p \cdot p \cdot p = p^3$$

Note that the exponent in each product above is the sum of the exponents of the factors. We may state, in general, that

$$x^m \cdot x^n = x^{m+n}$$

where x is any signed number and m and n are positive integers.

Rule: To multiply powers of the same base, add the exponents of the factors and make this sum the power of the common base in the product.

This rule may apply to two or more powers of the same base. Thus, $y^2 \cdot y^3 \cdot y^5 = y^{2+3+5} = y^{10}$. However, it does not apply to the product of powers of different bases. For example, $x^3 y^2$ cannot be written in any way with a single exponent.

Consider $(a^4)^3$:

$$(a^4)^3 = a^4 \cdot a^4 \cdot a^4 = a^{4+4+4} = a^{12}$$

We say that $(a^4)^3 = a^{12}$. Thus, if we are finding the power of a power, we must multiply the two exponents to find the power of a product. In general,

$$(x^r)^s = x^{rs}$$

where x is any signed number and r and s are positive integers.

Note also that $(a^2 b^3)^3 = (a^2)^3 (b^3)^3 = a^6 b^9$. That is, we apply the power to each factor in the parentheses.

Examples

Multiply:

1. $a^6 \cdot a^3 = a^{6+3} = a^9$

2. $p^2 \cdot p^5 = p^{2+5} = p^7$

3. $7^3 \cdot 7^8 = 7^{3+8} = 7^{11}$

4. $r \cdot r^3 = r^{1+3} = r^4$

5. $(t^3)^5 = t^{3 \cdot 5} = t^{15}$

6. $(c^2 d^3)^4 = c^8 d^{12}$

Exercises

Multiply:

1. $x^3 \cdot x^2$

2. $m^6 \cdot m$

3. $p^5 \cdot p^4$

4. $y^7 \cdot y$

5. $n^8 \cdot n^3$

6. $r^{10} \cdot r^5$

7. $3^5 \cdot 3^2$

8. $2^3 \cdot 2^4$

9. $10^3 \cdot 10^5$

10. $s^2 \cdot s^3 \cdot s^4$

11. $c^5 \cdot c \cdot c^6$

12. $d^3 \cdot d^7 \cdot d^3$

13. $2^3 \cdot 2^2 \cdot 2$

14. $1^3 \cdot 1^2 \cdot 1^4$

15. $4^5 \cdot 4^2 \cdot 4^3$

16. $g^8 \cdot g^2 \cdot g^5$

17. $x^5 \cdot x^a$

18. $y^3 \cdot y^n$

19. $(b^3)^2$

20. $(c^2)^3$

21. $(d^4)^5$

22. $(e^2)^5$

23. $(2^3)^4$

24. $(1^5)^3$

1. _____ 2. _____

3. _____ 4. _____

5. _____ 6. _____

7. _____ 8. _____

9. _____ 10. _____

11. _____ 12. _____

13. _____ 14. _____

15. _____ 16. _____

17. _____ 18. _____

19. _____ 20. _____

21. _____ 22. _____

23. _____ 24. _____

25. $(a^3)^2 \cdot (a^2)^3$ **26.** $(c^2 d^3)^2$

27. $(pq^2)^3$ **28.** $(mn)^4$

29. $(2^3 \cdot 3^2)^4$ **30.** $(3 \cdot 4^2)^3$

31. $b^2 \cdot b^4 \cdot c^3$ **32.** $x^5 \cdot y^3 \cdot y^7$

33. $r^7 \cdot s^2 \cdot r$

25. _____ **26.** _____

27. _____ **28.** _____

29. _____ **30.** _____

31. _____ **32.** _____

33. _____

4. Multiplying monomials

When we multiply monomials, we make use of the fact that we may arrange the factors in any order (the commutative property) and that we may group them as we wish (the associative law). Thus,

$$(3a)(4b) = 3 \cdot 4 \cdot a \cdot b = 12ab$$
$$(-6y^2)(+3y^3) = (-6)(+3) \cdot y^2 y^3$$
$$= -18y^5$$
$$(-7c^2 d)(-5cd^3) = (-7)(-5)(c^2 \cdot c)(d \cdot d^3)$$
$$= 35c^3 d^4$$

Rule: To multiply monomials:
1. **Multiply the numerical coefficients.**
2. **Multiply powers of the same base.**

Exercises

In 1 to 20, multiply.

1. $(+4a^2)(-5a^7)$

2. $(-15)(+4x)$

3. $(-6m)(-3n)$

4. $(-7p^2)(-5p^3 q)$

5. $(+3a)(-2b)(-4c)$

Examples

Multiply:

1. $(-3p)(+7q) = (-3)(+7)\,pq = -21pq$

2. $(-4x^3)(-2x^6) = (-4)(-2)\,x^3 \cdot x^6 = 8x^9$

3. $(9m^2)(-3m^3) = 9(-3)\,m^2 \cdot m^3 = -27m^5$

4. $(-3cd^2)(+5c^2 d^3)(-2c)$
$= (-3)(+5)(-2)\,c \cdot c^2 \cdot c \cdot d^2 \cdot d^3$
$= 30c^4 d^5$

1. _____

2. _____

3. _____

4. _____

5. _____

6. $(5c^2)(-8c^2d^3)$

6. _____

7. $\left(\dfrac{2}{3}r\right)(-9a)$

7. _____

8. $(-6p)\left(+\dfrac{1}{2}q\right)\left(-\dfrac{2}{3}r\right)$

8. _____

9. $(2x)^3$

9. _____

10. $(3ab)^2$

10. _____

11. $(-3x^2y)(+6xyz)$

11. _____

12. $(-9r^2s)(+7r^3s^4)$

12. _____

13. $(-2c)(+3cd)(-4d^2)$

13. _____

14. $(-.4b^2)^3$

14. _____

15. $(-3ak^2)(+5a^2k^3)$

15. _____

16. $(-5p)^2(-q)^3$

16. _____

17. $(+5c^2)(-5d^2)$

17. _____

18. $(-3ab^2)^3$

18. _____

19. $(-4d^2)(+3e^3)(-5de)$

19. _____

20. $\left(+\dfrac{1}{3}g\right)^2(9h)$

20. _____

21. Express the area of a rectangle whose length is $3t^2$ and whose width is $8t$.

21. _____

22. Express the area of a rectangle whose width is w and whose length is $3w$.

22. _____

23. Express the area of a square each of whose sides is $7k$ inches.

23. _____

24. Express the volume of a cube each of whose edges is $3y$ feet.

24. _____

25. Express the volume of a rectangular solid of height h, width $2h$, and length $3h$.

25. _____

5. Dividing powers of the same base

When we divide x^7 by x^3, we are in effect asking, "What quantity multiplied by x^3 results in x^7?" We have already learned that $x^4 \cdot x^3 = x^7$. Therefore, $x^7 \div x^3 = x^4$.

Likewise, $a^9 \div a^6 = a^3$, since $a^6 \cdot a^3 = a^9$.

Note that, in both these examples, the exponent of the quotient is the difference between the exponents of the dividend and the divisor. That is,

$$x^7 \div x^3 = x^{7-3} = x^4 \text{ and } a^9 \div a^6 = a^{9-6} = a^3$$

In general, then, we may write

$$x^m \div x^n = x^{m-n}$$

where $x \neq 0$, m and n are positive integers, and m is greater than n.

Rule: To divide two powers of the same base:
1. **Subtract the exponent in the divisor from that in the dividend.**
2. **Make this difference the exponent of the common base in the quotient.**

We know that any nonzero number divided by itself is 1, so that $x^5 \div x^5 = 1$. In general, $x^p \div x^p = 1$, where $x \neq 0$ and p is a positive integer.

Examples

Divide:

1. $y^{10} \div y^3 = y^{10-3} = y^7$

2. $b^9 \div b^5 = b^{9-5} = b^4$

3. $k^6 \div k = k^{6-1} = k^5$

4. $7^5 - 7^2 = 7^{5-2} = 7^3$

5. $\dfrac{r^7}{r^2} = r^{7-2} = r^5$

6. $\dfrac{x^a}{x^b} = x^{a-b}$

Exercises

Divide:

1. $a^5 \div a^2$ **2.** $p^{11} \div p^4$ **3.** $c^8 \div c$

4. $y^9 \div y^3$ **5.** $x^{10} \div x^5$ **6.** $d^8 \div d^7$

1. _____   **2.** _____   **3.** _____

4. _____   **5.** _____   **6.** _____

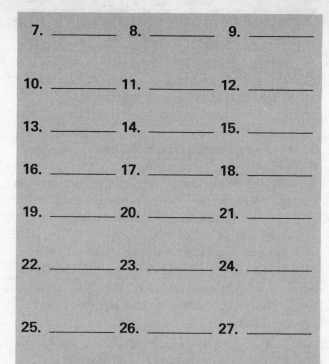

7. $\dfrac{n^6}{n^4}$ **8.** $\dfrac{t^5}{t^3}$ **9.** $\dfrac{m^{12}}{m^8}$

10. $2^5 \div 2^3$ **11.** $10^6 \div 10^2$ **12.** $3^6 \div 3^3$

13. $a^8 \div a^5$ **14.** $z^{11} \div z^{10}$ **15.** $b^8 \div b^5$

16. $k^2 \div k^2$ **17.** $c^9 \div c^9$ **18.** $s \div s$

19. $x^{2a} \div x^a$ **20.** $y^t \div y^3$ **21.** $b^x \div b^x$

22. $\dfrac{r^3 \cdot r^5}{r^2}$ **23.** $\dfrac{t^4 \cdot t^6}{t^5}$ **24.** $\dfrac{a^9 \cdot a^3}{a^3}$

25. $\dfrac{2^4 \cdot 2^7}{2^5}$ **26.** $\dfrac{10^4 \cdot 10^5}{10^3}$ **27.** $\dfrac{3^5 \cdot 3^2}{3^4}$

6. Dividing monomials

If we wish to divide $12x^5$ by $3x^2$, we are in effect asking, "What quantity multiplied by $3x^2$ results in a product of $12x^5$?" We already know that $(4x^3)(3x^2) = 12x^5$. Hence, $(12x^5) \div (3x^2) = 4x^3$.

Likewise, $(-10y^8) \div (5y^4) = -2y^4$, since $(-2y^4)(5y^4) = -10y^8$.

The above examples illustrate the following:

Rule: When dividing monomials:
1. **The coefficient of the quotient is the quotient of the coefficients of dividend and divisor.**
2. **The exponents in the quotient are the result of dividing powers of the same base.**

Examples

Divide:

1. $(-10b^7) \div (-5b^4) = +2b^3$

2. $\dfrac{-15x^8 y^5}{+3x^6 y^2} = \dfrac{-15}{+3} \cdot \dfrac{x^8}{x^6} \cdot \dfrac{y^5}{y^2} = -5x^2 y^3$

3. $\dfrac{+21a^7 b^5 c^4}{-3a^4 b^4 c^4} = \dfrac{+21}{-3} \cdot \dfrac{a^7}{a^4} \cdot \dfrac{b^5}{b^4} \cdot \dfrac{c^4}{c^4} =$

$-7a^3 b(1) = -7a^3 b$

Exercises

In 1 to 21, divide.

1. $30b^7$ by $10b^2$ **2.** $-21m^5 n^6$ by $7m^3$

3. $18ab$ by $6a$ **4.** $-42x$ by 6

5. $-20y^5$ by $4y^2$ **6.** $-35p^7$ by $-7p^3$

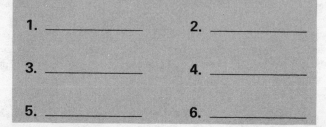

7. $(14a^7 k) \div (-2a^5 k)$　　**8.** $(6ab) \div (-3a)$

9. $(a^9 b^4) \div (a^6 b^3)$　　**10.** $(a^2 b^4) \div (ab^2)$

11. $(10p^4 q^3) \div (-5p^2 q^2)$

12. $(15x^2 y^3 z^4) \div (5xy^2 z^3)$

13. $\dfrac{21x^7}{-3x^4}$　　**14.** $\dfrac{150r^3 s^4}{-50r^3 s^4}$

15. $\dfrac{-40c^7 d^5}{+8c^6 d^4}$　　**16.** $\dfrac{-10a^3 b^4}{2a^2 b}$

17. $\dfrac{12x^5 y^5}{-4x^4 y}$　　**18.** $\dfrac{16a^6}{-4a^3}$

19. $\dfrac{-45r^7 s^5 t^4}{-9r^5 s^2 t^4}$　　**20.** $\dfrac{-31b^3 c^4}{-31b^3 c}$

21. $\dfrac{-56x^7 y^3 z^3}{8x^5 y}$

22. If the area of a rectangle is $48y^5$ and the width is $8y^3$, represent the length.

23. If a dozen eggs cost $36n$ cents, represent the cost of each egg.

24. If $3x$ books cost $21x^4$ dollars, represent the cost of each book.

25. Perform the operations indicated:

　a. $\dfrac{(7rs)(-4r^3 s^4)}{14r^2 s^2}$　　**b.** $\dfrac{(-5p^2 q^3)(-8p^4 q^5)}{10p^3 q^3}$

7. Adding polynomials

Expressions such as $3p$, $4x + 5$, and $y^2 + 2y + 7$ are called *polynomials*. A polynomial is merely a sum of terms. The polynomial $3p$ is called a monomial since it has only one term.

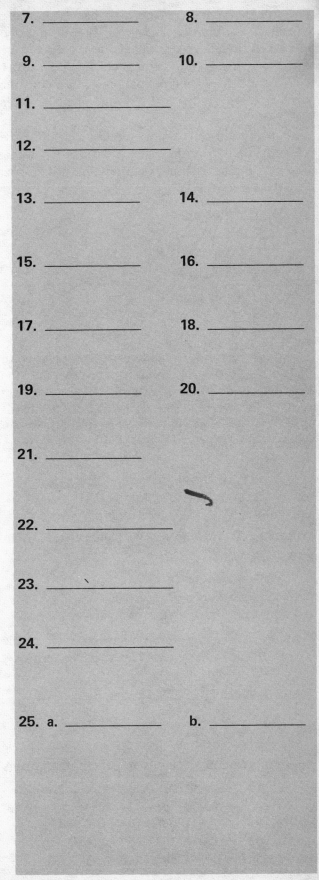

7. _____　8. _____

9. _____　10. _____

11. _____

12. _____

13. _____　14. _____

15. _____　16. _____

17. _____　18. _____

19. _____　20. _____

21. _____

22. _____

23. _____

24. _____

25. a. _____　b. _____

The polynomial $4x + 5$, which has two terms, is called a **binomial**; and $y^2 + 2y + 7$, a polynomial of three terms, is called a **trinomial**.

In general, the expression $2x^2 + (-5x) + (-6)$ is called a polynomial in x; the addition signs are generally omitted and it is written $2x^2 - 5x - 6$.

The addition of polynomials is simply the addition of like terms. This is similar to adding units of measure. For example, add 4 lb. 5 oz. to 6 lb. 4 oz.:

$$
\begin{array}{l}
4 \text{ lb.} + 5 \text{ oz.} \\
\underline{6 \text{ lb.} + 4 \text{ oz.}} \\
10 \text{ lb.} + 9 \text{ oz.} = 10 \text{ lb. } 9 \text{ oz.}
\end{array}
$$

Now add $3a + 4b$ to $6a + 2b$:

$$
\begin{array}{l}
3a + 4b \\
\underline{6a + 2b} \\
9a + 6b
\end{array}
$$

This method of adding polynomials is to place like terms in columns and to find the algebraic sum of the like terms. It may be convenient to arrange the terms alphabetically or in descending powers of one of the letters (decreasing exponents).

ILLUSTRATIVE PROBLEM 1

Add $2x - 3z + 4y$ to $5y - 7z + 2x$.

Solution: Arrange terms in alphabetical order. Now,

$$
\begin{array}{l}
2x + 4y - 3z \\
\underline{2x + 5y - 7z} \\
4x + 9y - 10z \quad (answer)
\end{array}
$$

In rearranging terms, remember that the sign to the left of any term is part of the term.

ILLUSTRATIVE PROBLEM 2

Add: $3a^2 - 2ab + b^2$, $\quad 4b^2 + 7ab - 13a^2$, $-2b^2 + 5a^2 - 3ab$

Solution: Rearrange terms in descending powers of a (decreasing exponents):

$$
\begin{array}{l}
3a^2 - 2ab + b^2 \\
-13a^2 + 7ab + 4b^2 \\
\underline{5a^2 - 3ab - 2b^2} \\
{-5a^2} + 2ab + 3b^2 \quad (answer)
\end{array}
$$

ILLUSTRATIVE PROBLEM 3

Simplify the polynomial $4x - 3y + 2x + 5y - 3x$.

Solution: Combine like terms in the polynomial:

$$4x + 2x - 3x - 3y + 5y$$

$$= (4x + 2x - 3x) + (-3y + 5y)$$

$$= 3x + 2y \quad (answer)$$

Exercises

In 1 to 12, add.

1. $3a + b$
   $\underline{2a + 5b}$

2. $5x - 2y$
   $\underline{3x + y}$

3. $2r - 3s + t$
   $\underline{5r + 9s - 5t}$

4. $6b - 4c$
   $-3b + 2c$
   $\underline{8b - 5c}$

5. $4y + 5z$
   $-3y - 2z$
   $\underline{y + z}$

6. $7x^2y - 5y^2z$
   ${-2}x^2y + 3y^2z$
   $\underline{-11x^2y + 8y^2z}$

7. $6x^2 - 3x + 8$
   $\underline{-2x^2 + 5x + 3}$

8. $3a^2 + 2ab + b^2$
   $\underline{a^2 + 4ab - 3b^2}$

9. $7r^2 - 8r + 9$
   $\underline{-2r^2 - 3r - 12}$

10. $4x + 2y$
    $3x - y + z$
    $\underline{x - z}$

11. $4c^2 - 2c + d$
    $-3c^2 + 7c + 5d$
    $\underline{9c^2 - 8c + 4d}$

12. $7a - 9b$
    $-3a + 2b - 4$
    $\underline{6a - 3b + 11}$

In 13 to 23, add.

13. $3a - 2c + 4b$ and $2a - 7b + 9c$.

14. $5x - 2y, y - x,$ and $3y + 4x$.

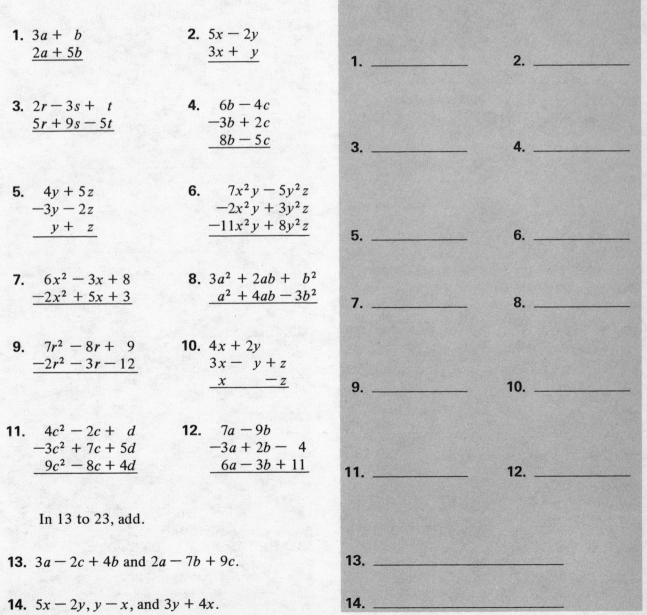

1. _____   2. _____

3. _____   4. _____

5. _____   6. _____

7. _____   8. _____

9. _____   10. _____

11. _____   12. _____

13. _____

14. _____

15. $4a + b + c, a + c - b,$ and $3a + 2b + 5c.$

15. _____

16. $-3x + 2y, 7x - 9y,$ and $-4x - 5y.$

16. _____

17. $8a - 2b, 10a + b,$ and $-2a - 3b.$

17. _____

18. $7x^2 - 2x + 9$ and $5 + 4x - 3x^2.$

18. _____

19. $a^2 - b^2 + c^2, 3a^2 - 2c^2,$ and $4b^2 - 5c^2 + 3a^2.$

19. _____

20. $5r^2 - 2rs + 4s^2, 3r^2 + s^2 - 6rs,$ and $-s^2 + r^2.$

20. _____

21. $3c^2 - c^3 + 2c - 7, 5 + 2c^2 + 3c^3,$ and $5c^2 - 9.$

21. _____

22. $7a^2 - 5ab + 3b^2, 8b^2 + 6a^2 - 9ab,$ and $-4ab + 3a^2 - 11b^2.$

22. _____

23. $9p - 3q + 2r, 4r - 3p + 8q,$ and $p - r.$

23. _____

In 24 to 37, simplify by combining like terms.

24. $6x - 4y + 3x + 9y$

24. _____

25. $7a - 3b - 5b + 6a$

25. _____

26. $3r - 5s + 6r - 9t + 7s$

26. _____

27. $-5a^2 - 3a + 8 + 2a + 12a^2 + 10$

27. _____

28. $7pq - 8qr - 9pq + 12qr$

28. _____

29. $10y^2 - 7 + 3y - 8 + 2y^2 - 7y$

29. _____

30. $3k + (2k - 7)$

30. _____

31. $(-8x + y) + 3y$

31. _____

32. $4t^2 + (-6t^2 - 9)$

32. _____

33. $8m^2 + (5m - 3m^2)$

33. _____

34. $(9s^2 - 3) + (4s^2 + 7)$

34. _____

35. $(12a + 7b) + (2b - 5a)$

35. _____

36. $(y^2 + 3 + 4y) + (3y^2 - 9y)$

36. _____

37. $(2p^3 - 7 + 9p^2) + (3 - 12p + 7p^2)$

37. _____

In 38 to 42, represent in simplest form the perimeters of the figures whose sides are given.

38. $2a - 9, \ 3a + 4, \ 5a - 2$

38. _____

39. $4x + 2y, \ 3x - 5y, \ x + 4y$

39. _____

40. $2r - 3s, \ 4r + 2s, \ 3r + 7s, \ 5r$

40. _____

41. $3a - 2, \ 2b + 4, \ 3a - 2, \ 2b + 4$

41. _____

42. $7s + 2t, \ 3s - 5t, \ 2s + 6t, \ 3t$

42. _____

43. Find the perimeter of a square each of whose sides is $2x - 3$.

43. _____

8. Subtracting polynomials

We can subtract polynomials in the same way we subtracted monomials; that is, we change the sign of the subtrahend and proceed as in addition.

For convenience, we may arrange like terms under one another as we did in the addition of polynomials.

ILLUSTRATIVE PROBLEM 1

Subtract: $(8a - 2b) - (10a + b)$

Solution:

$$\begin{array}{r} 8a - 2b \\ 10a + b \\ \hline -2a - 3b \end{array} \quad (answer)$$

ILLUSTRATIVE PROBLEM 2

Subtract $3x^2 - 2x + 5$ from $7 + 8x^2 - 4x$.

Solution 1: Arrange in descending order in columns:

$$8x^2 - 4x + 7$$
$$\underline{3x^2 - 2x + 5}$$
$$5x^2 - 2x + 2 \quad (answer)$$

Solution 2: We may use a horizontal arrangement:

$$(8x^2 - 4x + 7) - (3x^2 - 2x + 5)$$

Now change the signs of all terms in the subtrahend and change the operation of subtraction to addition ($-$ to $+$). Thus,

$$(8x^2 - 4x + 7) + (-3x^2 + 2x - 5)$$

$$(8x^2 - 3x^2) + (-4x + 2x) + (7 - 5)$$

$$5x^2 - 2x + 2 \quad (answer)$$

Exercises

In 1 to 12, subtract the lower polynomial from the upper one.

1. $7x + 5y$
  $\underline{2x + 3y}$

2. $8m - 5n$
  $\underline{2m + n}$

3. $12p - 5q$
  $\underline{-3p - 7q}$

1. _____ 2. _____ 3. _____

4. $12x^2 - 9y^2$
  $\underline{x^2 + y^2}$

5. $5a$
  $\underline{2a + 3b}$

6. $x^2 + 2x - 5$
  $\underline{3x^2 - 4x + 9}$

4. _____ 5. _____ 6. _____

7. 0
  $\underline{4r - 5s}$

8. $9y^2 + 3y$
  $\underline{7y^2 - 2y + 4}$

7. _____ 8. _____

9. $2a^2 - 11$
  $\underline{a^3 - 5}$

10. $8p - 9q + 3r$
  $\underline{-3p + 5r}$

9. _____ 10. _____

11. $10c - 3d + 7$
  $\underline{-2c - 3d}$

12. $3rs - 7st$
  $\underline{-6rs - 12st}$

11. _____ 12. _____

13. From $8x - 4y + 5z$ take $3z - 2y - 7x$.

13. _____

14. Subtract $a^2 + 12 - 7a$ from $19 + 3a^2 - 4a$.

14. _____

15. From $5c^2 - 7cd + d^2$ take $3d^2 - c^2 + 2cd$.

16. From $r - s - t$ take $s + t - r$.

17. From $2b^2 - 3bc + 4c^2$ take $2b^2 - 4c^2 - 3bc$.

18. Subtract $5k^2 - 12$ from 0.

19. How much greater is $9p - 7q$ than $3p + 2q$?

20. From the sum of $2x - 3y + 4z$ and $8x + 2y - 7z$, subtract $x + y + z$.

21. By how much does $3c^2 - 5cd + 9d^2$ exceed $2c^2 - 7d^2 - 2cd$?

22. How much less than $7x + 9$ is $3x - 2$?

23. Subtract $a^2 + b^2 - c^2$ from the sum of $3a^2 - 2b^2 + 5c^2$ and $-2a^2 + b^2 - 3c^2$.

In 24 to 33, simplify.

24. $(2a + b) - (3a + 5b)$

25. $(3x + 7) - (x + 6)$

26. $(5x^3y + 3x^2y) - x^3y$

27. $(4a^2 - b) - (2a^2 + b)$

28. $(8p + 2q) - (10p + q)$

29. $5r - (3r + 7)$

30. $(9y^2 - 8y + 1) - (3y^2 + 2y + 4)$

31. $(5a^2 + 3ab - 8b^2) - (a^2 - b^2)$

32. $(7x - 2) + (8x - 3) - (3x + 5)$

33. $(12k^2 - 4k + 7) - (3 - 7k^2)$

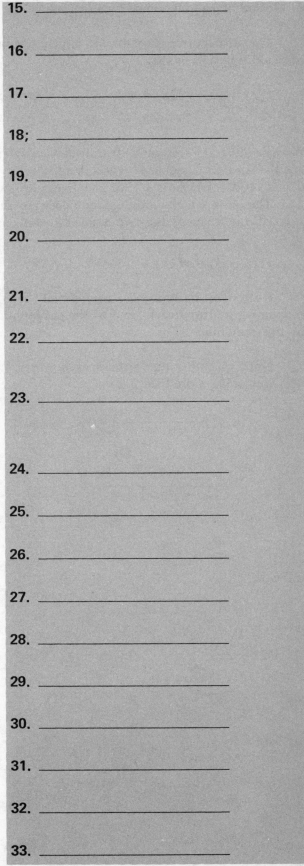

15. _____

16. _____

17. _____

18; _____

19. _____

20. _____

21. _____

22. _____

23. _____

24. _____

25. _____

26. _____

27. _____

28. _____

29. _____

30. _____

31. _____

32. _____

33. _____

9. Multiplying a polynomial by a monomial

The distributive property of multiplication over addition tells us that

$$x(2x + 3) = x(2x) + x(3)$$
$$= 2x^2 + 3x$$

We can illustrate this geometrically by considering the area of a rectangle whose length is $2x + 3$ and whose width is x. See the figure below.

The area of the original rectangle is the sum of the areas of the two smaller rectangles, so that

$$x(2x + 3) = x(2x) + x(3) = 2x^2 + 3x$$

Rule: To multiply a polynomial by a monomial, multiply each term of the polynomial by the monomial.

Note that this rule applies even when the polynomial has more than 2 terms.

Examples

Multiply:

1. $3(a + b) = 3a + 3b$

2. $2x(x - y) = 2x(x) - 2x(y) = 2x^2 - 2xy$

3. $4r^2(r^2 + 5r + 2) = 4r^2(r^2) + 4r^2(5r)$
$+ 4r^2(2) = 4r^4 + 20r^3 + 8r^2$

4. $5p - 3(2p - 1) = 5p - 3(2p) - 3(-1)$
$= 5p - 6p + 1 = -p + 1$

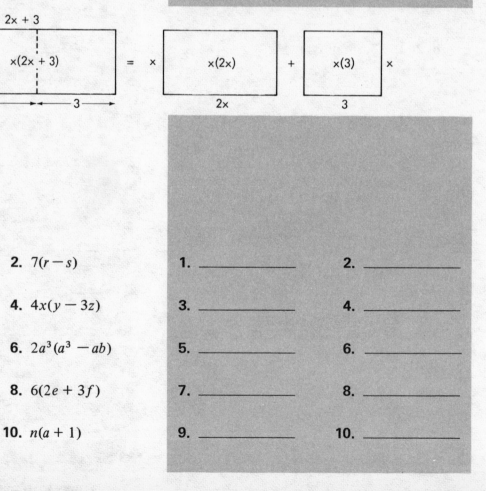

Exercises

In 1 to 28, multiply.

1. $5(2x + 3y)$　　　　**2.** $7(r - s)$

3. $-4(3 + 7a)$　　　　**4.** $4x(y - 3z)$

5. $3a(a + b)$　　　　**6.** $2a^3(a^3 - ab)$

7. $c(c^2 - 2d^2)$　　　　**8.** $6(2e + 3f)$

9. $-k(2k - 1)$　　　　**10.** $n(a + 1)$

1. _____　　　2. _____

3. _____　　　4. _____

5. _____　　　6. _____

7. _____　　　8. _____

9. _____　　　10. _____

11. $p^2(2p - 7)$

12. $-r(r^2 - s)$

13. $5m^2n(2m - 3n)$

14. $r^2t(r^2 - s^2)$

15. $-5xy^2(y^3 - x^2)$

16. $5(3p^2 - 2p - 7)$

17. $2k(k^2 - 2k + 1)$

18. $6c(2c^2 - c - 1)$

19. $x^2(3 - 5x + 7x^2 - x^3)$

20. $-1(q^2 - 3q + 2)$

21. $\frac{1}{2}p(4p^2 - 6p + 2)$

22. $.5r(r^2 - 10r)$

23. $-3n(n^2 - n - 4)$

24. $2ab(a^2 - 2ab + b^2)$

25. $\frac{3}{4}s(4s^2 - 8s + 12)$

26. $-30\left(\frac{2}{3}x^2 - \frac{1}{5}x + \frac{5}{6}\right)$

27. $5xy(y^2 - yx - x^2)$

28. $-2t(a^2t^2 - 3at + a^3)$

In 29 to 38, simplify by multiplying as indicated and combining like terms.

29. $5(n - 2) + 7n$

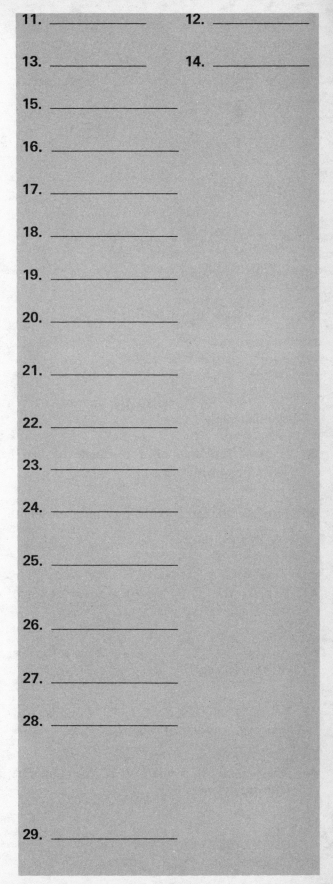

11. _____   **12.** _____

13. _____   **14.** _____

15. _____

16. _____

17. _____

18. _____

19. _____

20. _____

21. _____

22. _____

23. _____

24. _____

25. _____

26. _____

27. _____

28. _____

29. _____

30. $3t + 4(t - 3)$

30. _____

31. $7p + 1(p - 9)$

31. _____

32. $2r - 5(3 - r)$

32. _____

33. $-6(2k + 1) + 9k$

33. _____

34. $-1(5t - 4) - 6$

34. _____

35. $-3(4x + 5) + 20$

35. _____

36. $-4(2y - 3) + 5y - 1$

36. _____

37. $-1(c + d) + 3(c - d)$

37. _____

38. $5q(q^2 - 10) + 18q$

38. _____

In 39 to 44, represent the answer to each question in simplest form.

39. Express the area of a rectangle of length $3x - 4$ and width $5x$.

39. _____

40. Express the area of a rectangle of length $\frac{1}{2}p$ and width $(4p - 2)$.

40. _____

41. Express the perimeter of a square each of whose sides is $3x - 5$ inches.

41. _____

42. An egg costs $(3c - 2)$ cents. What is the cost of a dozen eggs?

42. _____

43. A can of milk weighs $(2k - 3)$ pounds. How many ounces does it weigh?

43. _____

44. The length of a board is $(2k - 1)$ meters. How many cm is this?

44. _____

10. Simplifying expressions with grouping symbols

In some of the exercises in the preceding section, we removed parentheses by multiplying and then simplified by combining like terms. We can do this in a number of cases by using the distributive property.

Occasionally, we find a parenthetic expression within a bracket [ ]. In cases of this kind, we begin by removing the parentheses first. For example,

$$5y - 3[2y - 7(y + 1)]$$
$$= 5y - 3[2y - 7y - 7] = 5y - 3[-5y - 7]$$
$$= 5y + 15y + 21 = 20y + 21$$

Note that first we remove the parentheses and combine, and then we remove the brackets and combine like terms.

Examples

Rewrite without parentheses and combine like terms.

1. $7 - 2(3x + 2) = 7 - 6x - 4 = 3 - 6x$

2. $4a + (5 - 2a) = 4a + 1(5 - 2a)$
   $= 4a + 5 - 2a = 2a + 5$

3. $4a - (5 - 2a) = 4a - 1(5 - 2a)$
   $= 4a - 5 + 2a = 6a - 5$

Exercises

Simplify:

1. $5 - (2b - 7)$
2. $10 - (3a + 7)$
3. $8 + (6k - 5)$
4. $12 - (-4c + 9)$
5. $6p + (5 - 2p)$
6. $12r - (3r - 6)$
7. $7c - 3c(2c - 1)$
8. $(9 + 5y) - (9 - 5y)$
9. $6a - 4b - (a + b)$
10. $3(x - y) - (y - x)$
11. $5d - (d - 3) + 4$
12. $m(m - 5) - m(m + 2)$
13. $3s + 4[s - 2(s - 7)]$
14. $9t - 3[t - 4(t - 6)]$
15. $5[p - 6(p - 1)] - 3p$

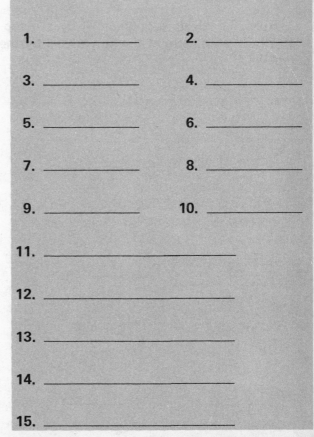

1. _____   2. _____

3. _____   4. _____

5. _____   6. _____

7. _____   8. _____

9. _____   10. _____

11. _____

12. _____

13. _____

14. _____

15. _____

16. $7[8z - 3(z - 4)]$

16. _____

17. $9[3e - (e - 4) + 1]$

17. _____

18. $p^2q - p[pq - p(q - r)]$

18. _____

11. Dividing a polynomial by a monomial

We already learned that

$3(a + b) = 3a + 3b$

It then follows that

$$\frac{3a + 3b}{3} = a + b$$

Note that the quotient $a + b$ can be obtained by dividing each term of the dividend $3a + 3b$ by 3 as follows:

$$\frac{3a + 3b}{3} = \frac{3a}{3} + \frac{3b}{3} = a + b$$

It thus appears that division by a monomial is also distributive over addition.

Rule: To divide a polynomial by a monomial, divide each term of the polynomial by the monomial.

Examples

1. $\dfrac{4p^2 + 8p}{4p} = \dfrac{4p^2}{4p} + \dfrac{8p}{4p} = p + 2$

2. $\dfrac{3r^3 - 6r^2 + 12r}{3r} = \dfrac{3r^3}{3r} - \dfrac{6r^2}{3r} + \dfrac{12r}{3r}$

$$= r^2 - 2r + 4$$

Exercises

In 1 to 31, divide.

1. $\dfrac{6m - 9n}{3}$ **2.** $\dfrac{15c - 20d}{-5}$

3. $\dfrac{21p - 14}{7}$ **4.** $\dfrac{cr + cs}{c}$

5. $\dfrac{k - tk}{k}$ **6.** $\dfrac{2m + 2}{-2}$

7. $\dfrac{6x^2 - 12y^2}{-3}$ **8.** $\dfrac{8p^2 - 20q^2}{4}$

1. _____   **2.** _____

3. _____   **4.** _____

5. _____   **6.** _____

7. _____   **8.** _____

9. $\dfrac{12d^2 - 6}{-6}$

10. $\dfrac{n^2 - 5n}{n}$

11. $\dfrac{15d^2 - 2d}{d}$

12. $\dfrac{9k^2 - 5k}{k}$

13. $(7x^2 - 3x) \div x$

14. $(18t^2 - 12t) \div (-t)$

15. $(a^2 - a) \div (-a)$

16. $\dfrac{7r^3 - 2r^2}{r^2}$

17. $\dfrac{9t^4 - 8t^2}{t^2}$

18. $\dfrac{15y^3 - 10y^2}{5y^2}$

19. $\dfrac{3p - 6q + 9r}{3}$

20. $\dfrac{7a + 14b - 28}{-7}$

21. $\dfrac{2x^2 - 4x - 8}{2}$

22. $\dfrac{\pi a^2 - \pi b^2}{\pi}$

23. $\dfrac{r^3 s^2 - r^2 s^2 + rs}{rs}$

24. $\dfrac{x^4 - x^2 + x}{-x}$

25. $\dfrac{-x^2 - xy + y^2}{-1}$

26. $\dfrac{21a^2 b - 14ab^2 + 7a^3 b}{7ab}$

27. $\dfrac{p^3 t - pt^3}{-pt}$

28. $\dfrac{22x^4 - 11x^3 + 33x^2}{11x^2}$

29. $\dfrac{18r^2 s^3 - 9r^2 s^2 + 27r^3 s^2}{9r^2 s^2}$

30. $\dfrac{3.2x^2 y - 2.4xy^2}{.8xy}$

9. _____	10. _____
11. _____	12. _____
13. _____	14. _____
15. _____	16. _____
17. _____	18. _____
19. _____	20. _____
21. _____	22. _____
23. _____	24. _____
25. _____	
26. _____	
27. _____	
28. _____	
29. _____	
30. _____	

31. $\dfrac{1.5p^3q^3 - 2.5p^2q^2 + 2p^3q^2}{.5p^2q^2}$

31. _____

32. The area of a rectangle is $15w^2 + 10w$. If the width is $5w$, represent the length in simplest form.

32. _____

33. Represent in simplest form the number of feet in $(24a + 36b)$ inches.

33. _____

34. Represent in simplest form the number of quarters in $(50n + 75)$ cents.

34. _____

35. A train travels $26h^2 + 39h$ miles in $13h$ hours. Express this rate in miles per hour in simplest form.

35. _____

36. The perimeter of a square is $8t^2 + 12$ inches. Express the length in inches of each side in simplest form.

36. _____

37. A building is $6x^2 + 9x$ feet high. Express, in simplest form, the height of the building in yards.

37. _____

Chapter review exercises

1. Add: $(-3x^2y) + (-5x^2y)$

1. _____

2. Combine like terms: $6.4x + 8.2x - 5.8x$

2. _____

3. Subtract $7a^2b$ from $12a^2b$.

3. _____

4. From the sum of $-3y^2$ and $8y^2$, take $-4y^2$.

4. _____

5. Multiply: $m^2 \cdot m^3 \cdot m^4$

5. _____

6. Multiply: $(-7r^2s^3)(+4rs^2)$

6. _____

7. Divide: $24p^3q^2r$ by $-6pqr$

7. _____

8. Represent in simplest form the number of days in:

    a. n weeks   **b.** $n + 3$ weeks

    c. $2n - 4$ weeks

9. Add: $-3x^2 + 4xy - 7y^2$, $5xy + 6x^2$, $x^2 - y^2$

10. Subtract $5a - 4c + 6b$ from $3b - 2c + 4a$.

11. Perform the indicated operations and simplify:

    a. $6(5p - 4q)$ **b.** $y - (3y + 7)$

    c. $8m^2 n(m^2 - n^2)$ **d.** $7n - 4(n - 8)$

12. Divide and simplify:

    a. $\dfrac{6x^2 - 9xy - 3y^2}{3}$ **b.** $\dfrac{15r^2 s - 10rs^2}{-5rs}$

13. Simplify: $(5p^2 - 3p + 7) - (2p^2 + 4p - 10)$

14. What number must be added to $5m^2 - 3$ to obtain $6m^2 + 7$?

15. Divide:

    a. $\dfrac{25n^2 - 15n}{-5n}$ **b.** $\dfrac{8x^3 - 6x^2 + 4x}{-2x}$

8. a. _____   **b.** _____

    c. _____

9. _____

10. _____

11. a. _____   **b.** _____

    c. _____   **d.** _____

12. a. _____   **b.** _____

13. _____

14. _____

15. a. _____   **b.** _____

EQUATIONS AND PROBLEM-SOLVING

1. Solving equations by adding signed numbers

In Chapter 2, we learned to solve simple equations by adding or subtracting the numbers of arithmetic. Thus, in the solution of $x + 3 = 8$, we subtracted 3 from both sides and arrived at the solution $x = 5$. We learned in our discussion of signed numbers that subtracting 3 is the same as adding -3, so that now we need use only the addition principle of equality. Here is an example:

ILLUSTRATIVE PROBLEM 1

Solve and check: $x + 11 = 4$

Solution: Add -11 to both members:

$$
\begin{array}{r}
x + 11 = 4 \\
-11 \quad -11 \\
\hline
x \quad\quad = -7 \quad (\textit{answer})
\end{array}
$$

Check: $\quad x + 11 = 4$

$\quad\quad\quad -7 + 11 = 4 \quad (x = -7)$

$\quad\quad\quad\quad\quad\quad 4 = 4 \;\checkmark$

Recall that our aim is always to get the unknown term by itself. In the above problem, we wanted to get the x by itself, so we added -11 to both sides of the equation. Since $+11$ and -11 add up to zero, the left member became $x + 0$, or x.

ILLUSTRATIVE PROBLEM 2

Solve and check: $y - 5 = 7$

Solution: Add $+5$ to both members:

$$
\begin{array}{r}
y - 5 = 7 \\
+5 \quad +5 \\
\hline
y \quad\quad = 12 \quad (\textit{answer})
\end{array}
$$

Check: $y - 5 = 7$

$+12 - 5 = 7$ $(y = 12)$

$7 = 7$ √

Exercises

Solve and check the following equations:

1. $y + 15 = 9$

2. $x - 10 = -4$

3. $18 = n - 6$

4. $7 + t = -15$

5. $-12 = -20 + r$

6. $-15 = s + 22$

7. $p + 2.4 = 8.7$

8. $7.6 + k = -15.4$

9. $n - 5\frac{1}{2} = 8$

10. $f - 6\frac{1}{3} = -7$

11. $g - 3\frac{1}{4} = -5\frac{1}{2}$

12. $3\frac{1}{8} + y = 7\frac{1}{2}$

13. $\frac{1}{2} + m = -\frac{3}{4}$

14. $3.14 = w + 6.28$

15. $-7 + x = -7$

16. $13 = y + 13$

1. _____   2. _____

3. _____   4. _____

5. _____   6. _____

7. _____   8. _____

9. _____   10. _____

11. _____   12. _____

13. _____   14. _____

15. _____   16. _____

2. Solving equations by multiplication and division of signed numbers

In Chapter 2, we solved equations by multiplying or dividing both members by the numbers of arithmetic. We may now extend these principles of equality to the same operations with signed numbers.

ILLUSTRATIVE PROBLEM 1

Solve and check: $6x = -24$

Solution: Divide both members by $+6$:

$$6x = -24$$

$$\frac{6x}{6} = \frac{-24}{6}$$

$$x = -4 \quad (answer)$$

Check:
$$6x = -24$$
$$6(-4) = -24$$
$$-24 = -24 \; \checkmark$$

ILLUSTRATIVE PROBLEM 2

Solve and check: $-\dfrac{3}{4}y = 15$

Solution: We may divide both sides by $-\dfrac{3}{4}$. As we learned in our study of fractions, this is the same as multiplying both sides by $-\dfrac{4}{3}$ (the reciprocal of $-\dfrac{3}{4}$). Thus,

$$-\frac{3}{4}y = 15$$

$$\left(-\frac{4}{3}\right)\left(-\frac{3}{4}y\right) = \left(-\frac{4}{3}\right)(15)$$

$$1 \cdot y = -20$$

$$y = -20 \quad (answer)$$

Check:
$$-\frac{3}{4}y = 15$$
$$\left(-\frac{3}{4}\right)(-20) = 15$$
$$15 = 15 \; \checkmark$$

ILLUSTRATIVE PROBLEM 3

Solve and check: $\dfrac{p}{8} = -3$

Solution: In order to obtain $1 \cdot p$ or p in the left member of the equation, we must multiply both members of the equation by 8. Thus,

$$\frac{p}{8} = -3$$

$$8\left(\frac{p}{8}\right) = 8(-3)$$

$$1 \cdot p = -24$$

$$p = -24 \quad (answer)$$

Check: $\quad \dfrac{p}{8} = -3$

$$\frac{-24}{8} = -3$$

$$-3 = -3 \quad \checkmark$$

Exercises

Solve and check.

1. $3t = -18$ **2.** $4y = -7$

3. $7k = -4$ **4.** $-6x = 42$

5. $-11r = 99$ **6.** $-8 = 3p$

7. $-5m = 15.5$ **8.** $-z = 17$

9. $-9a = -36$ **10.** $-12b = -6$

11. $-13c = -39$ **12.** $-8d = -44$

13. $-\dfrac{1}{5}p = 8$ **14.** $\dfrac{1}{6}m = -7$

15. $\dfrac{2}{3}k = -10$ **16.** $\dfrac{4}{5}r = -1.6$

17. $-\dfrac{5}{3}x = \dfrac{3}{5}$ **18.** $2\dfrac{2}{3}y = -48$

19. $-\dfrac{5}{2}t = -7\dfrac{1}{2}$ **20.** $\dfrac{a}{3} = -10$

1. _____   2. _____
3. _____   4. _____
5. _____   6. _____
7. _____   8. _____
9. _____   10. _____
11. _____   12. _____
13. _____   14. _____
15. _____   16. _____
17. _____   18. _____
19. _____   20. _____

21. $-\dfrac{f}{5} = 13$ **22.** $\dfrac{m}{-7} = -5$

21. _____ **22.** _____

23. $-\dfrac{3}{8}p = -15$ **24.** $\dfrac{b}{12} = -\dfrac{5}{6}$

23. _____ **24.** _____

25. $\dfrac{k}{8} = -\dfrac{5}{4}$ **26.** $-\dfrac{3s}{4} = \dfrac{5}{12}$

25. _____ **26.** _____

27. $\dfrac{r}{-7} = -\dfrac{3}{28}$

27. _____

3. Solving equations using two operations

If the solution of an equation requires two operations, it is usually simpler to use the addition principle first, and then the multiplication or division principle. However, before either principle is used, like terms (if any) should be combined.

ILLUSTRATIVE PROBLEM 1

Solve and check: $2x - 6x + 9 = -7$

Solution:

Combine like terms:
$$(2x - 6x) + 9 = -7$$
$$-4x + 9 = -7$$

Add -9 to both members:
$$\begin{array}{r} -9 \quad -9 \\ \hline -4x \quad\quad = -16 \end{array}$$

Divide both members by -4:
$$\frac{-4x}{-4} = \frac{-16}{-4}$$
$$x = 4$$
$$(answer)$$

Check:
$$2x - 6x + 9 = -7$$
$$2(4) - 6(4) + 9 = -7$$
$$8 - 24 + 9 = -7$$
$$-7 = -7 \;\checkmark$$

ILLUSTRATIVE PROBLEM 2

Solve and check: $\dfrac{y}{5} - 13 = 17$

Solution:

$$\frac{y}{5} - 13 = 17$$

Add 13 to both members:

$$\frac{+13 \quad +13}{\dfrac{y}{5} \quad = \quad 30}$$

Multiply both members by 5:

$$5\left(\frac{y}{5}\right) = 30 \cdot 5$$

$$y = 150$$
(answer)

Check:

$$\frac{y}{5} - 13 = 17$$

$$\frac{150}{5} - 13 = 17$$

$$30 - 13 = 17$$

$$17 = 17 \; \checkmark$$

Exercises

In 1 to 26, solve and check.

1. $4x + 3 = -21$ **2.** $9y - 5 = 22$

3. $6 = 7k - 15$ **4.** $-5 + 6t = -23$

5. $5p - 8 = 12$ **6.** $9 = 4a - 7$

7. $7r - 3r = -10$ **8.** $2s - 5s = 18$

9. $\dfrac{b}{3} - 7 = 1$ **10.** $\dfrac{c}{8} + 1 = -3$

11. $3x - 6x + 2 = -7$ **12.** $8y - 2y - 11 = 19$

13. $-\dfrac{3k}{4} + 7 = 13$ **14.** $\dfrac{5n}{8} - 8 = 2$

15. $-11 + \dfrac{2c}{3} = -15$ **16.** $-\dfrac{2a}{3} + 4 = 9$

17. $2x + 4 = 16$ **18.** $\dfrac{3p}{2} - 4 = 11$

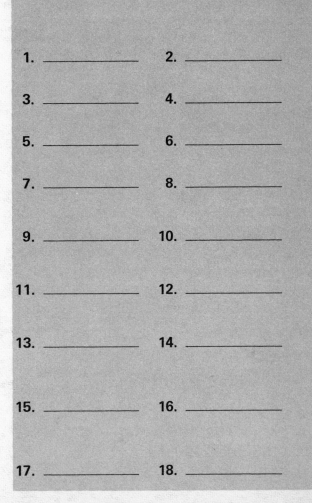

1. _____   2. _____

3. _____   4. _____

5. _____   6. _____

7. _____   8. _____

9. _____   10. _____

11. _____   12. _____

13. _____   14. _____

15. _____   16. _____

17. _____   18. _____

19. $8a + 3 = 11$ **20.** $\dfrac{t}{3} + 4 = 15$

21. $\dfrac{d}{8} + 45 = 64$ **22.** $2x - 6 = 0$

23. $2y - y + 7 = -9$ **24.** $8x + 4 - 7x = 9$

25. $6m - 8 - 3m = -17$ **26.** $-7 + 11y + y = 17$

27. If 3 times a number is added to 7, the result is 40. Find the number.

28. If six times a number is subtracted from 40, the result is -14. Find the number.

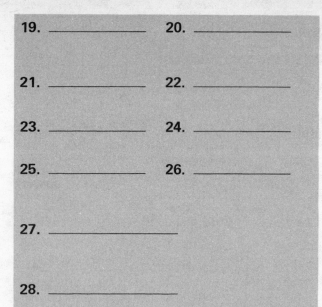

19. _____   **20.** _____

21. _____   **22.** _____

23. _____   **24.** _____

25. _____   **26.** _____

27. _____

28. _____

4. Solving equations with the unknown on both sides

If terms involving the unknown are on both sides of an equation, we try to eliminate the unknown on one side by adding a suitable monomial to both sides of the equation.

ILLUSTRATIVE PROBLEM 1

Solve and check: $7t = 24 - 5t$

Solution: Add $5t$ to both sides. Thus,

$$
\begin{array}{rr}
7t = 24 - & 5t \\
+5t & +5t \\
\hline
12t = 24 &
\end{array}
$$

Divide both members by 12:

$$\frac{12t}{12} = \frac{24}{12}$$

$$t = 2 \quad (answer)$$

Check: $7t = 24 - 5t$

$7(2) = 24 - 5(2)$

$14 = 24 - 10$

$14 = 14 \ \checkmark$

ILLUSTRATIVE PROBLEM 2

Solve and check: $4y + 12 = 48 - 2y$

Solution:

$$4y + 12 = 48 - 2y$$
$$\underline{+2y \qquad\qquad\quad +2y}$$
$$6y + 12 = 48$$

$$6y + 12 = 48$$
$$\underline{\qquad -12 \quad -12}$$
$$6y \qquad = 36$$

$$\frac{6y}{6} = \frac{36}{6}$$

$$y = 6 \quad (answer)$$

Check: $\quad 4y + 12 = 48 - 2y$

$$4(6) + 12 = 48 - 2(6)$$

$$24 + 12 = 48 - 12$$

$$36 = 36 \;\checkmark$$

Exercises

In 1 to 28, solve and check.

1. $8p = 10 + 3p$ **2.** $7p = 55 - 4p$

3. $15t = 6t + 36$ **4.** $17a = 28a + 44$

5. $9k = 70 - k$ **6.** $7d = 6 - 2d$

7. $9x = 36 + 5x$ **8.** $12r = 19r - 35$

9. $4y = 39y + 70$ **10.** $-3m = 4m - 49$

11. $.9s = .3s - 30$ **12.** $3\frac{3}{4}n = 60 - 1\frac{1}{4}n$

13. $15t + 19 = -3t - 17$

14. $8k - 17 = -29 - 4k$

15. $6p + 17 = -2p - 15$

16. $3x + 11 = 6x + 2$

1. _____   2. _____

3. _____   4. _____

5. _____   6. _____

7. _____   8. _____

9. _____   10. _____

11. _____   12. _____

13. _____

14. _____

15. _____

16. _____

17. $7b + 23 = 7 - b$

17. _____

18. $t - 7 = -6t + 21$

18. _____

19. $5r - 12 = 12r - 5$

19. _____

20. $-3m + 4 = -7m - 14$

20. _____

21. $10n - 2 = 3n + 47$

21. _____

22. $-a + 18 = 53 - 6a$

22. _____

23. $-7x = -8 + x - 14$

23. _____

24. $4y + 33 = 15y - 11$

24. _____

25. $10p - 6 - 5p = -5p + 4$

25. _____

26. $4m + 1 = 8m + 3$

26. _____

27. $15a = 30a + 33 - 4a$

27. _____

28. $14n + 3 = 15n + 8 - 6n$

28. _____

29. Seven times a number equals 45 more than twice the number. Find the number.

29. _____

30. Three times a number is equal to 20 less than five times the number. Find the number.

30. _____

31. If 3 times a number is increased by 12, the result is equal to 7 times the number. Find the number.

31. _____

32. If 5 times a number is decreased by 8, the result is the same as 3 times the number increased by 30.

32. _____

33. If 4 times a number is increased by 7, the result is the same as 31 more than the number. Find the number.

33. _____

34. If 3 times a number is increased by 7, the result is the same as when 72 is decreased by twice the number. Find the number.

34. _____

35. If 7 times a number is decreased by 8, the result is the same as when 80 is decreased by 4 times the number. Find the number.

35. _____

36. Six times a number exceeds 25 by the same amount that twice the number exceeds 15. Find the number.

36. _____

5. Solving equations containing parentheses

To solve an equation containing parentheses, first remove the parentheses by use of the distributive property or by performing the operation indicated. Then proceed to solve the resulting equation.

ILLUSTRATIVE PROBLEM 1

Solve and check: $6y - 3(y - 4) = -6$

Solution: $\qquad 6y - 3(y - 4) = -6$

Remove parentheses: $\qquad 6y - 3y + 12 = -6$

Combine terms: $\qquad\qquad 3y + 12 = -6$
Add -12 to both sides: $\qquad\quad \underline{ -12 \quad -12}$
$\qquad\qquad\qquad 3y \qquad\qquad = -18$

Divide both sides by 3: $\qquad\qquad y = -6$
$\qquad\qquad\qquad\qquad\qquad (answer)$

Check: $\qquad 6(-6) - 3(-6 - 4) = -6$

$-36 - 3(-10) = -6$

$-36 + 30 = -6$

$-6 = -6 \checkmark$

ILLUSTRATIVE PROBLEM 2

Solve and check: $9p - (p + 3) = 21$

Solution: $\qquad\qquad 9p - 1(p + 3) = 21$

Remove parentheses: $\qquad 9p - p - 3 = 21$

Combine like terms: $8p \quad -3 = 21$

Add +3 to both sides: $\dfrac{\qquad\qquad +3 \quad +3}{8p \qquad\qquad = 24}$

Divide both sides by 8: $p = \quad 3$
                                                    (*answer*)

Check: $9p - (p + 3) = 21$

$\qquad\qquad 9(3) - (3 + 3) = 21$

$\qquad\qquad\qquad 27 - 6 = 21$

$\qquad\qquad\qquad\qquad 21 = 21 \checkmark$

Exercises

In 1 to 18, solve and check.

1. $2t + 3(t - 5) = -20$ 1. _____

2. $3p - 2(p + 1) = 13$ 2. _____

3. $2n + (3n - 8) = -28$ 3. _____

4. $7k + (3k - 5) = 55$ 4. _____

5. $7n - (4n + 9) = -15$ 5. _____

6. $y - (8y - 11) = 46$ 6. _____

7. $(2k + 7) - 18 = +3$ 7. _____

8. $(4x - 7) - 12 = 13$ 8. _____

9. $a - (15 - a) = 45$ 9. _____

10. $5(7n - 3) = 20$ 10. _____

11. $6(2b - 3) = 54$ 11. _____

12. $8(y + 2) = 5(2y - 4)$ 12. _____

13. $8p - (4p + 6) = 46$ 13. _____

14. $8t - (5t + 3) = 12$ 14. _____

15. $4(2a - 9) - 6(10 - a) = 2$

15. _____

16. $2(c - 3) - 7 = 12 - 5(c - 2)$

16. _____

17. $10 + 3(5m + 2) = -m$

17. _____

18. $3(p - 2) - 19 = 13 - 5(p + 2)$

18. _____

19. The larger of two numbers is 7 more than the smaller. The larger number plus five times the smaller equals 67. Find the numbers.

19. _____

20. One number is 5 less than another. If 5 times the larger is subtracted from 8 times the smaller, the result is 11. Find the numbers.

20. _____

21. A shirt costs $7 more than a tie. Three shirts and 5 ties cost $53. Find the cost of each.

21. _____

22. The length of a rectangle is 7 inches shorter than four times its width. Find the width if the perimeter is 66 feet.

22. _____

6. Using equations to solve verbal problems

In Chapter 3, we learned to solve some simple verbal problems by the use of equations. Among others, we dealt with number problems, coin problems, perimeter problems, and problems arising from the use of various formulas.

Now that we have learned more about solving equations, we are in a position to solve more difficult verbal problems. Review the steps in Section 2, Chapter 3 for solving verbal problems. The following illustrative problems indicate how this method is extended to some slightly more difficult problems.

ILLUSTRATIVE PROBLEM 1

Find two consecutive integers whose sum is -31.

Solution:

Let n = first integer.

And $n + 1$ = second integer.

$$n + (n + 1) = -31 \quad \text{(write equation)}$$
$$n + n + 1 = -31 \quad \text{(remove parentheses)}$$
$$2n + 1 = -31 \quad \text{(combine like terms)}$$
$$\underline{\quad\quad -1 \quad\quad -1} \quad \text{(add } -1 \text{ to both sides)}$$
$$2n \quad\quad = -32$$
$$n \quad\quad = -16 \quad \text{(divide both sides by 2)}$$
$$n + 1 = -16 + 1 = -15$$

Answer: The numbers are -16 and -15.

Check: Do -16 and -15 add up to -31?

$$(-16) + (-15) = -31 \ \checkmark$$

ILLUSTRATIVE PROBLEM 2

Mary has 30 coins in her coin bank, consisting only of nickels and dimes. If the total value of the coins is $2.40, how many of each kind does she have?

Solution:

Let x = number of nickels.

Then $(30 - x)$ = number of dimes.

And $5x$ = value of the nickels in cents.

And $10(30 - x)$ = value of the dimes in cents.

$$5x + 10(30 - x) = 240 \quad \text{(write equation)}$$
$$5x + 300 - 10x = 240 \quad \text{(remove parentheses)}$$
$$-5x + 300 = 240 \quad \text{(combine like terms)}$$
$$\underline{\quad\quad -300 \quad -300} \quad \text{(add } -300 \text{ to both sides)}$$
$$-5x \quad\quad = -60$$
$$x \quad\quad = 12 \quad \text{(divide both sides by } -5)$$
$$30 - x = 30 - 12 = 18$$

Answer: Mary has 12 nickels and 18 dimes.

Check: Is the total value of 12 nickels and 18 dimes equal to $2.40?

$$12(5) + 18(10) = 60 + 180 = 240 \ \checkmark$$

ILLUSTRATIVE PROBLEM 3

Tom's father is now 3 times as old as Tom. Four years ago, he was 4 times as old as Tom. Find the age of each now.

Solution:

Let t = Tom's age now (in years).

Then $3t$ = father's age now.

And $t - 4$ = Tom's age 4 years ago.

And $3t - 4$ = father's age 4 years ago.

$$3t - 4 = 4(t - 4) \quad \text{(write equation)}$$

$$
\begin{array}{ll}
3t - 4 = 4t - 16 & \text{(remove parentheses)} \\
\underline{ +4 = +4} & \text{(add 4 to both sides)} \\
3t = 4t - 12 & \\
\underline{-4t -4t} & \text{(add } -4t \text{ to both sides)} \\
-t = -12 &
\end{array}
$$

$$t = 12 \quad \text{(divide both sides by } -1\text{)}$$

$$3t = 3(12) = 36$$

Answer: Tom's age is now 12 and his father's age is 36.

Check: Four years ago, Tom was 8 and his father was 32.

$$32 = 4(8)$$

$$32 = 32 \; \checkmark$$

ILLUSTRATIVE PROBLEM 4

The length of a rectangle is 8 inches more than its width. If the perimeter of the rectangle is 68 inches, find its dimensions.

Solution:

Let w = width in inches.

Then $w + 8$ = length in inches.

And perimeter = $2 \times$ length + $2 \times$ width.

$$
\begin{array}{ll}
68 = 2(w + 8) + 2w & \text{(write equation)} \\
68 = 2w + 16 + 2w & \text{(remove parentheses)} \\
68 = 4w + 16 & \text{(combine like terms)} \\
\underline{-16 -16} & \text{(add } -16 \text{ to both sides)} \\
52 = 4w & \\
w = 13 & \text{(divide both sides by 4)} \\
w + 8 = 13 + 8 = 21 &
\end{array}
$$

Answer: The dimensions are 21 in. and 13 in.

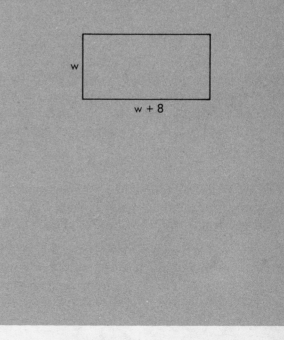

Check: perimeter $= 2l + 2w$

$$68 = 2(21) + 2(13)$$
$$68 = 42 + 26$$
$$68 = 68 \checkmark$$

Exercises

1. Jane has 20 coins in her purse consisting of dimes and quarters. If the total value of the coins is $3.50, find the number of each kind of coin.

2. The length of a rectangular room is 5 feet less than twice the width. If the perimeter is 110 feet, find the dimensions of the room.

3. In a math class of 34 pupils, there are 8 more boys than girls. How many boys and how many girls are in the class?

4. A ninth-grade class contributed $3.50 in nickels and dimes to the Red Cross. In all there were 45 coins. How many of each kind were there?

5. The larger of two numbers is 5 more than twice the smaller. The larger number exceeds the smaller by 14. Find the numbers.

6. The length of a rectangle is twice the width. If the length is increased by 4 and the width diminished by one, the new perimeter will be 198. Find the dimensions of the original rectangle.

7. One weekend Bill earned 3 times as much as Jim. Tom earned $5 more than Jim. In all, they earned $60. How much did each earn?

8. Nancy bought 50 postage stamps for which she paid $3.60. Some were 6-cent stamps and some were 10-cent stamps. How many of each did she buy?

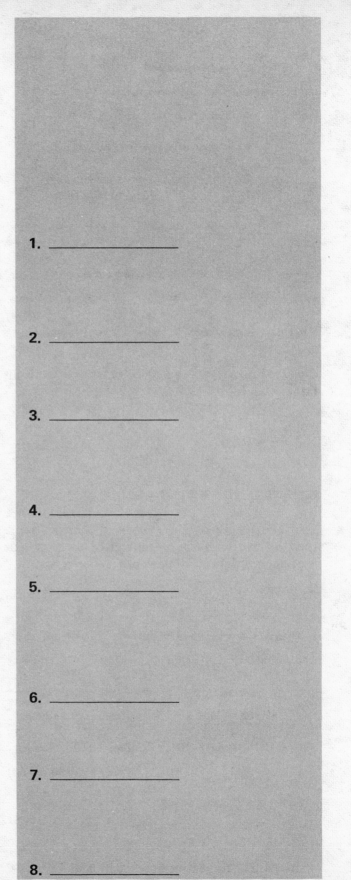

1. _____

2. _____

3. _____

4. _____

5. _____

6. _____

7. _____

8. _____

9. Arthur and Joe bought the same number of savings bonds. Arthur still has all of his. Joe has two-thirds of his. Together they still have 75 bonds. How many did each purchase?

9. _____

10. The perimeter of a rectangle is 40. The length is 2 more than 5 times the width. Find the dimensions.

10. _____

11. Peter has 5 times as many marbles as Don. Tony has 3 fewer than 4 times as many as Don. In all they have 167 marbles. How many does each have?

11. _____

12. At a basketball game, student tickets were 50¢ each and adult tickets were $1.00 each. If the total receipts from 900 tickets were $500, how many tickets of each kind were sold?

12. _____

13. Three partners in a business are to divide the profits in the ratio of $2:3:4$. If the profits for the first year are $7200, how much does each partner receive?

13. _____

14. Using the formula $C = \frac{5}{9}(F - 32)$, find F when $C = 20$.

14. _____

15. At an afternoon movie, tickets cost 42 cents for children, and 90 cents for adults. If a total of 550 tickets were sold and the receipts were $279, how many adults attended?

15. _____

16. The sum of the angles of any triangle is 180°. If the three angles of a triangle are in the ratio of $2:5:8$, find each angle of the triangle.

16. _____

17. A man is now 28 years of age and his daughter is 4 years old. In how many years will he be 4 times as old as his daughter?

17. _____

18. Separate 84 into two parts such that one part will be 12 less than twice the other.

18. _____

19. One number is 3 times another number. If 17 is added to each, the first result is twice the second resulting number. Find the two numbers.

19. _____

20. Find two consecutive integers such that twice the smaller diminished by the larger is 71.

20. _____

7. Motion problems: Introduction

If an auto travels at a rate (or speed) of 60 miles per hour, then, in 5 hours, it will travel $60(5) = 300$ miles. This relationship may be expressed by the formula

$$d = rt$$

where d is the distance (in miles), r is the rate or average speed (in miles per hour, mph), and t is the time (in hours).

By dividing both sides of the formula above, first by r and then by t, we obtain the equivalent formulas

$$t = \frac{d}{r} \quad \text{and} \quad r = \frac{d}{t}$$

which are also frequently used in solving uniform motion problems.

If a car travels 100 miles at the rate of 40 miles per hour, the time it takes is given by the formula $t = \dfrac{d}{r}$:

$$t = \frac{d}{r} = \frac{100}{40} = 2\frac{1}{2} \text{ hours}$$

If a plane flies 600 miles in 3 hours, then its average rate is

$$r = \frac{d}{t} = \frac{600}{3} = 200 \text{ mph}$$

Problems may be literal as well as numerical. How many miles does a boy ride his bike if his rate is x miles per hour for 4 hours?

$$d = rt$$

$$d = x(4) = 4x \text{ miles}$$

Exercises

1. How far will a plane fly it it goes 250 mph for:

   a. 3 hours?   **b.** $4\frac{1}{2}$ hours?   **c.** n hours?

   1. a. _____ **b.** _____ **c.** _____

2. How far will a plane fly it it goes y miles an hour for:

   a. 3 hours?   **b.** h hours?

   c. $(h + 2)$ hours?

   2. a. _____ **b.** _____

   c. _____

3. **a.** If a man walks 9 miles in 3 hours, what is his rate?

   b. If a man walks m miles in h hours, what is his rate?

   3. a. _____

   b. _____

4. How long does it take a boy to ride his bike 15 miles:

   a. at 5 miles per hour?

   b. at 3 miles per hour?

   c. at k miles per hour?

   4. a. _____

   b. _____

   c. _____

5. How fast must a train travel to cover 350 miles:

   a. in 7 hours?   **b.** in 5 hours?

   c. in $(n + 3)$ hours?

   5. a. _____ **b.** _____

   c. _____

6. How far will an auto travel in 4 hours at an average speed of:

   a. 45 miles per hour?   **b.** 58 miles per hour?

   c. $(r - 10)$ miles per hour?

   6. a. _____ **b.** _____

   c. _____

7. Two cars start from the same place and travel for h hours in opposite directions at rates of 40 mph and 50 mph.

   a. Represent in terms of h the distance traveled by the slower car.

   b. Represent in terms of h the distance traveled by the faster car.

   7. a. _____

   b. _____

c. Represent how far apart the two cars are at the end of *h* hours.

d. Write an equation which would indicate that the cars are 270 miles apart at the end of *h* hours.

8. Two planes started from different points and flew toward each other. The slower plane flew at 200 mph and the faster at 250 mph. They met in *n* hours.

a. Represent in terms of *n* the distance traveled by the slower plane.

b. Represent in terms of *n* the distance traveled by the faster plane.

c. Represent in terms of *n* the total distance they traveled.

d. Write an equation which would indicate that the planes were originally 1000 miles apart.

c. _____

d. _____

8. a. _____

b. _____

c. _____

d. _____

8. Solving motion problems

ILLUSTRATIVE PROBLEM 1

Two trains are 700 miles apart. In how many hours will they meet if one is moving at 40 mph and the other at 30 mph?

Solution: Draw a diagram of the situation, as shown at the right.

Let t = no. of hours until they meet.

Then $40t$ = distance traveled by faster train.

And $30t$ = distance traveled by slower train.

$$40t + 30t = 700$$
$$70t = 700$$
$$t = 10 \text{ hours} \quad (answer)$$

Check: $40t = 40(10) = 400$ miles
$30t = 30(10) = 300$ miles
$400 + 300 = 700$ miles $\checkmark$

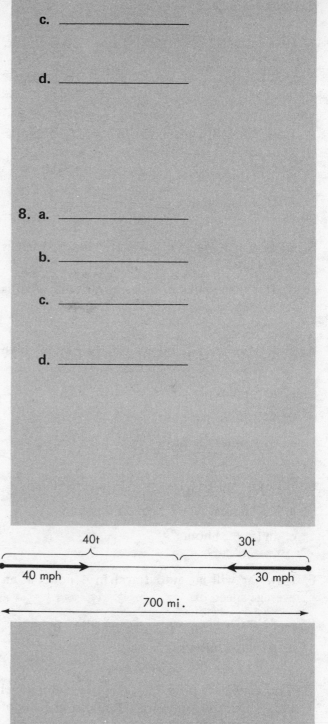

40t   30t

40 mph →   ← 30 mph

←——— 700 mi. ———→

ILLUSTRATIVE PROBLEM 2

Two planes start from the same point and travel in opposite directions, one at 60 mph faster than the other. In 5 hours they are 1500 miles apart. How fast is each plane flying?

Solution: Draw a diagram, as shown at the right.

Let r = rate of slower plane.

Then $r + 60$ = rate of faster plane.

And $5r$ = distance traveled by slower plane.

And $5(r + 60)$ = distance traveled by faster plane.

$5r + 5(r + 60) = 1500$

$5r + 5r + 300 = 1500$

$10r + 300 = 1500$

$$\frac{-300 \qquad -300}{10r \qquad = 1200}$$

$r \qquad = 120$ mph (slower plane)

$r + 60 = 180$ mph (faster plane)

Check: $5(120) = 600$ mi. (distance, slower plane)

$$5(180) = \underline{900 \text{ mi.}} \quad \text{(distance, faster plane)}$$
$$1500 \text{ mi. } \checkmark$$

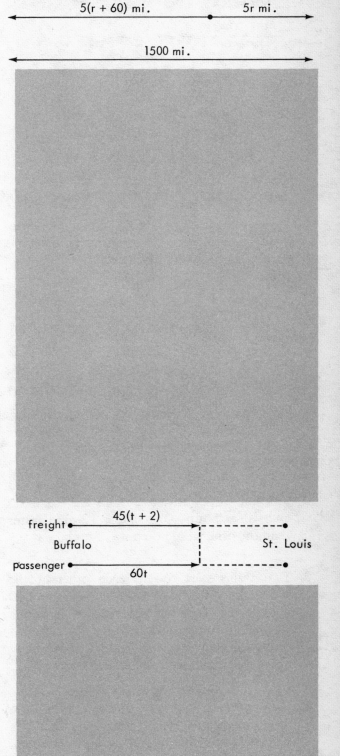

ILLUSTRATIVE PROBLEM 3

A freight train leaves Buffalo for St. Louis traveling at the rate of 45 mph. Two hours later a passenger train leaves Buffalo for St. Louis traveling at 60 mph. In how many hours will the passenger train overtake the freight train?

Solution: Since the freight train left 2 hours earlier, it travels 2 hours longer than the passenger train.

Let t = no. of hours passenger train travels.

Then $t + 2$ = no. of hours freight train travels.

And $60t$ = distance traveled by passenger train.

And $45(t + 2)$ = distance traveled by freight train.

The distance traveled by the passenger train is the same as the distance traveled by the freight train. Thus,

$$60t = 45(t + 2)$$

$$60t = 45t + 90$$

$$\begin{array}{r} -45t \quad -45t \\ \hline 15t = 90 \end{array}$$

$$t = 6 \text{ hours} \quad (answer)$$

Check: $60(6) = 360$ miles
                    (distance, passenger train)

$45(6 + 2) = 45(8) = 360$ miles
                    (distance, freight train)

Distances are equal. ✓

Note that, in the preceding illustrative problems, it is helpful to draw distance diagrams to clarify the relationship needed to form an equation.

Exercises

1. Two cars leave the same place at the same time and travel in opposite directions. At the end of 7 hours, they are 455 miles apart. Find the rate of each if one travels 5 mph faster than the other.

   1. _____

2. Two trains starting from the same place and traveling in opposite directions are 432 miles apart in 6 hours. One rate is 12 mph faster than the other. Find the rate of each.

   2. _____

3. Two trains start toward each other at the same time from stations which are 570 miles apart. One is a passenger train which averages 55 mph, while the other is a freight train which averages 40 mph. In how many hours will they meet?

   3. _____

4. Two airplanes start from Chicago at the same time and fly in opposite directions. One flies 20 mph faster than the other. After 3 hours,

they are 1140 miles apart. Find the rate of each plane.

4. _____

5. Two trains are 276 miles apart, and are traveling toward each other at rates of 42 mph and 50 mph respectively. In how many hours will they meet?

5. _____

6. Two planes leave the airport at the same time, traveling in opposite directions. The rate of one plane is 30 mph faster than that of the other. If they are 860 miles apart at the end of 2 hours, what is the rate of each plane?

6. _____

7. An eastbound freight train left the station at 8 A.M. traveling at the rate of 40 mph. At 10 A.M. an eastbound passenger train left the same station traveling 60 mph. At what time will the passenger train overtake the freight train?

7. _____

8. A truck and a car leave the city at the same time traveling along the same road. The car is traveling twice as fast as the truck. If, at the end of 3 hours, the car is 72 miles ahead of the truck, find the rate of each.

8. _____

9. A boy walked a certain distance at the rate of 3 mph. One and one-half hours after he left, his father followed him at the rate of 4 mph. How many miles had the boy gone when his father overtook him?

9. _____

10. Ted left home on his bicycle traveling at the rate of 6 mph. One hour later Jack set out to overtake him traveling at the rate of 8 mph. In how many hours will Jack overtake Ted?

10. _____

11. A jet and a propeller plane leave the same airport at the same time and travel in opposite directions. The rate of the jet is 550 mph and the rate of the propeller plane is 300 mph.

   a. In how many hours will they be 2550 miles apart?

11. a. _____

b. How many miles from the airport will the jet be at this time?

12. At 10 A.M. two men start from two different towns which are 270 miles apart. They travel toward each other and meet at 1 P.M. If one man's rate is 10 mph faster than the rate of the other, find the rate of each.

Chapter review exercises

In 1 to 16, solve and check.

1. $n - 9 = -3$ **2.** $-k + 11 = -4$

3. $y + 12 = -5$ **4.** $4x = 3$

5. $-3p = 10$ **6.** $4t + 7 = 6$

7. $3a + 7 = a - 5$ **8.** $3r + 7 + 2r = 2$

9. $3y + 1 = 8y + 16$

10. $10n - 2(3n + 1) = 26$

11. $7b + 5 = 3b + 17$ **12.** $2(3r - 1) = 5r + 4$

13. $6t + 13 = 4t + 15$

14. $4(d + 6) + d = 8d - 3$

15. $5a - 4 = 3a + 6$ **16.** $6(y + 3) = 2y - 2$

17. Three children each contributed toward a birthday present for their mother. The oldest contributed three times as much as the youngest, while the second oldest contributed 50 cents more than the youngest. If the present cost $3.50, how much did each contribute?

18. A rectangular playground is enclosed by 440 feet of fencing. If the length of the play-

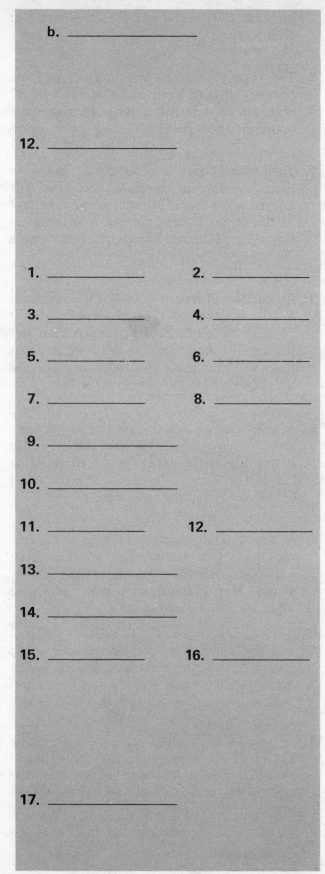

b. _____

12. _____

1. _____   2. _____

3. _____   4. _____

5. _____   6. _____

7. _____   8. _____

9. _____

10. _____

11. _____   12. _____

13. _____

14. _____

15. _____   16. _____

17. _____

ground is 20 feet less than three times the width, find the dimensions of the playground.

19. Two trains left the station at the same time traveling in opposite directions. The rate of one train was 12 mph faster than the other train. At the end of 3 hours, the trains were 276 miles apart. What was the rate of each train?

20. There are 153 pupils in the senior class. If the ratio of boys to girls is 5:4, how many boys are in the class?

21. A boy saved nickels and dimes until he had $1.45. If he had 8 more nickels than dimes, how many dimes did he have?

22. During May, Jack, Bob, and Jerry earned a total of $115. If Bob earned twice as much as Jack, and Jerry earned $15 more than Jack, how much did each earn?

23. Bill is now twice as old as his sister. Four years ago the sum of their ages was 10. What are their ages now?

24. A salesman sold 200 pairs of sneakers. Some were sold at $6 per pair and the remainder were sold at $11 per pair. Total receipts from this sale were $1600. How many pairs of sneakers were sold at $6 each?

18. _____

19. _____

20. _____

21. _____

22. _____

23. _____

24. _____

GRAPHING LINEAR
EQUATIONS

1. Graphing
a formula

In some of our work in previous grades, we learned to read and make graphs of a statistical nature, such as bar and line graphs. It is frequently desirable for us to graph a formula or an equation.

For example, if a boy is riding his bicycle at 4 miles per hour, the distance (d), in miles, which he travels is given by the formula $d = 4t$, where t is the number of hours he travels.

The relation between d and t may also be shown by a table:

When t is:	0	1	2	3	4	5
Then d is:	0	4	8	12	16	20

The table can show only a few of the possible pairs of values for t and d, since t can have any positive or zero value and d will vary as t varies. Thus, we call t and d *variables* of the formula.

Another way in which we can picture the relations between variables is by graphing the relations. We shall illustrate this below by using the table we established above for the formula $d = 4t$.

Draw a vertical and a horizontal line meeting at a point. These lines are called the *vertical axis* and the *horizontal axis*, respectively. The point of intersection of the axes is called the *origin*. See Fig. 1.

We now choose appropriate scales for each axis so that we can repre-

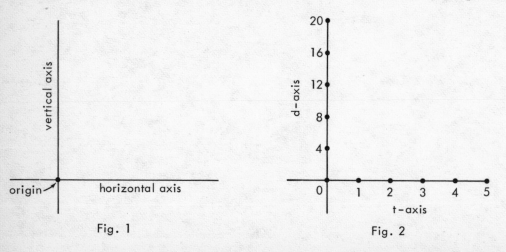

Fig. 1

Fig. 2

sent all the values in the table on the graph. In Fig. 2, each space on the horizontal axis is 1 and each space on the vertical axis is 4.

We now represent each pair of numbers on the table as a point. The point for $t = 3$ and $d = 12$ is located by moving 3 units to the right on the horizontal or t-axis and then moving vertically up until we reach the line representing $d = 12$ on the vertical or d-axis. For the point representing $t = 5$ and $d = 20$, we move 5 to the right from the origin and then up to 20.

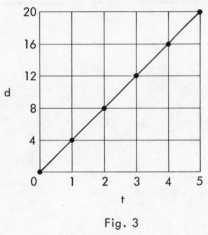

Fig. 3

We thus obtain five points from the pairs of numbers in the table. When we locate these points, we say that we are "plotting" them. In Fig. 3, note that the five points so plotted lie in a straight line, which is then drawn on the graph. The line starts at the origin and extends infinitely to the right and up. Any pair of values that satisfies the formula $d = 4t$ would be represented on the graph as a point on this line, and any point on this line would give us values of t and d that would satisfy the relation $d = 4t$.

The relation $d = 4t$ is a first-degree equation with two variables. It is first degree because the exponents of d and t are both understood to be 1. Since the graph of a first-degree equation is always a straight line, such an equation is often called a *linear equation*.

Once we have drawn the graph, we may take readings from it which were not in the original table. For example, when $t = 7$, find d.

Using Fig. 4, locate $t = 7$ on the horizontal axis. Draw a vertical line

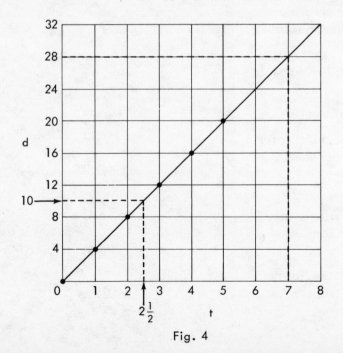

Fig. 4

up to the graph and, at that point, draw a horizontal line across to the d-axis. We see that $d = 28$.

Likewise, to find t when $d = 10$: locate 10 on the d-axis, draw a horizontal line across to the graph and, at that point, draw a vertical line down to the t-axis. We see that $t = 2\frac{1}{2}$.

Exercises

Use separate paper to make the tables of values; use graph paper to make the graphs.

1. The perimeter (p) of a square is given by the formula $p = 4s$ where s is the length of a side of the square.

  a. Make a table of values for this formula, using whole number values of s, from 1 to 5 inclusive.

  b. Make a graph from the table.

  c. From the graph, find (1) the value of p when $s = 7$; (2) the value of s when $p = 14$.

  1. c. (1) _____   **(2)** _____

2. The velocity V of an object (speed in feet per second) falling to the ground is given by the formula $V = 32t$ where t is the time in seconds that the object is falling.

  a. Make a table of values for the formula using $t = 0, 2, 4, 6, 8, 10$.

  b. Make a graph from the table of values.

  c. From the graph find (1) the value of V when $t = 7$; (2) the value of t when $V = 176$.

  2. c. (1) _____   **(2)** _____

3. d, the distance in miles a car travels at 30 miles per hour, is given by the formula $d = 30t$ where t is the number of hours it travels.

  a. Make a table of values for the formula using $t = 0, 2, 4, 6,$ and 8 hours.

  b. Make a graph from the table of values.

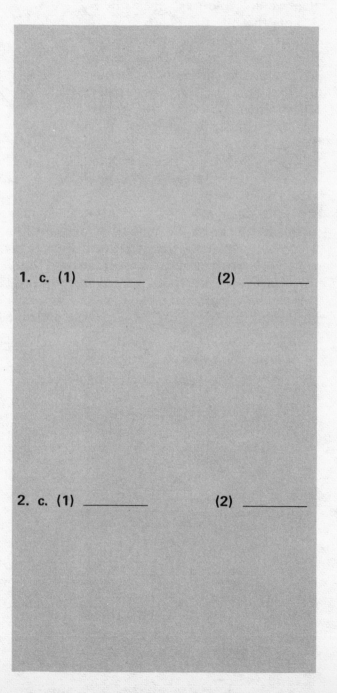

c. From the graph find (1) the value of *d* when *t* is 9; (2) the value of *t* when *d* = 195 miles.

4. The approximate number of miles *m* that is equivalent to a given number of kilometers *k* is given by the formula $m = .6k$. Make a table of values and a graph for this formula for values of $k = 0, 10, 20, 30, 40, 50$.

5. The equation $p = 2l + 5$ shows a relation between the length *l* and the perimeter *p* of a rectangle whose width is $2\frac{1}{2}$ inches.

a. Make a table of values for this formula using values of $l = 2, 5, 9, 12$.

b. Make a graph from the table of values.

c. From the graph find (1) the value of *p* when *l* is 7 inches; (2) the value of *l* when *p* is 28 inches.

6. Draw graphs of the relations shown by the following equations:

a. $r = \frac{2}{3}n$ $(n = 0, 3, 6, 9, 12)$

b. $s = 3t + 2$ $(t = 0, 2, 4, 6, 8)$

3. c. (1) _____   **(2)** _____

5. c. (1) _____   **(2)** _____

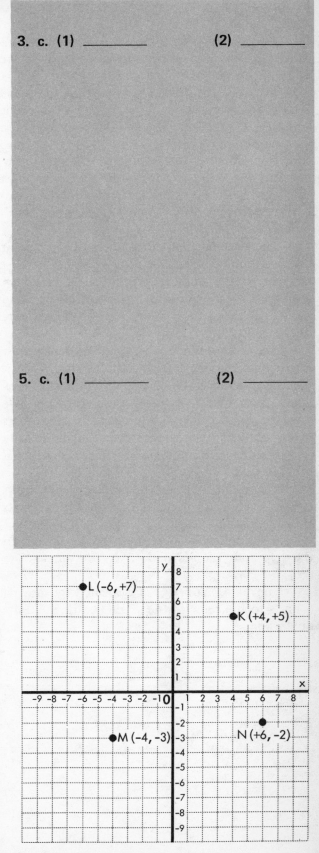

2. Graphs using signed numbers

Thus far, we have discussed only graphs that use positive numbers or zero as values of the variables. However, many formulas and relations may also use negative numbers as values of the variables. For example, a formula involving temperatures must also allow for negative values of temperature. The question then arises as to how to represent negative numbers on a graph.

We extend the horizontal axis to the left of the origin; we extend the vertical axis below the origin. We call the horizontal axis the *x*-axis and the vertical axis the *y*-axis, as shown in the diagram at the right.

On the *x*-axis, negative numbers are indicated

to the left of the origin (or 0); positive numbers are indicated to the right of the origin, as before. Likewise, on the y-axis, negative numbers are indicated below the origin; positive numbers are above the origin, as before.

To locate the point K on the graph, we move 4 units to the right of the origin along the x-axis and then 5 units up. The point K is designated by the number pair $(4, 5)$ or $(+4, +5)$. Note that the order of the numbers in a pair is important; the point $(5, 4)$ would give us a point other than K. Therefore, we refer to the numbers associated with any point on the graph as an *ordered number pair*.

The ordered pair of numbers for any point represents the *coordinates* of the point. The first number of the number pair is called the **x-*coordinate*** or the *abscissa* of the point. The second number is called the **y-*coordinate*** or the *ordinate* of the point.

The x-coordinate of a point indicates how many units to the left or right of the y-axis it is. The y-coordinate of a point indicates how many units above or below the x-axis it is. We must be careful not to interchange the numbers in an ordered pair as the reversed pair usually represents a different point than the original ordered pair.

The point L is located by moving 6 units to the left of the origin and then 7 units up. Its coordinates are $(-6, +7)$.

The point M is located by moving 4 units to the left and 3 units down. Its coordinates are $(-4, -3)$.

The point $N(+6, -2)$ is located by moving 6 units to the right of the origin and then 2 units down.

Exercises

1. Write as ordered number pairs the coordinates of points A, B, C, D, E, F, G, H, and O in the following graph:

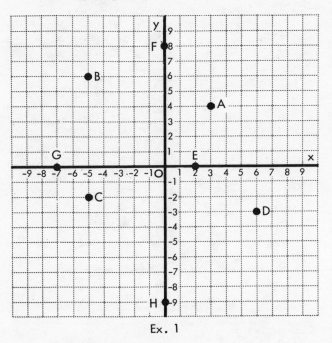

Ex. 1

1. A _____

   B _____

   C _____

   D _____

   E _____

   F _____

   G _____

   H _____

   O _____

2. Draw a pair of coordinate axes on a sheet of graph paper, place numbers along the axes, and plot the following points:
   $A(4, 7)$, $B(-2, 5)$, $C(-1, -6)$, $D(4, -5)$,
   $E(0, -3)$, $F(-4, 0)$, $G\left(-2\frac{1}{2}, -3\right)$, $H(0, 0)$,
   $J(6.4, -4.5)$

3. Draw axes on graph paper and locate the points $P(4, -3)$ and $Q(-3, 4)$. Join them with a straight line.

   a. At what point does the line cut the y-axis?

   b. At what point does the line cut the x-axis?

3. **a.** _____

   b. _____

4. Draw axes on graph paper and locate the points $R(11, 4)$ and $S(3, -4)$. Draw the line RS and extend it in both directions.

   a. At what point does the line cut the x-axis?

   b. At what point does the line cut the y-axis?

4. **a.** _____

   b. _____

5. Draw axes on graph paper and locate these points: $A(4, 2)$, $B(0, 2)$, $C(-1, -1)$, and $D(3, -1)$. Join them in succession. What is the name of the geometric figure $ABCD$?

5. _____

6. Draw axes on graph paper and locate these points: $(3, 4)$, $(3, 6)$, $(3, 0)$, $(3, -2)$, $(3, -5)$.

a. What is true of the abscissas of all five points?

6. a. _____

b. If you join all the points in succession, what geometric figure do you get?

b. _____

7. On the same axes as in exercise **6**, locate these points: $(6, 2)$, $(3, 2)$, $(0, 2)$, $(-2, 2)$, $(-5, 2)$.

a. What is true of the ordinates of all five points?

7. a. _____

b. If you join all the points in succession, what geometric figure do you get?

b. _____

8. Plot the points $C(-2, 1)$ and $D(2, -3)$. Draw the straight line CD and extend it in both directions. At what point does this line cut:

a. the x-axis?

8. a. _____

b. the y-axis?

b. _____

3. Graphs of linear equations

The equation $y = x - 2$ shows us how the two variables x and y are related. It tells us that any value of y is 2 less than the corresponding value of x. For ·example, if $x = 3$, then $y = 3 - 2 = 1$. Thus, the ordered pair $(3, 1)$ satisfies the equation $y = x - 2$. Or we may say that $(3, 1)$ is a solution of the equation $y = x - 2$, where it is understood that 3 is the x-value and 1 the y-value.

By making a table of values that satisfy the equation, we can determine several solutions of the equations.

When x is	−3	−2	−1	0	1	2	3
Then y is	−5	−4	−3	−2	−1	0	1

We may now plot these points on a pair of axes and obtain the graph of $y = x - 2$. Note that there is an infinite number of ordered pairs that satisfy the equation, but we are using only a few. Remember that we may use fractional or decimal values of the variables as well as whole numbers.

The number pairs in the table are plotted as points on the graph at the right. Note that all the points lie in a straight line, which is extended indefinitely in both directions.

This line is the graph of the equation $y = x - 2$. Every ordered pair of numbers that satisfies this equation represents a point on the line, and every point on the line has coordinates which satisfy the equation.

Since we need only two points to draw a straight line, we need only two ordered pairs of numbers. However, we usually take a third pair of numbers as a check. If all three do not lie in a straight line, then we know we have made an error in calculating our pairs of values.

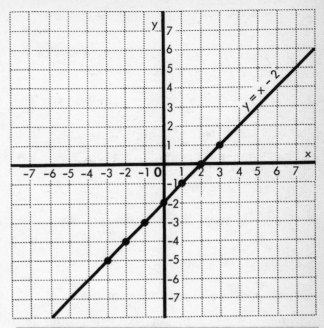

ILLUSTRATIVE PROBLEM

Draw the graph of $y = 2x - 3$.

Solution: First make a table showing at least three pairs of numbers satisfying the equation. Choose a value for x and calculate the corresponding value of y. Thus, if $x = 2$, then $y = 2(2) - 3 = 4 - 3 = 1$.

When x is	0	2	4
Then y is	−3	1	5

Now, plot a point for each number pair. Note that the three points lie in a straight line. Draw the line and extend it indefinitely in both directions. Lable the line with the equation $y = 2x - 3$.

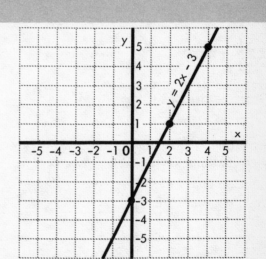

Exercises

On separate paper, make a table with at least three pairs of values for each equation below. Using graph paper, draw the graph of each equation.

1. $y = x + 3$ **2.** $y = 3x - 4$

3. $y = 4x + 1$ **4.** $y = 2x$

5. $y = 5x - 4$ **6.** $y = -3x + 2$

7. $y = \dfrac{1}{2}x + 2$ **8.** $y = 4 - 3x$

9. $y = 5 + \dfrac{1}{3}x$ **10.** $y = -\dfrac{2}{5}x + 4$

4. Graphing more difficult linear equations

ILLUSTRATIVE PROBLEM 1

Graph the equation $3x + 2y = 6$.

Solution: Here y is not expressed directly in terms of x. However, we may form a table of values by substituting values of x in the equation and solving for y; or by substituting values of y and solving for x.

For example, if $x = 4$, then $y = ?$

$$3(4) + 2y = \quad 6$$
$$12 + 2y = \quad 6$$
$$\underline{-12 \qquad\;\; = -12}$$
$$2y = \;\; -6$$

$$y = \;\; -3$$

Substituting $x = 0$ and $y = 0$ usually gives us easy calcuations for the table. Thus,

x	0	4	2
y	3	-3	0

The calculation of the pair $(2, 0)$ is as follows:

$$3x + 2(0) = 6$$
$$3x + \quad 0 = 6$$
$$3x = 6$$
$$x = 2$$

We may then proceed to plot the three points and draw the graph as before.

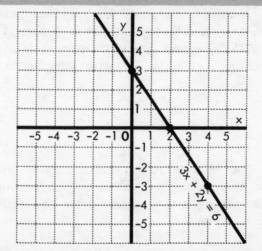

ILLUSTRATIVE PROBLEM 2

Which of the following points lies on the graph of $2x + 3y = 4$?   *a.* $(3, 0)$ *b.* $(-1, 2)$ *c.* $(-2, 2)$

Solution: Here we need only substitute the number pair in the equation to see if the pair satisfies the equation.

a. $2(3) + 3(0) = 4$

   $6 + 0 = 4$

Not true. Point $(3, 0)$ is not on the line.

b. $2(-1) + 3(2) = 4$

   $-2 + 6 = 4$

True. Point $(-1, 2)$ is on the line.

c. $2(-2) + 3(2) = 4$

   $-4 + 6 = 4$

Not true. Point $(-2, 2)$ is not on the line.

ILLUSTRATIVE PROBLEM 3

If the point whose abscissa (*x*-value) is 3 lies on the graph of $2x + y = 1$, what is the ordinate (*y*-value) of the point?

Solution: Substitute $x = 3$ in $2x + y = 1$. Thus,

   $2(3) + y = 1$

   $6 + y = 1$

   $\underline{-6 \quad\quad = -6}$

   $y = -5$ (*answer*)

Exercises

In 1 to 4, choose your answers from the given choices.

1. Which point lies on the graph of $2x + y = 10$?

   a. $(10, 0)$ *b.* $(3, 4)$ *c.* $(0, 8)$ *d.* $(4, 3)$

1. _____

2. Which number pair corresponds to a point which lies on the graph of $3x + 2y = 4$?

   a. $(-1, 2)$ *b.* $(-4, 4)$ *c.* $(2, -1)$ *d.* $(2, 0)$

2. _____

3. The graph of $x + 3y = 6$ intersects the y-axis in which point?

  a $(0, 2)$ *b.* $(0, 18)$ *c.* $(6, 0)$ *d.* $(3, 6)$

3. _____

4. Which is an equation whose graph does *not* pass through the point whose coordinates are $(2, 3)$?

  a. $2x - y = 1$ *b.* $3x - 2y = 0$
  c. $x + y = 5$ *d.* $x - y = 5$

4. _____

5. If a point whose ordinate (y-value) is 3 lies on the graph of $x + y = 2$, what is the abscissa (x-value) of the point?

5. _____

6. Point P lies on the graph of $2x - y = 1$. If the abscissa of P is 2, what is the ordinate of P?

6. _____

In 7 to 16, graph the equations. (Use graph paper.)

7. $2x + y = 8$ **8.** $x + 3y = 10$

9. $y - 2x = 0$ **10.** $3x + y = 6$

11. $2x - y = 5$ **12.** $4x + 3y = 12$

13. $2x - 3y = 6$ **14.** $3x + 4y = -12$

15. $3x + 6y = 0$ **16.** $5x + 3y = 15$

5. Graphing lines parallel to the axes

ILLUSTRATIVE PROBLEM 1

Graph the equation $y = 3$.

Solution: We may think of this equation as $y = 0 \cdot x + 3$. Now, make a table:

$$y = 0 \cdot x + 3$$

x	-2	0	$+4$
y	3	3	3

Note that, regardless of the value of x chosen, y is always 3. The graph is a straight line parallel to the x-axis and passing through the point $(0, 3)$.

The **y-*intercept*** of a line is the y-coordinate of the point where the line crosses the y-axis. In Problem 1, the y-intercept is 3.

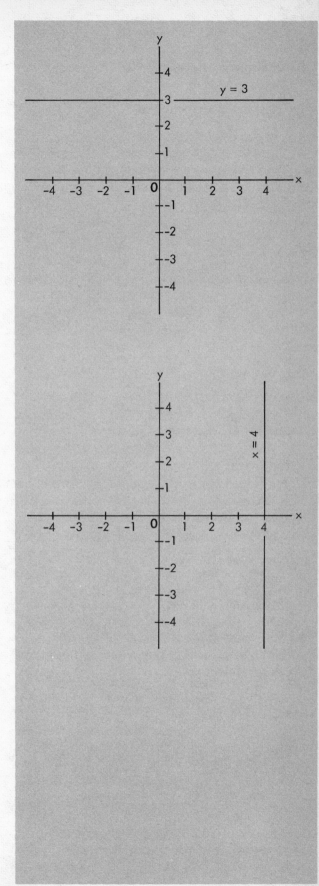

ILLUSTRATIVE PROBLEM 2

Graph the equation $x = 4$.

Solution: We may think of this equation as $x = 0 \cdot y + 4$. Now make a table choosing values of y and calculating values of x:

$$x = 0 \cdot y + 4$$

x	4	4	4
y	-2	0	3

The graph is a straight line parallel to the y-axis and passing through the point $(4, 0)$.

The **x-*intercept*** of a line is the x-coordinate of the point where the line crosses the x-axis. In Problem 2, the x-intercept is 4.

Summary:
1. **The graph of the equation $y = k$, where k is a constant, is a line parallel to the x-axis and k units away from it.**
2. **The graph of the equation $x = c$, where c is a constant, is a line parallel to the y-axis and c units away from it.**

Exercises

In 1 to 6, draw the graph of each equation. (Use graph paper.)

1. $x = 5$ **2.** $x = -2$ **3.** $x = 2\dfrac{1}{2}$

4. $y = 4$ **5.** $y = -3$ **6.** $y = 3.5$

7. What line is the graph of $x = 0$?

7. _____

8. What line is the graph of $y = 0$?

8. _____

9. Write an equation of a line that is parallel to the y-axis and whose x-intercept is: **a.** 7

9. **a.** _____

           b. -7

    b. _____

           c. $4\dfrac{1}{2}$

    c. _____

10. Write an equation of a line that is parallel to the x-axis and whose y-intercept is: **a.** 6

10. **a.** _____

           b. -5

    b. _____

           c. $3\dfrac{1}{4}$

    c. _____

Chapter review exercises

1. On a graph, the points $(-3, 2)$ and $(-1, 6)$ are joined by a line segment. If this segment is extended so as to intersect the x-axis, it does so at which of the following points? *a.* $(0, -4)$ *b.* $(4, 0)$ *c.* $(-4, 0)$ *d.* $(0, 8)$

1. _____

2. The point P lies on the graph of $x + 2y = 7$. If the ordinate of P is 6, what is its abscissa?

2. _____

3. The point Q lies on the graph of $5x + 2y = 6$. If the abscissa of Q is 4, what is its ordinate?

3. _____

    In 4 to 7, choose your answer from the given choices.

4. Which ordered pair is a solution of the equation $x - y = -1$? *a.* $(2, -3)$ *b.* $(2, 3)$ *c.* $(3, -2)$ *d.* $(3, 2)$

4. _____

5. The graph of $x + y = 4$ crosses the y-axis at the point whose coordinates are: *a.* $(0, -4)$ *b.* $(-4, 0)$ *c.* $(0, 4)$ *d.* $(4, 0)$

5. _____

6. The graph of $x = -3$:   *a.* passes through the origin   *b.* is parallel to the *x*-axis *c.* is parallel to the *y*-axis *d.* has a *y*-intercept of -3.

6. _____

7. Which number pair does *not* belong to the solution set of $x - 2y = 10$? *a.* $(-4, -7)$ *b.* $(0, -5)$ *c.* $(5, 0)$ *d.* $(6, -2)$

7. _____

8. The equation of a line is $3x - 2y = 9$. The abscissa of a point on this line is 6. What is the ordinate of this point?

8. _____

For 9 to 11, use graph paper.

9. Graph the equation $x + 2y = 10$.

10. Graph the equation $2x + 3y = -4$.

11. The formula $F = \dfrac{9}{5} C + 32$ is used to convert Celsius temperature readings (C) to Fahrenheit temperature readings (F).

  a. On separate paper, make a brief table of values for this formula using $C = -20$, 0, 20, 40, 100.

  b. Make a graph from the table of values placing C on the horizontal axis and F on the vertical axis; use a suitable scale for each.

  c. From the graph, determine the following:

    (1) For what temperature are the readings the same?

11. c. (1) _____

    (2) Water boils at 100°C. What is the corresponding Fahrenheit reading?

(2) _____

    (3) Normal body temperature is 98.6°F. What is the corresponding Celsius reading?

(3) _____

INEQUALITIES

13

1. Meaning and symbols of inequality

Thus far, we have dealt only with equations or statements of equality. Frequently, we deal with problems that involve statements indicating that quantities are not equal.

We may say that $5 + 3 \neq 7$, where the symbol $\neq$ is read "is not equal to." Such a statement is called an *inequality*.

To compare two unequal numbers, we use the following symbols:

$>$ is read "is greater than." Thus $5 > 3$ is read "5 is greater than 3."

$<$ is read "is less than." Thus $2\frac{1}{2} < 6$ is read "$2\frac{1}{2}$ is less than 6."

Note that in each case the symbol points to the smaller number.

If we write the inequality $x > 3$, we mean that x may assume any value that is greater than 3; thus, x may be equal to $3\frac{1}{2}$, 4.2, 7, etc. There is an infinite set of numbers that satisfies this inequality, and we call this set the solution set of the inequality.

Note that a temperature of $-20°$ is lower than a temperature of $-10°$. Thus we say that $-20 < -10$. The more negative a number is, the smaller it is.

In the case of the inequality $x < 3$, the solution set would consist of all values of x that are less than 3; thus, members of the solution set would be $2, 1\frac{1}{2}, 0, -3, -7.4$, etc. $x < 3$ $x = 2\ 1\frac{1}{2}$

Consider the inequality $x + 5 > 11$. What positive integers less than 10 satisfy this inequality? Substitute integers less than 10.

Let $x = 9$. Is $9 + 5 > 11$? Is $14 > 11$? Yes
Let $x = 8$. Is $8 + 5 > 11$? Is $13 > 11$? Yes
Let $x = 7$. Is $7 + 5 > 11$? Is $12 > 11$? Yes
Let $x = 6$. Is $6 + 5 > 11$? Is $11 > 11$? No
Let $x = 5$. Is $5 + 5 > 11$? Is $10 > 11$? No

By continuing this process, we see that 7, 8, and 9 are the only positive integers less than 10 that satisfy the inequality $x + 5 > 11$.

Consider the inequality $2x + 1 < 5$. What integers greater than -5 satisfy this inequality? Substitute integers greater than -5.

Let $x = -4$. Is $2(-4) + 1 < 5$? Is $-8 + 1 < 5$? Is $-7 < 5$? Yes.
Let $x = -3$. Is $2(-3) + 1 < 5$? Is $-6 + 1 < 5$? Is $-5 < 5$? Yes.

By continuing this process, we see that $-4, -3, -2, -1, 0$, and $+1$ are the only integers greater than -5 that satisfy the inequality $2x + 1 < 5$.

Exercises

In 1 to 10: for each inequality, list the integers from 0 to $+5$ inclusive which satisfy the inequality.

1. $y + 4 > 6$ **2.** $x + 2 > 3$

3. $p + 2\frac{1}{2} > 5$ **4.** $k - 2 > 1$

5. $4t > 16$ **6.** $a + 6 < 9$

7. $3t < 5$ **8.** $3x + 2 > 7$

9. $\frac{r}{3} < 1$ **10.** $5m - 3 < 6$

In 11 to 20: for each inequality, list the integers from 0 to -5 inclusive which satisfy the inequality.

11. $x + 4 > 1$ **12.** $p + 3 < -1$

13. $t + 3\frac{1}{2} < 0$ **14.** $K + 8\frac{1}{4} > 5$

15. $3y - 4 < -13$ **16.** $\frac{s}{3} > -1$

17. $5b < -20$ **18.** $2x + 7 < 2$

19. $\frac{a}{6} < -\frac{1}{2}$ **20.** $3p + 8 < 8$

1. _____	2. _____
3. _____	4. _____
5. _____	6. _____
7. _____	8. _____
9. _____	10. _____
11. _____	12. _____
13. _____	14. _____
15. _____	16. _____
17. _____	18. _____
19. _____	20. _____

In 21 to 28: for each exercise, replace the question mark by one of the symbols >, <, or = so as to make the statement true.

21. When $a = 4$, $2a + 3$? 7.

21. _____

22. When $x = 0$, $3x - 5$? 8.

22. _____

23. When $t = 2$, $t - 5$? -2.

23. _____

24. When $y = 2$, $4y - 5$? 3.

24. _____

25. When $p = 5$, $2p - 7$? 9.

25. _____

26. When $r = 3$, $\dfrac{r}{4}$? 2.

26. _____

27. When $k = 6$, $3k - 7$? $2\dfrac{1}{2}$.

27. _____

28. When $b = -2$, $2b - 7$? 5.

28. _____

2. Representing inequalities on the number line

In previous chapters, we used the number line to illustrate operations on signed numbers. We will find that using the number line to show inequalities gives us a better understanding of them.

On the number line at the right, we may represent all signed numbers, positive and negative. Note that, as we move to the right, the numbers grow larger. As we move to the left, the numbers grow smaller. Thus, we can verify that

$$-5 < -2 \text{ or } -3\frac{1}{2} < 0 \text{ or } -\frac{1}{2} > -1,$$ etc., by

checking the *order* of these numbers on the line: For any two numbers on the line, the smaller number is always to the *left*.

When we represent an inequality with one variable on the number line, we call this the graph of the inequality. At the right is the graph of $x < 2$.

The heavy line indicates all values of x less

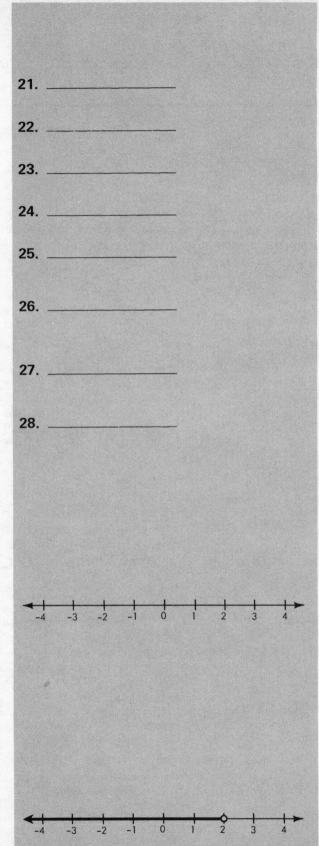

than 2. The open circle at 2 indicates that 2 is not a member of the solution set.

The arrowhead at the left of the heavy line indicates that the solution set continues indefinitely to the left.

At the right is the solution set of $x > 1$.

The heavy line indicates all values of x greater than 1. Note the open circle at 1 to indicate it is not included in the solution set. The arrowhead at the right indicates that the graph extends indefinitely to the right.

If we wish to include an endpoint in an inequality, we use a double symbol combining the $=$ symbol and the $<$ or $>$ symbol. For example, $x \geq 1$ is read "x is greater than or equal to 1." In this case, the open circle on the graph becomes a heavy dot, as indicated at the right:

This symbol is frequently convenient. For example, the voting age is now 18 years or over. If V is the voting age, we may then write $V \geq 18$.

If we wish to indicate that the speed limit (s) is now 55 mph, we may write the inequality $s \leq 55$, which indicates that speeds of 55 mph or less are legal.

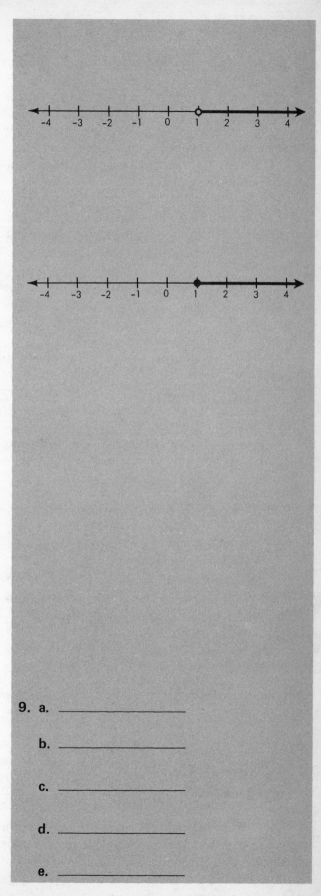

Exercises

In 1 to 8, use separate paper to graph the inequalities on a number line.

1. $x > 3$ **2.** $x < 4$ **3.** $x < -3$

4. $x > -2$ **5.** $x \leq -2$ **6.** $x \geq -1$

7. $x \leq 0$ **8.** $x \geq 1$

9. Express as an inequality in symbols:

  a. n is greater than or equal to $4\frac{1}{2}$.

  b. p is less than or equal to 3.14.

  c. The greatest number of pupils (n) allowed in a class is 35.

  d. The minimum speed (s) permitted on a highway is 30 mph.

  e. Use a suitable scale on the number line and graph the inequality in **d.**

9. a. _____

  b. _____

  c. _____

  d. _____

  e. _____

3. Properties of inequalities

If we start with the inequality $5 > 3$, and add 4 to both sides, we obtain the inequality $5 + 4 > 3 + 4$ or $9 > 7$; this is apparently a true inequality. When the inequality symbol is the same in two inequalities, we say they are of the same *order*, or *the order remains unchanged*.

This suggests the following addition principle of inequalities:

Principle: If the same number is added to (or subtracted from) both members of an inequality, the order of the inequality remains unchanged.

In a similar manner, if we start with the inequality $6 > 4$, and multiply both members by 3, we get $6 \times 3 > 4 \times 3$ or $18 > 12$; this is apparently a true inequality.

However, if we start with $6 > 4$, and multiply both members by -3, the left member becomes -18 and the right member becomes -12. Now $-18 < -12$. We say that *the order of the inequality has been reversed*.

These illustrations suggest the following multiplication principle of inequalities:

Principle:
1. If both members of an inequality are multiplied (or divided) by the same positive number, the order of the inequality remains unchanged.
2. If both members of an inequality are multiplied (or divided) by the same negative number, the order of the inequality is reversed.

Note that we include division in the multiplication property because dividing by 3 is the same as multiplying by $\dfrac{1}{3}$ or, in general, division by a number (other than 0) is the same as multiplication by the reciprocal of that number.

4. Solving inequalities

By using the addition and multiplication principles of inequalities, we are able to find their solution sets.

ILLUSTRATIVE PROBLEM 1

Solve the inequality $x - 2 > 1$ and graph the solution set.

Solution:

$$x - 2 > 1$$
$$\underline{+2 \quad +2} \quad \text{(add 2 to both members)}$$
$$x \quad\;\; > \;\; 3 \quad \text{(order of inequality stays the same)}$$

The heavy line indicates all values of x for which $x > 3$, which is also the solution set of the original equation $x - 2 > 1$. Note that 3 is not included in the graph.

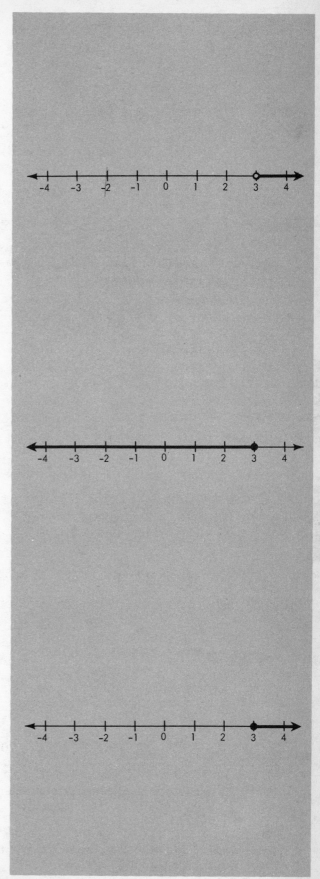

ILLUSTRATIVE PROBLEM 2

Solve the inequality $x + 2 \le 5$ and graph the solution set.

Solution:

$$x + 2 \le 5$$
$$\underline{-2 \quad -2} \quad \text{(add } -2 \text{ to both members)}$$
$$x \quad\;\; \le \;\; 3 \quad \text{(order of inequality stays the same)}$$

Note that 3 is included in the graph.

ILLUSTRATIVE PROBLEM 3

Solve the inequality $\frac{1}{3}p \ge 1$ and graph the solution set.

Solution:

$$\frac{1}{3}p \ge 1$$

$$3 \cdot \frac{1}{3}p \ge 1 \cdot 3 \quad \text{(multiply both members by 3)}$$

$$p \ge 3 \qquad \text{(order of inequality stays the same)}$$

ILLUSTRATIVE PROBLEM 4

Solve the inequality $-3x + 2 \le 8$ and graph the solution set.

Solution:

$$-3x + 2 \le 8$$
$$\underline{ -2 -2} \quad \text{(add } -2 \text{ to both members)}$$
$$-3x \le 6$$

$$\frac{-3x}{-3} \le \frac{6}{-3} \quad \text{(divide both members by } -3\text{)}$$

$$x \ge -2 \quad \text{(order of inequality is reversed)}$$

Exercises

In 1 to 18, solve the inequalities. On separate paper, graph their solution sets.

1. $x - 3 > 2$ 2. $p + 5 > 3$

3. $K - 2 < 1$ 4. $r + \dfrac{1}{3} > 3$

5. $y - \dfrac{1}{2} > 0$ 6. $t + 2.5 < 3.5$

7. $s + 2 < 0$ 8. $4z > 8$

9. $3m \le 9$ 10. $-2y > 4$

11. $-3a \ge -9$ 12. $.6x \ge -3$

13. $4K - 2 > 2$ 14. $6 + \dfrac{n}{2} \ge 0$

15. $\dfrac{1}{2}z - 2 < -8$ 16. $4x - 3 > 13$

17. $3t - 6 \ge 15$ 18. $-8b - 3b - 2 \le 20$

1. _____ 2. _____

3. _____ 4. _____

5. _____ 6. _____

7. _____ 8. _____

9. _____ 10. _____

11. _____ 12. _____

13. _____ 14. _____

15. _____ 16. _____

17. _____ 18. _____

In 19 to 22, write an inequality and then solve it.

19. Seven times a number is less than 63. What numbers satisfy this condition?

19. _____

To draw the graph of $y \geq 2$, we draw the line $y = 2$ as a solid line and shade the half-plane above this line. See Fig. 6.

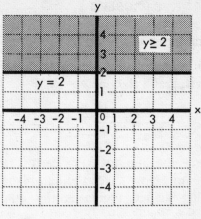

Fig. 6

To draw the graph of $y \leq 2$, we draw the line $y = 2$ as a solid line and shade the half-plane below this line. See Fig. 7.

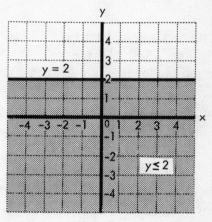

Fig. 7

If we wish to graph the inequality $x > 2$, we draw the broken vertical line $x = 2$ and shade the half-plane to the right of this line. See Fig. 8. All points in this region have abscissas greater than 2.

For the graph of $x \geq 2$, we would draw the vertical line $x = 2$ as a solid line. The graph would then consist of the shaded area and the solid line.

To draw the graph of $x < 2$, we would shade the region to the left of the vertical broken line $x = 2$. This half-plane would be the graph of all points in the plane with abscissas less than 2.

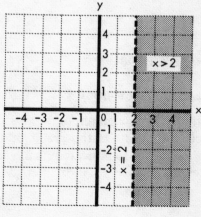

Fig. 8

ILLUSTRATIVE PROBLEM 1

Graph the inequality $y > 3x + 1$.

Solution:

First, graph the line $y = 3x + 1$.

x	0	1	-1
y	1	4	-2

Draw the line dotted since it is not included in the graph. Now shade the half-plane above this line. This shaded region is the graph of $y > 3x + 1$. See Fig. 9.

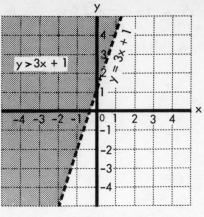

Fig. 9

ILLUSTRATIVE PROBLEM 2

Graph the inequality $y \leq 2x - 2$.

Solution:

First, graph the line $y = 2x - 2$.

x	0	1	-1
y	-2	0	-4

Draw the line solid since it is included in the graph. Now shade the half-plane below this line. This shaded region and the line make up the graph of $y \leq 2x - 2$. See Fig. 10.

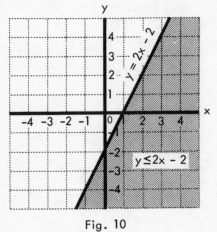

Fig. 10

ILLUSTRATIVE PROBLEM 3

Graph the inequality $y \leq 1$.

Solution: Draw the graph of $y = 1$. The half-plane below this line is the graph of $y < 1$. We draw the line solid to indicate it is included in the graph. See Fig. 11.

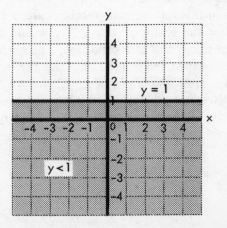

Fig. 11

Exercises

In 1 to 18, graph the inequalities. Use graph paper.

1. $y > x$ **2.** $y < 3x$

3. $y \geq x + 3$ **4.** $y \leq 2x + 1$

5. $y < x$ **6.** $y \leq x - 2$

7. $y > -2x$ **8.** $y \geq 3x - 4$

9. $y < -x + 2$ **10.** $y \geq \dfrac{1}{2}x + 3$

11. $y \leq 2x + 5$ **12.** $y > -x + 6$

13. $y > \dfrac{2}{3}x$ **14.** $y \leq \dfrac{3}{4}x - 2$

15. $2y \geq x - 4$ **16.** $y \geq 3$

17. $x \leq -1$ **18.** $y < -2$

In 19 to 26, write an inequality representing the statement. Then graph the inequality.

19. The ordinate of a point is less than its abscissa.

19. _____

20. The ordinate of a point is greater than or equal to 3 less than its abscissa.

20. _____

21. The ordinate of a point is greater than 3 times its abscissa.

21. _____

22. The ordinate of a point is less than 3 more than twice its abscissa.

22. _____

23. The ordinate of a point is greater than 4 less than half its abscissa.

23. _____

24. The ordinate of a point is less than one-third its abscissa.

25. The ordinate of a point is greater than −1.

26. The abscissa of a point is negative.

24. _____

25. _____

26. _____

Chapter review exercises

In 1 to 10, choose your answer from the given choices.

1. A value of x that satisfies the inequality $x >$ −2 is $a.$ −4 $b.$ −3 $c.$ −2 $d.$ −1

1. _____

2. A value of y that satisfies the inequality $y -$ $2 > -3$ is $a.$ 0 $b.$ −4 $c.$ −1 $d.$ −2

2. _____

3. The solution set of the inequality $2t + 3 > 5$ consists of all values of t for which $a.$ $t > 1$ $b.$ $t < 1$ $c.$ $t > 4$ $d.$ $t < 4$

3. _____

4. The graph shown is the graph of $a.$ $y > x$ $b.$ $y < x$ $c.$ $y \leq x$ $d.$ $y \geq x$

4. _____

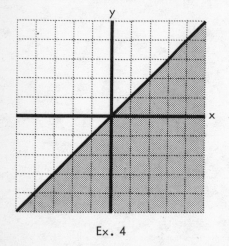

Ex. 4

5. The graph indicates the solution set of $a.$ $x < 0$ $b.$ $x \leq 0$ $c.$ $x > 0$ $d.$ $x \geq 0$

5. _____

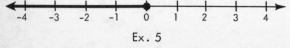

Ex. 5

6. If $3x - 1 \geq 4$, a member of the solution set is
a. 1   *b.* 0   *c.* 3   *d.* −1

6. _____

7. The solution set of $3x - 3 > 2x + 1$ consists of all values of x for which   *a.* $x < 4$
b. $x > -2$ *c.* $x > 4$ *d.* $x > -4$

7. _____

8. Which number pair does not belong to the solution set of $y \geq 2x - 3$?   *a.* $(0, -3)$
b. $(1, -2)$ *c.* $(1, 0)$ *d.* $(2, 3)$

8. _____

9. The solution set of $3y - 3 > 12$ is   *a.* $y > 3$
b. $y < 3$ *c.* $y > 5$ *d.* $y < 5$

9. _____

10. Which relation is shown in the graph?
a. $y < 1$ *b.* $y > -1$ *c.* $x > -1$
d. $x < -1$

10. _____

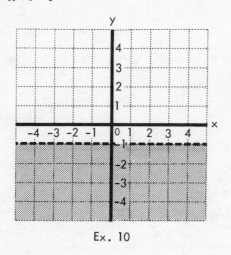

Ex. 10

11. Solve the inequality: $1 + 2x < 0$

11. _____

12. Solve the inequality: $2x - 1 < 8$

12. _____

For 13 to 16, use separate graph paper.

13. Graph the inequality: $y \geq -x + 1$

14. Graph the inequality: $y < 3x - 6$

15. Graph the set of all points whose ordinates are less than −2.

16. Graph the set of all points whose abscissas are positive or zero.

APPENDIX I: ARITHMETIC OF WHOLE NUMBERS

Preliminary note

If you are having difficulty with some of the computational skills or concepts of the arithmetic of whole numbers, you should review this appendix. Read carefully the descriptive material in each section and work out the exercises at the end of each section. In each section, an attempt is made to give an understanding of the rules of arithmetic and why these rules are true.

1. The system of whole numbers

Whole numbers are formed from various combinations of the digits from 0 to 9. When we write the number 734, we mean

7 hundreds plus 3 tens plus 4 units

or

$$7 \times 100 + 3 \times 10 + 4 \times 1$$

The value of each digit in a whole number is determined by its placement, so that we call our number system a "place value" system. The **units** or **ones** are shown in the first place on the right, the **tens** in the second place from the right, and so on.

The following table shows place values in whole numbers:

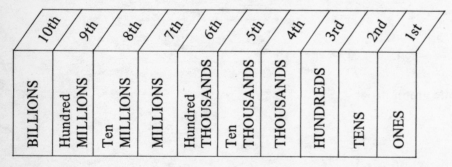

10th	9th	8th	7th	6th	5th	4th	3rd	2nd	1st
BILLIONS	Hundred MILLIONS	Ten MILLIONS	MILLIONS	Hundred THOUSANDS	Ten THOUSANDS	THOUSANDS	HUNDREDS	TENS	ONES

To read a number, separate its digits into groups of three, beginning at the right side. For 5-digit numbers and larger, commas are used to separate these groups. A number is read from the left side after the proper grouping is recognized. Thus, 2,375,208 is read two million, three hundred seventy-five thousand, two hundred eight. The word "and" is not used in reading whole numbers.

Here are some examples of reading and writing whole numbers:

1. Read the number 85,042 and write it as a word statement.
   Answer: eighty-five thousand, forty-two
      Note: The "0" serves as a place-holder to indicate that there are no hundreds, but we do not read it as such.

2. Write the word statement as a number: eight thousand, four hundred ninety-two.
   Answer: 8492

3. What is the value of the 7 in the number 4703?
   Answer: Since the 7 is the third digit to the left, it is in the hundreds place and represents a value of 7 × 100, or 700.

Exercises

In 1 to 10, read the number and write it as a word statement.

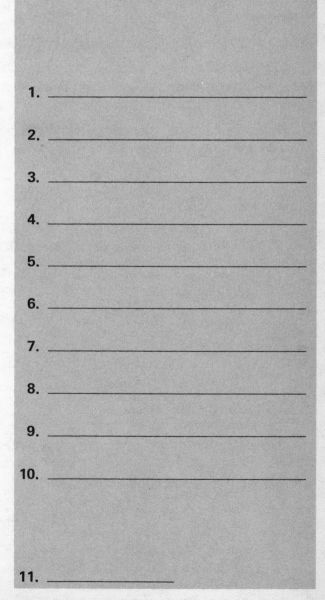

1. 582

   1. _____

2. 304

   2. _____

3. 9254

   3. _____

4. 18,723

   4. _____

5. 7008

   5. _____

6. 423,601

   6. _____

7. 6,000,000

   7. _____

8. 12,472,000

   8. _____

9. 6,425,000,000

   9. _____

10. 22,500,000,000

    10. _____

In 11 to 20, write the word statement as a number.

11. seven hundred twenty-one

    11. _____

12. two thousand, eight hundred forty-two

13. nine thousand, fifty-seven

14. ninety-three million

15. two hundred twenty-three million, eight hundred fifty thousand

16. fourteen billion

17. six thousand, two hundred forty-five

18. fifteen thousand, eight

19. three billion, two hundred sixty-eight million

20. eight million, eight thousand, eight hundred

21. Write the number that means 7 hundreds, 5 tens, and 8 ones.

22. Write the number that means 2 thousands, 6 hundreds, and 3 ones.

In 23 to 25, give the value of the 7 in each number.

23. 372   **24.** 27,245

25. 58,702

12. _____

13. _____

14. _____

15. _____

16. _____

17. _____

18. _____

19. _____

20. _____

21. _____

22. _____

23. _____   **24.** _____

25. _____

2. Addition of whole numbers

The operation of addition is indicated by a plus sign (+), as in $7 + 4 = 11$. The numbers, 7 and 4, are called the *addends* and the result, 11, is called the *sum* or *total*.

Most of us are now well aware that $4 + 7$ also equals 11; that is, it doesn't matter in what *order* we add the two numbers. Likewise, $8 + 5 = 5 + 8 = 13$. The sum is the same regardless of the order of the addends. We say that addition is *commutative*, and we refer to this order principle as the *commutative principle*.

When we add three or more numbers, we may use the principle of *grouping*. We use parentheses ( ) as symbols of grouping; they indicate that the operations within the parentheses are to be done first.

Thus, $(4 + 5) + 6 = 9 + 6 = 15$.

And $4 + (5 + 6) = 4 + 11 = 15$.

Note that the sums are the same no matter how we group them. We say that addition is *associative;* that is, it doesn't matter whether we *associate* the 4 and 5 first or the 5 and 6 first when adding $4 + 5 + 6$.

Using the commutative and associative principles of addition, we conclude that

$$(4 + 5) + 6 = 4 + (5 + 6)$$
$$= 4 + (6 + 5)$$
$$= (5 + 4) + 6$$
$$= 5 + (4 + 6), \text{etc.}$$

Since the sum is 15 in any case, we generally omit the parenthesis and write $4 + 5 + 6 = 15$.

The commutative principle and the principle of grouping justify our adding three or more numbers in *any order* and *grouping* them any way we please.

If several large numbers are to be added, the addends are placed beneath one another so that the digits are lined up correctly: ones digits in the right-hand column, tens digits in the next column to the left, etc. For example, $548 + 85 + 1324 + 459$ is arranged like this:

$$
\begin{array}{r}
548 \\
85 \\
1324 \\
459 \\
\text{carry} \quad \underline{1\,2\,2} \\
2416 \quad (sum)
\end{array}
$$

When we add the digits in the ones column, we get 26. We write the 6 in the ones column and carry the "2" to the tens column, since the "2" really means 2 tens or 20. We then add the tens column and get 21, which now means 21 tens or 210. Again, we place the 1 in the tens column and carry the "2" into the hundreds column.

We then add the hundreds column and get 14, which now means 14 hundreds or 1400. We place the 4 in the hundreds column and the "1" in the thousands column. We then add the thousands column and get 2, which now means 2000.

This method of column addition, with its use of the carrying of digits, shows us one of the great advantages of place value in our number system.

We may check the addition by using the commutative and associative principles. One way is merely to reverse the addition by adding upward:

```
carry   1 2 2
          548
           85
         1324
          459
         ─────
         2416  √
```

Exercises

1. Add the following columns and check:

a. 43	**b.** 36
27	29
52	84
60	98

c. 148	**d.** 347
321	85
707	1140
423	139

2. Arrange the following numbers in columns and add:

a. 235; 3423; 57; 109

b. 1147; 532; 84; 903

c. 4283; 20,147; 709; 3283

d. 304; 29; 1612; 75; 237

3. Bill spent 98 cents for a notebook, 62 cents for paper, 32 cents for a ruler, 47 cents for pencils, and 55 cents for graph paper. How many cents did he spend altogether?

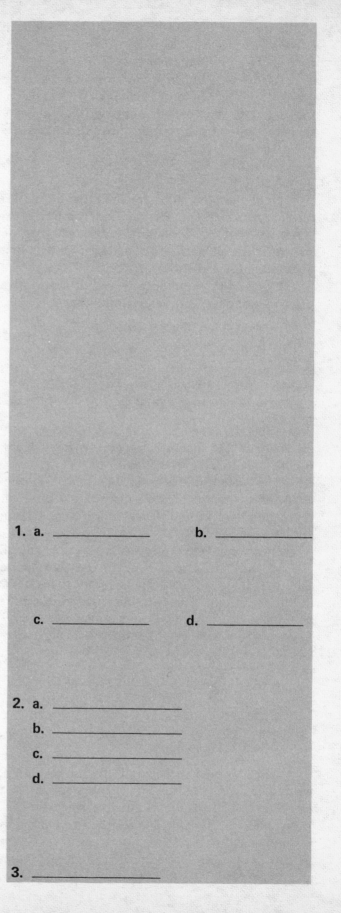

1. a. _____   b. _____

   c. _____   d. _____

2. a. _____

   b. _____

   c. _____

   d. _____

3. _____

4. In a junior high school, there are 420 seventh graders, 503 eighth graders, and 487 ninth graders. Find the total number of pupils in the school.

4. _____

5. How much does a set of bedroom furniture cost if the bed costs $189, the dresser $240, the night table $68, the vanity $312, and a book rack $45?

5. _____

6. In taking a trip, a man and his wife drove 420 miles the first day, 388 miles the second day, 175 miles the third day, 412 miles the fourth day, and 78 miles the fifth day. How many miles did they travel altogether?

6. _____

7. Mr. Burns makes the following purchases in a department store: a suit for $140, a topcoat for $128, a shirt for $12, a tie for $7, and a pair of shoes for $35. How much did he spend?

7. _____

8. Henry bought a new car for $4,250. He also bought air-conditioning for $415, power steering for $184, power brakes for $97, and a stereo radio for $132. Find his total cost.

8. _____

3. Subtraction of whole numbers

The operation of subtraction is indicated by a minus sign (−), as in 9 − 3 = 6. The number 9 is called the *minuend*, 3 is called the *subtrahend*, and 6 is called the *difference* or *remainder*. The number zero is the difference whenever the minuend and subtrahend are equal. Thus, 7 − 7 = 0.

Subtraction is the opposite (or inverse) of addition. When we write 9 − 3 = ?, we are really asking for the number that must be added to 3 to give us 9. Thus, if we know our addition combinations, we can readily determine our subtraction combinations.

With positive integers, the subtrahend must be less than the minuend. Hence, we cannot speak of a *commutative principle* for subtraction. For example, 3 − 9 would have no meaning at this point. A simple example would readily convince us that the *associative principle* does not apply to subtraction either. Is $10 - (6 - 3)$ equal to $(10 - 6) - 3$?

The following illustrative problems will serve to explain the actual process of subtraction.

ILLUSTRATIVE PROBLEM 1

Subtract 43 from 58.

Solution:

$$\frac{\begin{array}{r}58\\-43\end{array}}{} = \frac{\begin{array}{l}5 \text{ tens} + 8 \text{ ones}\\4 \text{ tens} + 3 \text{ ones}\end{array}}{1 \text{ ten } + 5 \text{ ones} = 15 \quad (answer)}$$

This shows that we are subtracting ones from ones and tens from tens.

ILLUSTRATIVE PROBLEM 2

Find the difference between 53 and 28.

Solution:

$$\frac{\begin{array}{r}53\\-28\end{array}}{} = \frac{\begin{array}{l}5 \text{ tens} + 3 \text{ ones}\\2 \text{ tens} + 8 \text{ ones}\end{array}}{}$$

Since we cannot take 8 ones from 3 ones, we change 53 to 4 tens + 13 ones. We are then able to subtract 8 ones from 13 ones.

$$\frac{\begin{array}{r}53\\-28\end{array}}{} = \frac{\begin{array}{l}4 \text{ tens} + 13 \text{ ones}\\2 \text{ tens} + 8 \text{ ones}\end{array}}{2 \text{ tens} + 5 \text{ ones} = 25}$$
$$(answer)$$

ILLUSTRATIVE PROBLEM 3

How much greater is 830 than 397?

Solution:

$$\frac{\begin{array}{r}830\\-397\end{array}}{} = \frac{\begin{array}{l}8 \text{ hundreds} \quad 3 \text{ tens} \quad 0 \text{ ones}\\3 \text{ hundreds} \quad 9 \text{ tens} \quad 7 \text{ ones}\end{array}}{}$$

$$= \frac{\begin{array}{l}8 \text{ hundreds} \quad 2 \text{ tens} \quad 10 \text{ ones}\\3 \text{ hundreds} \quad 9 \text{ tens} \quad 7 \text{ ones}\end{array}}{}$$

$$= \frac{\begin{array}{l}7 \text{ hundreds} \quad 12 \text{ tens} \quad 10 \text{ ones}\\3 \text{ hundreds} \quad 9 \text{ tens} \quad 7 \text{ ones}\end{array}}{4 \text{ hundreds} \quad 3 \text{ tens} \quad 3 \text{ ones} = 433}$$
$$(answer)$$

Note: We usually indicate subtraction like this:

$$\begin{array}{r}\overset{4}{\cancel{5}}\overset{1}{3}\\-28\\\hline 25\end{array}$$

Note: This subtraction example would usually be done like this:

$$\begin{array}{r} {}^{7}8{}^{12}3{}^{1}0 \\ -397 \\ \hline 433 \end{array}$$

Here we first changed 830 to 8 hundreds, 2 tens, and 10 ones. When we could not subtract 9 tens from 2 tens, we then further changed 830 to 7 hundreds, 12 tens, and 10 ones.

ILLUSTRATIVE PROBLEM 4

Subtract 328 from 700.

Solution:

$$\begin{array}{r} {}^{6}7{}^{9}0{}^{1}0 \\ -372 \\ \hline 328 \end{array}$$

Here, when we increased the first zero on the right by 10, we could not "borrow" 10 from the tens column. Instead, we changed the two left digits in the minuend from 70 to 69. In effect, we are changing 700 to 690 + 10. The column-by-column digit subtraction is then possible.

All of these subtraction problems may be checked by adding the subtrahend to the remainder. The sum should then be the minuend.

For instance, in illustrative problem 4:

Check:
$$\begin{array}{r} 372 \quad \text{(subtrahend)} \\ +328 \quad \text{(remainder)} \\ \hline 700 \;\checkmark\; \text{(minuend)} \end{array}$$

Exercises

1. Subtract and check:

   a. 58
      24

   b. 428
      113

   c. 781
      256

   d. 902
      427

2. Subtract and check:

   a. 892
      374

   b. 5374
        249

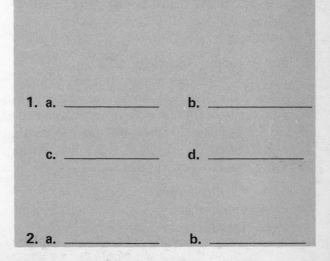

1. a. _____   b. _____

   c. _____   d. _____

2. a. _____   b. _____

c. 7620
    359

d. 5400
    728

3. Subtract and check:

  a. 297 − 58   **b.** 5275 − 1492

  c. 64,000 − 9700

4. Subtract 329 from 1100.

5. Take 847 from 1252.

6. From 1848 take 1088.

7. Find the difference between 685 and 278.

8. A boy weighed 128 pounds one year and 144 pounds the following year. How many pounds did he gain?

9. Mr. Tobin bought a house for $38,500 and sold it five years later for $46,250. How much more did he sell it for?

10. Mrs. Andrews bought a color television set for $528. She made a down payment of $150. How much more does she still have to pay?

11. Carlos went to the supermarket with a $20 bill. He spent $6.20 for meats, $2.40 for fruits and vegetables, $3.37 for detergents, and $2.76 for baked goods. How much did he have left?

4. Multiplication of whole numbers

If a classroom has 4 rows of seats with 5 seats in each row, then we can say it has a total of 5 + 5 + 5 + 5 = 20 seats. We can also say that 4 is *multiplied* by 5, or 4 × 5 = 20. Written vertically, the problem appears as

    5   (multiplicand)
   ×4   (multiplier)
   20   (product)

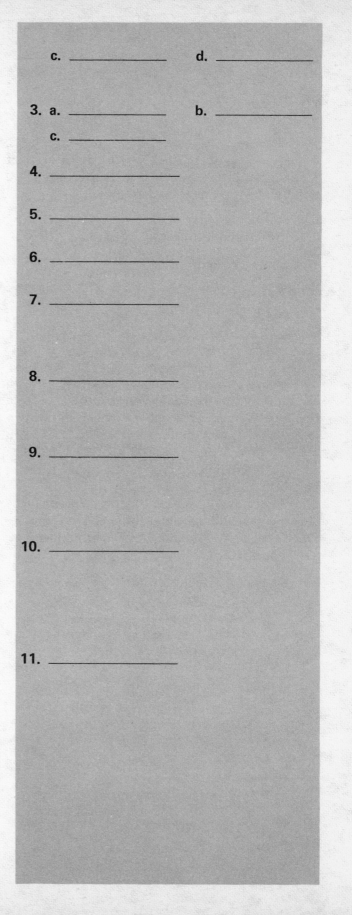

c. _____   d. _____

3. a. _____   b. _____

   c. _____

4. _____

5. _____

6. _____

7. _____

8. _____

9. _____

10. _____

11. _____

The *multiplier* indicates the number of times the *multiplicand* is to be written down and added. The result of multiplication is the *product*. The multiplication symbol (✕) is read *times*; we sometimes also use a dot placed in the middle of the line of writing—thus, $5 \cdot 4 = 20$. We may also indicate multiplication by putting one or both of the numbers in parentheses; thus, $5(4) = 20$. Numbers that are multiplied together to form a product are also called *factors* of the product. Thus, 5 and 4 are factors of 20.

In the example above, note that 4×5 also yields 20, the total number of seats in the room; that is, $5 \times 4 = 4 \times 5$. This indicates to us that the *commutative principle* also applies to multiplication. This principle permits us to check a multiplication problem by interchanging the multiplicand and the multiplier.

A simple illustration shows that the *associative principle* of multiplication also holds true. Note that $(3 \times 4) \times 5 = 12 \times 5 = 60$.

Note also that $3 \times (4 \times 5) = 3 \times 20 = 60$.

Thus, $(3 \times 4) \times 5 = 3 \times (4 \times 5)$.

Since the manner in which we *group* the factors does not matter, we usually write the product above as $3 \times 4 \times 5$.

If we wish to find the product $2 \times (3 + 4)$, we may add 3 and 4 and multiply the sum by 2. Thus,

$$2 \times (3 + 4) = 2 \times 7 = 14$$

Note that, if we multiply each addend by 2 and then add, we get the same result. Thus,

$$2 \times (3 + 4) = 2 \times 3 + 2 \times 4 = 6 + 8 = 14$$

This example illustrates that *multiplication is distributive over addition* (or subtraction). In the example above, the multiplier 2 is "distributed" over the 3 and the 4. The distributive principle states that, when the sum of two or more addends is to be multiplied by a number, the product is the same as the result obtained when each of the addends is multiplied by the number and *these products* are then added. These latter products are called *partial products*.

The distributive principle is used when we multiply numbers with two or more digits. Thus,

$$3 \times 23 = 3 \times (20 + 3) = 3 \times 20 + 3 \times 3$$
$$= \quad 60 \quad + \quad 9 \quad = 69$$

Written vertically, this appears as

$$
\begin{array}{r}
23 \\
\times 3 \\
\hline
69
\end{array}
$$

Note that the ones digits are aligned and that the multiplier (usually the smaller number) is the bottom number. Then multiply from right to left, starting with the ones digit in the multiplicand. "Carrying" will usually be necessary, as shown in the following illustrative problems:

ILLUSTRATIVE PROBLEM 1

Multiply 237 by 5.

Solution: First, $5 \times 7 = 35$. Write the 5 under the ones column and carry the 3 to the tens column.

$$
\begin{array}{r}
\overset{3}{2}37 \\
\times 5 \\
\hline
5
\end{array}
$$

Then $5 \times 3 = 15$, plus the 3 that was carried, equals 18. Write the 8 in the tens column and carry the 1 to the hundreds column.

$$
\begin{array}{r}
\overset{13}{2}37 \\
\times 5 \\
\hline
85
\end{array}
$$

Then $5 \times 2 = 10$, plus the 1 that was carried, equals 11. Write 1 in the hundreds column and 1 in the thousands column.

$$
\begin{array}{r}
\overset{13}{2}37 \\
\times 5 \\
\hline
1185
\end{array}
$$

Answer: $237 \times 5 = 1185$

The following illustrates how we multiply two numbers with two or more digits:

ILLUSTRATIVE PROBLEM 2

Multiply 345×32.

Solution: First multiply the 2 in the multiplier by 345.

$$
\begin{array}{r}
345 \\
\times 32 \\
\hline
690
\end{array}
$$

Now multiply the 3 in the multiplier by 345. Start by placing the 5 in the partial product under the 3 in the multiplier (tens column) and the other digits of the partial product to the left. Then draw a line and add the two partial products.

$$
\begin{array}{r}
345 \\
\times 32 \\
\hline
690 \\
10\ 35 \\
\hline
11{,}040
\end{array}
$$

Answer: $345 \times 32 = 11{,}040$

The same procedure is followed when the multiplier has 3 or more digits. Multiply with

every digit in the multiplier beginning with the ones digit. Place the first right-hand digit of each partial product directly under the digit you are multiplying by.

You may check your result by reversing the multiplicand and multiplier.

Remember that any number multiplied by zero yields zero. This fact can be used to simplify problems in multiplication where zero digits appear. When there are one or more zeros in the multiplier, there is no need to write down horizontal lines of zeros. If you come to a zero in the multiplier, just bring down the zero *in a straight line* as a place holder and then continue the multiplication with the next digit to the left. See examples **1** and **2,** at the right.

A simple rule for multiplying a number by 10, 100, 1000, etc., is merely to write 1, 2, 3, etc., zeros, respectively, after the extreme right-hand digit of the number. See example **3**.

Exercises

1. Multiply and check:

  a. 72
     X6

  b. 42
     X27

  c. 325
     X58

  d. 719
     X32

2. Find the product and check:

  a. 409
     X78

  b. 732
     X30

  c. 547
     X203

  d. 76,008
       X45

Example 1

Multiply 74 X 30.

Solution:

$$\begin{array}{r} \overset{1}{74} \\ \times 30 \\ \hline 2220 \end{array}$$

Example 2

Multiply 345 by 201.

Solution:

$$\begin{array}{r} 3\overset{1}{4}5 \\ \times 201 \\ \hline 345 \\ 69\,00 \\ \hline 69{,}345 \end{array}$$

Example 3

Multiply 47 by 10, by 100, and by 1000.

Solution:

$$47 \times 10 = 470$$
$$47 \times 100 = 4700$$
$$47 \times 1000 = 47{,}000$$

1. a. _____   **b.** _____

   c. _____   **d.** _____

2. a. _____   **b.** _____

   c. _____   **d.** _____

3. Multiply:

    a. 763 × 200   **b.** 4752 × 101

    c. 854 × 1000   **d.** 8720 × 230

4. An auto mechanic earns $325 per week. What does he earn in a year (52 weeks)?

5. An appliance dealer bought 18 toasters, each costing $27. How much did he pay for all of them?

6. An auto dealer sells 134 cars at $4250 each. How much did he receive for all of them?

7. How many envelopes are there in 145 boxes, packed 500 to the box?

8. A hotel manager is carpeting 125 rooms and needs 37 square yards of carpet per room. How many square yards of carpet must he order?

9. A housing development is having air-conditioning units installed in 137 houses. If each installation costs $1450, what is the total cost?

10. A clothing store sells the following items during the course of one month:

        178 shirts at $12 each
        256 ties at $8 each
        235 suits at $142 each
        43 raincoats at $52 each

How much money did the store take in that month?

11. A construction firm sells 245 homes for $48,500 each. Find the total amount it receives for the sale.

12. A trucking company purchases 352 new trucks costing $9270 each. How much does it pay for all of them?

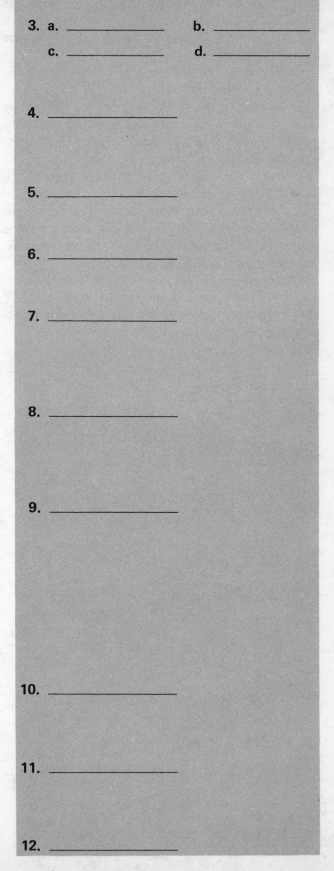

3. a. _____   **b.** _____

    c. _____   **d.** _____

4. _____

5. _____

6. _____

7. _____

8. _____

9. _____

10. _____

11. _____

12. _____

5. Division of whole numbers

In a class of 18 students, a gym teacher wants to form squads of 6 each; we say that he is **dividing** the 18 students into groups of 6. In this case, he divides 18 by 6 and sees that he gets exactly 3 squads. This division may be indicated in any of three different ways:

(1) $18 \div 6 = 3$

(2) $\dfrac{18}{6} = 3$

(3) $6\overline{)18}^{\,3}$

Division is the *opposite*, or *inverse*, of multiplication. When we say 18 divided by 6 ($18 \div 6$), we mean: What number multiplied by 6 will give us 18? The number 18 is called the **dividend**, 6 is called the **divisor**, and the result 3 is called the **quotient**. The quotient tells us how many times the divisor is contained in the dividend.

As in multiplication, division is also *distributive over addition*.

For example, $\dfrac{18 + 12}{6} = \dfrac{30}{6} = 5.$

Also, $\dfrac{18 + 12}{6} = \dfrac{18}{6} + \dfrac{12}{6} = 3 + 2 = 5.$

Note that distributing the divisor among the addends in the dividend gives the same result. The *distributive law* provides the basis for the process of dividing whole numbers.

For example, if we wish to divide 36 by 3, we may write

$$\frac{36}{3} = \frac{30 + 6}{3} = \frac{30}{3} + \frac{6}{3} = 10 + 2 = 12$$

Using the division box, we usually write this division example as

$$3\overline{)36}^{\,12}$$

This is an abbreviated form for

$$3\overline{)3\ \text{tens} + 6\ \text{ones}}^{\,1\ \text{ten}\ +\ 2\ \text{ones} \,=\, 12}$$

The following illustrative problems show how to proceed in more difficult cases of division:

ILLUSTRATIVE PROBLEM 1

Divide 52 by 4.

Solution: We say 4 is contained in 5 once and write 1 in the tens place over the 5; then 1 X 4 = 4, write 4 in the tens place under 5, take the difference and bring down 2. Now 4 is contained in 12 three times; write 3 in the units place over the 2 in the dividend.

Thus, 52 ÷ 4 = 13.

We may check by multiplying:

4 X 13 = 52 √

$$\begin{array}{r} 13 \\ 4\overline{\smash{)}52} \\ \underline{4} \\ 12 \\ \underline{12} \end{array}$$

ILLUSTRATIVE PROBLEM 2

Divide 352 by 11.

Solution: Remember that 35 here is really 35 tens; therefore, 35 tens ÷ 11 is about 3 tens; we place the 3 in the tens column above the 5. Now 3 X 11 = 33; place this under 35 and subtract, giving 2. Carry down the 2 in the dividend. Now 22 ÷ 11 = 2 exactly; place this over the 2 in the dividend; then multiply 2 by 11, giving 22.

Thus, 352 ÷ 11 = 32.

$$\begin{array}{r} 32 \\ 11\overline{\smash{)}352} \\ \underline{33} \\ 22 \\ \underline{22} \end{array}$$

Check:
$$\begin{array}{r} 32 \\ \underline{\times 11} \\ 32 \\ \underline{32} \\ 352 \ \checkmark \end{array}$$

ILLUSTRATIVE PROBLEM 3

Divide 15,750 by 25.

Solution: Since 25 is greater than 15, the first 3 digits in the dividend are required to obtain the first digit in the quotient. 157 ÷ 25 is about 6. Proceed as in problem 2 above. When there is no remainder after the second digit in the quotient, we place a zero in the quotient over the final 0 in the dividend.

15,750 ÷ 25 = 630

$$\begin{array}{r} 630 \\ 25\overline{\smash{)}15{,}750} \\ \underline{15\ 0} \\ 75 \\ \underline{75} \\ 00 \end{array}$$

ILLUSTRATIVE PROBLEM 4

Divide 42 by 5.

Solution: Here we see that the quotient is 8, and we are left with a *remainder* of 2. We may write the result as 8 R 2, or we may write the result as $8\frac{2}{5}$ where the remainder is above the fraction line and the divisor below it. In Chapter 4, we saw that this latter result is correct by showing that

$$5 \times 8\frac{2}{5} = 42$$

That is, divisor $\times$ quotient = dividend.

Thus, $42 \div 5 = 8$ R 2 or $8\frac{2}{5}$.

$$
\begin{array}{r}
8 \\
5\overline{)42} \\
40 \\
\hline
2
\end{array}
$$

ILLUSTRATIVE PROBLEM 5

Divide 6532 by 74.

Solution:

1. Divide. How many 74's in 659? Try 9; then multiply 9 by 74. The product is larger than 659. Try 8. Write the 8 over the 9.
2. Multiply 74 by 8. Place the product 592 under 659.
3. Subtract 592 from 659. The remainder must be smaller than 74, the divisor.
4. *Bring down* the next digit, 2, and place it to the right of the remainder 67.
5. Now *repeat* the 4 steps above. Divide 672 by 74. Write the 9 over the 2, multiply 9 by 74, and write the product under 672. The remainder is then 6. The quotient is 89 R 6 or $89\frac{6}{74}$.

To check, multiply the quotient 89 by the divisor 74. Then add the remainder 6 to the product. The sum should be the dividend.

$$
\begin{array}{r}
89 \\
74\overline{)6592} \\
592 \\
\hline
672 \\
666 \\
\hline
6
\end{array}
$$

$$
\begin{array}{r}
89 \\
\times 74 \\
\hline
356 \\
623 \\
\hline
6586 \\
+6 \\
\hline
6592 \; \checkmark
\end{array}
$$

ILLUSTRATIVE PROBLEM 6

Divide 64,528 by 128.

Solution: Here $645 \div 128$ is about 5. (Think of $600 \div 100 = 6$. This is too large because $128 \times 6 = 768$, so try 5.) When we multiply 5 by 128, the product is 640. When we subtract and bring down the 2, we are left with 52, which is smaller than the divisor, 128. In this case, we place a zero over the 2 in the dividend and bring down the next digit, 8. Then repeat the process.

The quotient is 504 R 16 or $504\dfrac{16}{128}$.

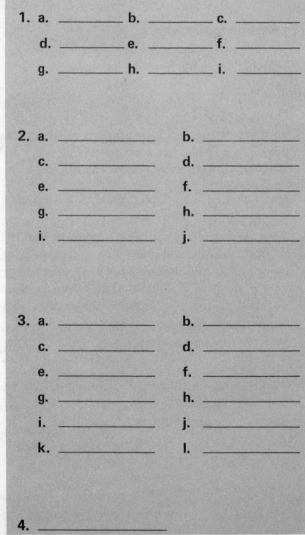

Exercises

1. Divide and check.

    a. $4\overline{)484}$ **b.** $3\overline{)936}$ **c.** $7\overline{)518}$

    d. $6\overline{)4596}$ **e.** $34\overline{)7582}$ **f.** $26\overline{)910}$

    g. $48\overline{)3648}$ **h.** $37\overline{)2072}$ **i.** $79\overline{)6557}$

2. Divide and check.

    a. $127\overline{)896}$ **b.** $620\overline{)4340}$

    c. $183\overline{)4758}$ **d.** $4590 \div 135$

    e. $24,909 \div 437$ **f.** $49,296 \div 632$

    g. $87,710 \div 358$ **h.** $249,888 \div 274$

    i. $24,800 \div 800$ **j.** $325,000 \div 5000$

3. Divide and express each remainder as a fraction.

    a. $5\overline{)658}$ **b.** $3\overline{)245}$

    c. $8\overline{)247}$ **d.** $7\overline{)503}$

    e. $9\overline{)435}$ **f.** $100 \div 37$

    g. $54\overline{)2130}$ **h.** $78\overline{)5796}$

    i. $4508 \div 98$ **j.** $528\overline{)38,676}$

    k. $64\overline{)74,816}$ **l.** $218,541 \div 42$

4. A bushel basket contains 936 eggs, which are then placed in boxes holding one dozen eggs each. How many boxes are filled?

---

1. a. _____ **b.** _____ **c.** _____

   d. _____ **e.** _____ **f.** _____

   g. _____ **h.** _____ **i.** _____

2. a. _____ **b.** _____

   c. _____ **d.** _____

   e. _____ **f.** _____

   g. _____ **h.** _____

   i. _____ **j.** _____

3. a. _____ **b.** _____

   c. _____ **d.** _____

   e. _____ **f.** _____

   g. _____ **h.** _____

   i. _____ **j.** _____

   k. _____ **l.** _____

4. _____

5. Mrs. Petrillo earns $12,220 per year. What are her average weekly earnings? (Use 52 weeks per year.)

5. _____

6. A tourist drives 544 miles in one day and uses 32 gallons of gasoline. How many miles does he travel on one gallon?

6. _____

7. There are 16 ounces in 1 pound. How many pounds are there in 2960 ounces?

7. _____

8. On a field day, a school orders buses, each of which carries 38 students. How many buses should it order for 722 students?

8. _____

9. There are 12 inches in a foot. How many feet in 157 inches?

9. _____

10. A car is traveling on a highway at constant speed. It covers 287 miles in 5 hours. How many miles does it travel each hour?

10. _____

11. The *average* of a group of numbers is obtained by *dividing* the sum of the numbers by the number of items in the group. Find the average of the following test marks: 82, 75, 89, 68, 78.

11. _____

12. During four weeks in February, a salesman earned the following commissions: $285, $340, $315, $296. What was his average weekly commission?

12. _____

13. In a certain junior high school, the ninth grade classes have the following class registers: 32, 29, 27, 31, 26, 30. What is the average class size?

13. _____

14. At the end of one term, Jennifer gets the following grades in her five major subjects: 85, 92, 84, 75, 93. What is her grade average for the term?

14. _____

APPENDIX II:
SETS

1. Meaning of terms and symbols

The notion of *sets* has become very popular in the study of mathematics in recent years. The use of sets frequently helps to clarify ideas in elementary mathematics, so we will review here some of the basic concepts and terminology.

In ordinary speech, we talk about a set of dishes, a set of books, a set of golf clubs, and so on. A *set* is a collection of objects or ideas. In mathematics, we speak of a set of numbers or a set of triangles. The set of digits, for example, consists of the whole numbers from 0 to 9 inclusive. Each of these numbers is called an *element* or *member* of the set of digits.

One way of indicating a set is to list the elements between braces. Thus, we may represent the set of digits as $\{0, 1, 2, 3, 4, 5, 6, 7, 8, 9\}$. The set of vowels is $\{a, e, i, o, u\}$. This way of representing the elements of a set is called the *list method* or the *roster method*.

We frequently use a capital letter to refer to a particular set. For example, $P = \{1, 3, 5\}$ may be read "*P* is the set whose elements are 1, 3, and 5." To indicate that 3 is an element of *P*, we write $3 \in P$. To indicate that 4 is not an element of *P*, we write $4 \notin P$.

It does not matter in what order the elements are listed. For example, the set of vowels may be written as $\{e, i, a, u, o\}$ or $\{u, o, i, e, a\}$.

If there are many elements in a set, we do not use the roster method. Instead, we *describe* the set. We may write $\{$counting numbers from 1 to 50$\}$, which is read "the set of counting numbers from 1 to 50."

Sometimes a set has no element. For example, the set of Presidents of the United States under 25 years of age has no elements. We refer to a set with no elements as the *empty set* or *null set*. We represent the empty set by empty braces $\{\ \}$ or by the symbol ϕ. If *M* is the set of months beginning with the letter Z, we write $M = \phi$ or $M = \{\ \}$. Note that $\{0\}$ is not the empty set since it has the number 0 as a single element.

We can readily tell by counting that the set of digits has 10 elements and that the set of vowels has 5 elements. If the number of elements in a set can be counted, we call it a *finite set*.

Let us consider the set *E* of positive even numbers. We may write

$$E = \{2, 4, 6, 8, 10, \ldots\}$$

where the dots indicate that we are to go on writing consecutive even numbers. Here we cannot count the elements of the set since they go on forever.

Such a set is called an *infinite set*. The set of counting numbers (or natural numbers) is also an infinite set:

$$\{1, 2, 3, 4, 5, 6, \ldots\}$$

To write the month "August," six letters are used. But the letter "u" is repeated. In writing the set of letters of this word, we write {A, u, g, s, t}. We do not repeat the "u." When we describe a set by the roster method, we list the same element only once.

If two sets have the same number of elements, they are said to be *equivalent sets*. Thus, the set $A = \{1, 3, 5, 7\}$ and the set $B = \{p, q, r, s\}$ are equivalent, since they both contain 4 elements.

If two sets have *exactly* the same elements, they are said to be *identical sets* or *equal sets*. Thus, $P = \{a, e, i, o, u\}$ and $Q = \{u, e, i, a, o\}$ are equal sets. Note that they have the same number of members as well as the same members.

Exercises

In 1 to 10, represent each set by the roster method (list the elements of each set between braces).

1. The set of all months that begin with the letter J.

2. The set of even numbers between 1 and 11.

3. The set of months that have fewer than 30 days.

4. The set of U.S. Presidents since John Kennedy.

5. The set of odd numbers between 1 and 33 that are divisible by 5.

6. The set of all female U.S. Presidents.

7. The set of all days of the week beginning with the letter T.

8. The set of letters in the word "null."

9. The set of whole numbers between 7 and 8.

10. The set of even numbers between 9 and 19.

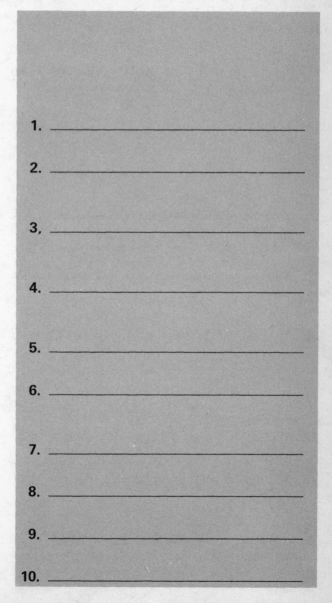

1. _____

2. _____

3. _____

4. _____

5. _____

6. _____

7. _____

8. _____

9. _____

10. _____

In 11 to 15, describe in words the set whose elements are given by the roster method.

Example

{ 1, 3, 5, 7, 9} is the set of odd numbers from 1 to 9.

11. {2, 4, 6, 8}

11. _____
_____

12. {Alaska, Oregon, Washington, California}

12. _____
_____

13. {1, 2, 3, 4, 5, 6}

13. _____
_____

14. {March, May}

14. _____
_____

15. {3, 6, 9, 12, 15}

15. _____
_____

In 16 to 25, state whether the set is an *infinite set*, a *finite set*, or an *empty set*.

16. The set of odd numbers.

16. _____

17. The set of people living in Arizona.

17. _____

18. The set of states of the U.S. smaller in size than Rhode Island.

18. _____

19. The set of counting numbers greater than 1000.

19. _____

20. The set of months of the year beginning with K.

20. _____

21. The set of rectangles.

21. _____

22. The set of 3-digit numbers beginning with 5.

22. _____

23. The set of whole numbers that are multiples of 7.

23. _____

24. {months of the year having 25 days}

24. _____

25. {5, 10, 15, 20, 25, . . .}

25. _____

In 26 to 34, state whether the two sets in each exercise are *equivalent*, *equal*, or *neither*.

26. {p, q, r, s} and {r, s, q, p}

26. _____

27. {Bill, Mary, Ed, Sue} and {a, b, c, d}

27. _____

28. {5, 7, 9, 11, 13} and {p, q, r, s}

28. _____

29. {a, b, l, e} and {e, l, b, a}

29. _____

30. {2, 3, 4, 5} and $\left\{\dfrac{1}{2}, \dfrac{1}{3}, \dfrac{1}{4}, \dfrac{1}{5}\right\}$

30. _____

31. ϕ and {0}

31. _____

32. {M, I, T} and {T, I, M}

32. _____

33. {counting numbers from 1 to 10} and {digits from 0 to 9}

33. _____

34. {days in the week} and {months in the year}

34. _____

2. Subsets

In a particular discussion, the set of all objects being considered is called the **universal set** or the **universe**. If we are talking about numbers, the set of counting numbers could be the universal set. If we are talking about American citizens, the set of residents of the U.S. could be the universal set. We designate such a set by the letter U.

Now let us consider the sets $U = $ {citizens of U.S.} and $T = $ {citizens of Texas}.

All the elements of T are also elements of U. In such a case, we say that T is a **subset** of U, and we write $T \subset U$.

If we consider U as {a, e, i, o, u}, we can see that there are many possible subsets of U; for example, {a, e, i} or {i, o}. Also, we can write {e} $\subset U$ or {i} $\subset U$. We may also consider {a, e, i, o, u} as a subset of U since *all* of its elements are also elements of U. Such a subset is called an **improper subset** of U, whereas subsets with fewer elements than U are called **proper subsets** of U.

The example above illustrates that *every set is a subset of itself*. Mathematicians have also agreed to consider the empty set to be a subset of every set.

Let us list all the subsets of the set {a, b, c}. These would be: {a}, {b}, {c}, {a, b}, {a, c}, {b, c}, {a, b, c}, and { }.

Let us consider the sets V = {a, e, i, o, u} and L = {a, b, c, d, e}. Clearly, V is not a subset of L and L is not a subset of V. However, V and L have 2 elements in common, a and e. V and L are called *overlapping sets*. Two sets are overlapping if they have elements in common but neither set is a subset of the other.

Two sets are called *disjoint sets* if no element of one is an element of the other. Thus, {a, b, c} and {1, 2, 3} are disjoint sets.

Exercises

In 1 to 10, two sets are given in each exercise. State whether the two sets are *overlapping sets*, *disjoint sets*, or one is a *subset* of the other. In the latter case, indicate which set is the subset.

Example

P = {a, b, c} and Q = {a, b, c, d}

Answer: subset; $P \subset Q$

1. A = {5, 6, 7} and B = {5, 6, 7, 8}

2. {dogs} and {birds}

3. C = {cows} and A = {animals}

4. A = {2, 4, 6, 8} and B = {1, 2, 3, 4}

5. S = {Seniors in the school} and J = {Juniors in the school}

6. ϕ and A = {residents of Alabama}

7. S = {ships} and B = {battleships}

8. A = {p, q, r} and B = {q, r, p}

1. _____

2. _____

3. _____

4. _____

5. _____

6. _____

7. _____

8. _____

9. C = {Mary, Harry, Ed} and D = {Jane, Tony, Harry}

9. _____

10. E = {all even numbers} and F = {4, 8, 12, 16}

10. _____

In 11 to 14, list all subsets of the given set.

11. {p}

11. _____

12. {3, 4}

12. _____

13. {r, s, t}

13. _____

14. {Sue, Tom}

14. _____

In 15 to 18, state whether the first set is a *proper* subset or an *improper* subset of the second set.

15. {mackerel} $\subset$ {fish}

15. _____

16. {b, c, d} $\subset$ {d, b, c}

16. _____

17. {w, x, y, z} $\subset$ {z, w, y, x}

17. _____

18. {all multiples of 6} $\subset$ {all even numbers}

18. _____

3. Operations on sets

Let us consider two overlapping sets P = {a, e, i, o, u} and Q = {a, b, c, d, e}. Note that a and e are elements of both sets. We refer to the set {a, e} as the **intersection** of sets P and Q.

The intersection of two sets P and Q is the set containing only those elements of P which also belong to Q.

The intersection of sets P and Q is represented by the symbol $P \cap Q$, which is read "P intersection Q" or "P cap Q." Thus, if P is the set of counting numbers from 1 to 10 and Q = {8, 10, 12, 14}, then $P \cap Q$ = {8, 10}.

It is convenient to represent the relationships of sets by means of **Venn diagrams**. We represent the universal set by a rectangle and its interior. We usually label the rectangle with a U in one corner, as shown in Fig. 1.

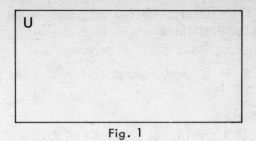

Fig. 1

If we want to picture a subset P of U, we place a circle within the rectangle and mark its interior with a P, as shown in Fig. 2.

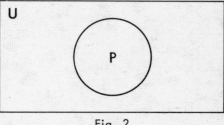

Fig. 2

Now let us consider the possible diagrams for $P \cap Q$, when P and Q are subsets of U.

When P and Q are overlapping sets, we draw overlapping circles, as shown in Fig. 3. The shaded part of the two circles represents $P \cap Q$.

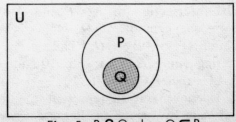

Fig. 3. P ∩ Q when P and Q are overlapping sets.

Fig. 4 pictures two disjoint sets. Since the sets do not overlap, there is no shaded area. Thus, $P \cap Q = \phi$.

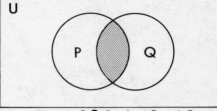

Fig. 4. P ∩ Q when P and Q are disjoint sets.

Fig. 5 shows the situation when $Q \subset P$. The circle representing Q is completely within the circle representing P. The shaded area represents $P \cap Q$. Note that $P \cap Q = Q$ in this case.

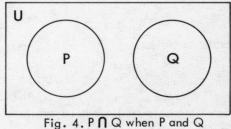

Fig. 5. P ∩ Q when Q ⊂ P.

The **union** of two sets P and Q is the set of all elements which belong to P or Q or both. The union of P and Q is represented by $P \cup Q$, read "P union Q" or "P cup Q."

If $P = \{6, 7, 8, 9\}$ and $Q = \{8, 9, 10, 11\}$, then $P \cup Q = \{6, 7, 8, 9, 10, 11\}$. Note that P and Q are both subsets of $P \cup Q$.

The Venn diagrams for $P \cup Q$ are shown in Figs. 6, 7, and 8:

The shaded region in each diagram shows $P \cup Q$. In Fig. 8, when $Q \subset P$, note that $P \cup Q = P$.

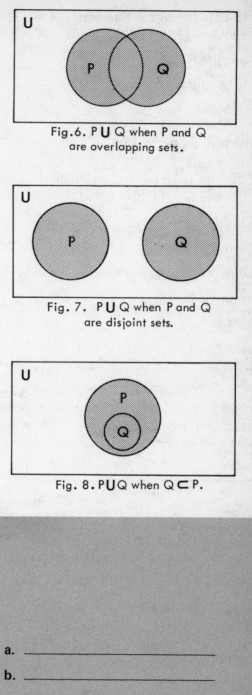

Fig. 6. P ∪ Q when P and Q are overlapping sets.

Fig. 7. P ∪ Q when P and Q are disjoint sets.

Fig. 8. P ∪ Q when Q ⊂ P.

Exercises

1. If $P = \{2, 4, 6\}$ and $Q = \{1, 2, 3, 4\}$, find:

    a. $P \cap Q$

    b. $P \cup Q$

2. If $A = \{p, q, r, s\}$ and $B = \{r, s, t\}$, find:

    a. $A \cap B$

    b. $A \cup B$

3. If $C = \{10, 11, 12\}$ and $D = \{13, 14\}$, find:

    a. $C \cap D$

    b. $C \cup D$

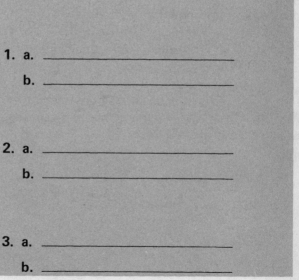

1. a. _____

   b. _____

2. a. _____

   b. _____

3. a. _____

   b. _____

4. If $U = \{$counting numbers$\}$, $A = \{3, 4, 5\}$, and $B = \{3, 4, 5, 6, 7\}$, find:

    a. $A \cap B$

    b. $A \cup B$

4. a. _____

    b. _____

ILLUSTRATIVE PROBLEM

    If $U = \{$letters of the alphabet$\}$, $V = \{$a, e, i, o, u$\}$, and $L = \{$a, b, c, d, e, f$\}$:

a. Find $V \cap L$.

b. Find $V \cup L$.

c. Draw Venn diagrams to show **a** and **b**.

Solution:

a. $V \cap L = \{$a, e$\}$

b. $V \cup L = \{$a, e, i, o, u, b, c, d, f$\}$

c.

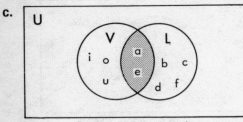

V∩L (shaded area)

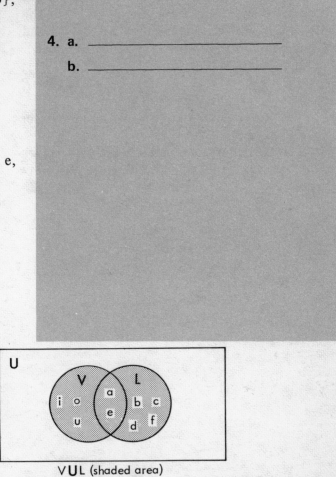

V∪L (shaded area)

Exercises (continued)

5. If $T = \{$triangles$\}$, $R = \{$rectangles$\}$, and $U = \{$geometric figures$\}$:

    a. Find $T \cap R$.

    b. On separate paper, draw a Venn diagram to show $T \cap R$.

5. a. _____

6. a. Find $\{2, 4, 6, 8\} \cap \{4, 6\}$.

    b. Find $\{2, 4, 6, 8\} \cup \{4, 6\}$.

6. a. _____

    b. _____

7. Find: **a.** $P \cap \phi$ **b.** $P \cup \phi$

          c. $P \cap P$ **d.** $P \cup P$

7. a. _____ **b.** _____

    c. _____ **d.** _____

8. If $U = \{$people$\}$, $L = \{$blue-eyed people$\}$, and $R = \{$brown-eyed people$\}$, draw a Venn diagram to show:

   a. $L \cap R$ b. $L \cup R$

9. If P and Q are disjoint sets, what is $P \cap Q$?

   9. _____

10. If $A \subset B$:

    a. Find $A \cap B$.

    b. Find $A \cup B$.

    10. a. _____

          b. _____

INDEX

Abscissa, 252
Absolute value, 181
Addends, 278
Addition
  associative principle of, 279
  commutative principle of, 279
  of decimals, 87
  distributive property of division
    over, 289
  distributive property of multi-
    plication over, 199, 216, 285
  grouping in, 279
  of like fractions, 56–57
  of like terms, 5
  of monomials, 199–200
  of polynomials, 210–211
  of signed numbers, 181–183
  solving equations by, 17–18,
    224–225
  solving inequalities by, 266–267
  of unlike fractions, 58–60
  of whole numbers, 278–280
Addition principle
  of equality, 18
  of inequalities, 266
Algebraic expressions, 4–5
  factors of, 19
  with signed numbers, 194
  simplifying, 219
  See also Monomials, Polynomials
Algebraic representation, 2, 30–31
  of inequalities, 262
  of problems, 34–42
Algebraic sum, 181–183
Amount (returned on loan), 144
Annual interest, 144
Area, 155
  changing units of, 158–159
  of circle, 166–167
  of rectangle, 155–156
  of triangle, 160–161
Associative principle
  of addition, 183, 279
  of multiplication, 190, 285
  and subtraction, 282
Axes of graph, 248, 251–252
  lines parallel to, 258–259

Balance principle, 17–18
Base, 163
  dividing powers of same, 207
  multiplying powers of same,
    203–204
Binomial, 210
Braces, 294
Brackets, 219

Cancellation, 66–67
Carrying digits, 279–280, 286
Circle
  area of, 166–167
  ratio of circumference to diam-
    eter of, 118
Circumference, 118
Clearing equation of decimals,
  98–99
Coefficient, numerical, 4, 19, 21
Coin problems, 39–40
Combination
  of like terms, 4–5, 25–26
  of signed numbers, 181–183
Common denominator, 58
  least, 58, 59
Common fractions, 47–48, 85–86
Common literal factor, 5
Commutative principle
  of addition, 183, 279
  of multiplication, 65, 190, 285
  and subtraction, 281
Comparison
  of decimals, 82
  by division, 102
  by subtraction, 102
Complex fractions, 74–75
Consecutive integers, 37
  even, 39
  odd, 39
  problems about, 37–38
Coordinates of point, 252
Cross-multiplying, 109–110
Cubic units, 171

Decimal equations, 98–99
Decimal fractions, 78–80
  See also Decimals

Decimal point, 78
Decimals, 78
  adding, 87
  changed to common fractions,
    85–86
  clearing equation of, 98–99
  comparing, 82
  dividing, 93–98
  equations containing, 98–99
  mixed, 80, 125
  multiplying, 89–92
  and percents, 124–125
  place value in, 79
  rounding off, 83–84
  subtracting, 87–88
  zeros in, 79–80
Denominator, 47
  fractions with different, 58–60,
    61–62
  fractions with same, 56–57, 61
  least common, 58, 59
Diagrams, Venn, 299–301
Difference, 185, 281
Directed numbers
  See Signed numbers
Discount(s), 139
  problems about, 138–140
  rate of, 139
  successive, 140
Disjoint sets, 298, 300
Distributive property
  of division over addition, 289
  of multiplication over addition,
    199, 216, 285
Dividend, 192, 289
Division
  over addition, distributive prop-
    erty of, 289
  changing improper fraction to
    mixed number by, 54
  comparison by, 102
  of decimals, 93–98
  fraction as form of, 48
  of fractions, 68–70
  in inequalities, 266
  of monomials, 208
  of polynomial by monomial, 220

Means of proportion, 109
Measurement
    of area, 155-156, 160-161,
        166-167
    English system of, 152
    of length, 149-150
    metric system of, 152-153
    of volume, 171-172
Members
    of equation, 16
    of set, 294
Metric system, 152-153
Minuend, 185, 281
Mixed decimals, 80, 125
Mixed numbers, 48
    adding, 59-60
    and improper fractions, 53-55
    as percents, 125
    subtracting, 62-63
Monomial(s), 199
    adding, 199-200
    dividing monomial by, 208
    dividing polynomial by, 220
    multiplying polynomial by, 216
    multiplying two, 205
    subtracting, 201
Motion problems, 240, 242-244
Multiplicand, 285
Multiplication
    over addition, distributive prop-
        erty of, 199, 216, 285
    algebraic representation of, 2
    associative principle of, 285
    changing mixed number to frac-
        tion by, 54-55
    commutative law of, 65, 285
    of decimals, 89-92
    of fractions, 65-67
    of inequalities, 266
    of monomials, 205
    of number by letter, 2, 4-5
    of polynomial by monomial, 216
    of powers of same base, 203-204
    by powers of ten, 287
    raising fraction by, 51
    by reciprocal to divide, 69-70
    of signed numbers, 189-190
    solving equations by, 21-22,
        225-227
    of whole numbers, 284-287
    by zero, 287
Multiplication principle
    of equality, 22
    of inequalities, 266
Multiplier, 285

Negative numbers, 178
    See also Signed numbers
Net price, 139

Null set, 294
Number line
    inequalities on, 264-265
    signed numbers on, 178, 185
Number pair, ordered, 252
Numbers
    consecutive, 37
    consecutive even, 39
    consecutive odd, 39
    directed, 178
    found from fractional parts, 72-73
    mixed, 48
    finding percents of, 131
    found from percents, 136-137
    ordered pair of, 252
    rational, 47
    signed, 178-179
    whole, 276-277
Numerator, 47
Numerical coefficient, 4, 5
Numerical expressions, 9-10

Odd integers, consecutive, 39
Operations
    inverse, 281, 289
    on sets, 299-301
    solving equations by two, 23-24,
        228-229
    See also Order of operations
Order of inequality, 264-265, 266
Order of operations, 6-7
    in addition, 183, 279
    and grouping symbols, 9-10, 219
    in multiplication, 65, 190
Ordered number pair, 252
Ordinate, 252
Origin
    on graph, 248
    on number line, 178
Overlapping sets, 298, 300

Parentheses
    within brackets, 219
    in equations, 233-234
    in formulas, 9-10
Partial products, 285
Percent(s), 122-123
    and decimals, 124-125
    and discount problems, 138-140
    finding number from, 136-137
    and fractions, 127-128
    and interest, 143-145
    of a number, 131
    one number is of another, 134
Perimeter of triangle, 2-3
Pi (π), 118
Place value
    in decimals, 79
    in whole numbers, 276

Plotting points, 249
Point (on graph)
    coordinates of, 252
    of origin, 248
    plotting ordered number pair as,
        249, 252
Point, decimal, 78
Point, zero, 178
Polynomials, 209-210
    adding, 209-211
    dividing monomial into, 220
    multiplying monomial by, 216
    subtracting, 213-214
Positive numbers, 178
    See also Signed numbers
Powers, 163-164
    of same base, 203-204, 207
    of ten, 92, 97, 287
Price
    list, 138-139
    marked, 138-139
    net, 139
    sale, 139
Principal, 144
Principles
    of equality, 18, 20, 22
    of inequalities, 266
    of proportions, 109
Problems, 34-35, 235-238
    coin, 39-40
    consecutive number, 37-38,
        235-236
    discount, 138-140
    formulas to solve, 1-3
    geometric, 41-42
    motion, 240, 242-244
    ratio, 107
Product(s), 284-285
    algebraic representation of, 2
    of letter and number, 4-5
    of means and extremes of propor-
        tion, 109-110
    partial, 285
    of signed numbers, 189-190
Proper fraction, 48
Proper subset, 297
Proportion, 109-111
    extremes of, 109
    means of, 109
    and scale drawings, 113-115
    testing for, 109-110

Quotient, 192, 289

Raising fractions, 51-52
Rate, 103
    of discount, 139
    of interest, 144
Rational number, 47